JOHN RAMSAY'S CATALOGUE OF
BRITISH DIE-CAST MODEL TOYS

THIRD EDITION

A Swapmeet Toys and Models Ltd Publication
PO Box 21, Bury St Edmunds, Suffolk. England. IP33 2ED

Compiled by John Ramsay

1st Edition published 1984
2nd Edition published 1986
3rd Edition published 1988

ISBN 0 9509319 2 6

Typeset by TND Serif Ltd, Hadleigh and printed
in Great Britain by W. S. Cowell Ltd, Ipswich

CONTENTS

GIFT SETS are shown at end of each section.

SPOT ON MODELS

4

INTRODUCTION

Since the first edition was published late in 1983 there have been tremendous changes in the diecast collecting world. Firstly, and most importantly, the diecast toymaking industry appears to be in fine fettle compared to five years ago when the Mettoy Co PLC (Corgi) had just asked its bankers to call in the receivers. Similarly Lesney & Co. (Matchbox) were close to being taken over and lastly it appeared as though 'Dinky Toys' had disappeared for ever.

What a transformation has taken place since those uncertain days just a few short years ago. Firstly the Mettoy Company PLC were taken over in a management buy out and have simply gone from strength to strength ever since. Similarly with Lesney & Co having been taken over and absorbed into the mighty worldwide Matchbox Group of companies, the future of Matchbox Toys has been secured. Furthermore the same company has clearly expressed its confidence in the diecast model future by purchasing the 'Dinky Toys' trademark and by announcing its plans to reintroduce the famous old name back into the market place.

It is not surprising that Matchbox have shown such confidence in the future for there have been strong signs of growth taking place within the toy collecting market.

Firstly has been the increasing numbers of new die-cast collectors. Many of them no doubt today's parents who grew up in the fifties and sixties which was a golden era for British produced die-cast models. It was an age when every boy certainly had toy models bought for him. It would seem that many of these 'boys' have made a nostalgic return to the 'days of their youth'. Days when hard-saved pocket money of a few shillings could purchase perhaps a model of Dad's car.

To cater for all of the new collectors there has been a big increase in the number of Toy Fairs which are now being held. Indeed there can be few parts of Britain where collectors nowadays do not have regular access to a Toyfair. Furthermore it's not just the dads who attend, for increasingly they are accompanied by the rest of the family as well.

Several excellent new toy museums have opened up, all displaying a good range of die-cast models.

One often hears the cry 'I had one of those' and perhaps it is this that explains why nostalgia has played such a large part in the revival of the toy industry.

Certainly the toymakers have responded to the demand by producing superb models all resplendent in accurate liveries from the past.

There has been a growing awareness of the marketing value associated with die-cast products and so there has been a big upsurge in the number of promotional models produced and this will undoubtedly continue.

All of this is a long way from the early thirties when the first Dinky Toys promotional model (HORNBY TRAINS) was introduced. Frank Hornby could have had little idea of how the seeds he sowed then would have flourished into the fascinating hobby of die-cast model collecting that we see today.

CATALOGUE IMPROVEMENTS

Much more information has been included in the 3rd Edition as follows:

i) CORGI TOYS
   a. The model listings have been completely updated.
   b. The commercial vehicle section has been redesigned on a model type basis.
   c. A complete section has been devoted to the superb new 'CORGI CLASSICS' series.

ii) DINKY TOYS
   New variations have been included plus full details of 'THE DINKY COLLECTION'

iii) MATCHBOX TOYS
   a. The 'Models of Yesteryear' listings have been linked to the Matchbox Toy book, 'THE COLLECTION', thereby ensuring total accuracy.
   b. The '1—75' Series listings have been greatly enhanced by the addition of many new variations and much more detail.
   c. Early Lesney Toys — now listed.
   d. 'King Size' models — now listed.
   e. Giftware models — now listed.

iv) SPOT ON MODELS
   Many new colour variations have been included.

v) BUDGIE TOYS — now listed.

vi) MORESTONE TOYS — now listed.

vii) CRESCENT TOYS — now listed.

viii) LLEDO — MODELS OF DAYS GONE
   Model listing brought up to date plus information on the promotional issues.

ix) TRI-ANG — MINIC SHIPS now included

x) AUCTION PRICE RESULTS
   Much more information has been provided.

xi) USE OF ABBREVIATIONS
   Many fewer have been used.
   e.g. The 'Models of Yesteryear' section now has no abbreviations at all.

MARKET SURVEY OF PRICE AND RARITY GRADINGS

A fresh market survey was undertaken in 1988. The survey was conducted on the basis of requesting information from the trade and then checking the findings against information collected direct from shops, toy-fairs and mail order listings. In addition a close watch was kept on the prices realised for the rarer models at auction and this information has been published in the Catalogue to help underpin the price levels shown.

The qualifying standards concerning model and box condition were the same as for the 1983 and 1985 surveys:

Pre-War Models— Fine — Good condition (No fatigue)
1946-53 Models — Good — Excellent Unboxed
1953-88 Models — Excellent Boxed to Mint Boxed

From the results which emerged it was apparent that the older rarer models in pristine condition, which were truly mint boxed, did command a considerably higher price. These higher price levels contrasted considerably with the prices requested for models sometimes described as mint boxed but really being in the good to excellent categories. Similarly large prices are being requested for models with the rarer colour or components as against the normal issue model. The survey found that the rarer models are harder to find so it is hardly surprising that those which have come onto the market in pristine condition have commanded an increased premium.

As a consequence the Catalogue Price and Rarity gradings have reflected this price gap much more so than in the 1st edition. Just how this has been achieved is explained in 'THE MODEL PRICE AND RARITY GRADING SYSTEM' section which follows.

We believe that by combining the results of our own survey with the trade supplied information, the Price and Rarity gradings shown are as accurate and credible as it is possible to make them and we trust they provide a useful guide to collectors. However it cannot be over-emphasised that irrespective of any price guidance given in this Catalogue it would be inadvisable for collectors to expect their local collectors shop, toyfair traders or mail order lists to charge similar prices in every case. A trader will charge exactly what he wants for a model and will NOT be governed by any figures shown in this Catalogue nor could he be reasonably expected to do so.

PRICE AND RARITY CHANGES

At the beginning of each main chapter a comparison of the findings of the past three surveys has been shown. Various examples have been included to provide collectors with an at a glance review of the changes.

THE MODEL RARITY AND PRICES GRADING SYSTEM

Based on the Market Survey each model and set has been placed into one of the following grades. In each case a market price or price range has been shown followed by the rarity grade code as described below. The only exception to this being the grading where just the (NRP) abbreviation has been shown.

Where the Market Price Range (MPR) coding has been given collectors should bear the following in mind:

Where a large gap exists between the lower and the top end of the Market Price Range the reasons will be as follows:

i) Only models in pristine condition qualify for the top market price — e.g. this is highly relevant to Spot On models and some Dinky models, e.g. 514 Guy Van 'Lyons' which is extremely difficult to find with pristine decals. Similarly the Matchbox 1—75 model 37a 'Coca-Cola' (uneven) is notoriously difficult to find with undamaged decals.

ii) The top market price will only refer to the rarer colours — again very relevant for Spot On models.

1. NPE   No Prices Estimate
This coding has been shown alongside models and gift sets which were never encountered in the survey and about which no up-to-date asking price or auction price information was obtained. The price shown against the model therefore is the compiler's estimate of what it would cost should it come onto the market. This grading particularly applies to many of the pre-war Dinkies and also to the Spot On model range.

Consequently because of rarity considerations, expect to see large price fluctuations occur over and above the catalogue estimate, especially at auctions.

2. GP   Guidance Price
This coding has been shown alongside models which the survey found were only rarely available and about which only limited price and auction price information was obtained. The price shown against the model therefore reflects this limited information and has been given for guidance purposes only. Consequently because of rarity considerations, expect to see the occasional largish price fluctuation from the figure shown, especially at auctions.

3. MPR   Market Price Range
eg £25-£30
This category is by far the most common grading used in the catalogue and applies to all those models which were found to be reasonably available most of the time. The two figures shown indicate the range of asking prices seen having discounted exceptionally high or low figures. Expect slight price fluctuations above and below the range shown in respect of the laws of supply and demand. A large gap between the figures indicates some issues/colours are rarer or models in pristine condition are rare.

Large gaps for the foregoing reasons will be found in the 'Spot On' model listings.

4. NC   Not Common
This coding has been shown alongside models which are fairly scarce but not rare and about which sufficient information was produced by the survey to give reasonable asking price guidance. Nevertheless expect to see asking price fluctuations from the figure shown because of scarcity.

5. NRP   Normal Retail Price
This is shown alongside models which have usually been recently issued or for models which have yet to attain a real collectable value. One would not expect to see asking prices for models in this grade set higher than a few pounds unless a model happens to be particularly large, eg. a common gift set containing several models.

6. NPP   No Prices Possible
This is shown alongside models never encountered in the survey and about which there is doubt whether they were ever actually issued, even though it may have been pictured in a catalogue. This particularly applies to some of the Spot On models and the odd Dinky toy. Readers will appreciate that unlike postage stamps or coins, no birth records are available in respect of all the die-cast models issued.

7. NGPP   No Grading Possible at Present
Where a model or gift set is particularly rare and no price information whatsoever is available, no rarity or price grading has been shown as the compiler believes this is carrying rarity and value grading into the realms of pure guesswork.

As and when information becomes available concerning these rarities it will be included in the catalogue.

NB 'Models of Yesteryear'
The foregoing grading system does not apply to models in this range. Please see MoY chapter for further details.

AUCTION PRICES REALISED

Some of the price gradings shown have been supported by reports of the prices actually realised at auction.

This has only been done in those instances where a model is either rare or is representative of a group of similar models.

Collectors should be aware that many factors govern a model's price and the amount a model makes at auction on a particular day can only be taken as a guide.

CLASSIFYING THE CONDITION OF MODELS AND BOXES

The condition of a model and its accompanying box does of course have a direct bearing on its value which makes accurate condition grading a matter of key importance.

Unlike most other collecting hobbies such as stamps and coins, no one universal grading system is used to classify the condition of models and boxes.

Nevertheless whilst several variants exist there are really two main condition classification systems in operation in the UK as follows:—

1. The 'Specific Condition' Grading System
The following example is fairly typical of the types of descriptions and gradings seen on Mail Order Lists.

M   Mint
AM   Almost Mint
VSC   Very Slightly Chipped
SC   Slightly Chipped
C   Chipped
VC   Very Chipped

If a model is described as Mint Boxed, the condition of its box is not normally separately described. However it is expected to be in a first class and as near original condition as is possible, bearing in mind the age of the model concerned.

If a box is damaged the flaws are usually separately described. This method has always seemed to work out quite well in practice, for all reputable dealers automatically offer a 'sale or return if not satisfied' deal to their clients, which provides the necessary safeguard against the misrepresentation of a model's condition. The compiler would stress that the foregoing is only an example of a mail order condition grading system and stricter box grading definitions are known to exist.

2. The 'General Condition' Grading System
This method is often seen used by auctioneers, although it is seen used on the odd Mail Order Lists as well.

(M)   Mint
(E)   Excellent
(G)   Good
(F)   Fair
(P)   Poor

Usually these gradings are separately applied to describe firstly the condition of the model and secondly the condition of the box.

From our observations and purely for guidance purposes, we would suggest the following descriptions approximately represent the different grades.

a.   Model Condition Gradings

1.   MINT (M)
The model must be complete and as fresh, new and original in appearance as when first received from the manufacturers.

2.   EXCELLENT (E)
The model is almost in mint condition and is only barred from this classification by having a few slight flaws — eg slight paintwork chipping in unimportant areas.

3.   GOOD (G)
The model is in a complete and original condition and retains an overall attractive collectable appearance despite having a few chips or rubbed paintwork.

4.   FAIR (F)
The model may not be in its original state eg. broken bumper, replacement radiator or windscreen, or have signs of metal fatigue. The paintwork may be faded, well chipped, retouched or repainted. There may be signs of rust. Unless the model is rare it is in a barely collectable condition.

5.   POOR (P)
The model may be damaged, incomplete, repainted, metal fatigued, have bad rust on the base plate, or be heavily chipped etc. Unless the model is rare it has little real value to a collector other than as a candidate for a complete restoration or spares.

b.   Box Condition Gradings

1.   MINT (M)
The box must be complete both inside and out and contain all the original packing materials, manufacturer's leaflets and box labels. It should be as fresh, new and original in appearance as when first received from the manufacturers.

2.   EXCELLENT (E)
The box is in almost mint condition but is barred from this classification by just the odd minor blemish eg. there may be slight damage to the display labels caused by bad storage. The original shop price label may have been carelessly removed and caused slight damage. The cover of a bubble pack may be cracked or there may be very slight soiling etc.

3.   GOOD (G)
The box is complete both inside and out and retains an overall attractive collectable appearance. Furthermore despite showing a few signs of wear and tear it does not appear 'tired'.

4.   FAIR (F)
The box will appear to be 'tired' and show definite signs of wear and tear. It may well be incomplete and not contain the original packing materials or leaflets. In addition it may not display all the exterior identification labels or they may be torn or soiled or it may have a box-end flap missing or be otherwise slightly damaged. In this condition unless the model is particularly rare, it will have only a small effect on a model's value.

5.   POOR (P)
The box will show considerable signs of wear and tear. It will almost certainly be badly damaged, incomplete or heavily soiled and being in this condition, unless it is very rare, is of little value to a collector.

MODEL AND BOX
VALUATION GUIDELINES

The research has produced the following comparative price information concerning the values of both unboxed models and separate boxes in the various condition classifications.

The guidelines have been based on the 'General Condition' grading system as described in the previous section. The percentage value ranges are designed to reflect the relatively higher values of the rarer models and boxes.

BOX CLASSIFICATION	% VALUE OF MINT BOXED MODEL
Mint	15%-25%
Excellent	10%-20%
Good	5%-15%
Fair	5%-10%
Poor	0%- 5%

N.B. The same model may have been issued in two types of box eg. 'Yesteryears'. The model in the earlier box is normally more valuable.

Rare Models and Sets

The exceptions to the foregoing guidelines are in respect of rare models or boxes, or models seldom found in first class condition such as some pre-war Dinkies. In these situations rarity commands a premium and the asking price or the price realised at auction will almost certainly reflect it.

UNBOXED MODEL CLASSIFICATION	% VALUE OF MINT BOXED MODEL
Mint	65%-75%
Excellent	55%-65%
Good	35%-55%
Fair	15%-35%
Poor	0%-15%

SELLING MODELS TO THE TRADE

The model value figures produced by the Price Grading System always refer to the likely *asking prices* for models.

They have been prepared solely to give collectors an idea of the amount they might reasonably expect to pay for a particular model.

The figures given are *not* intended to represent the price which will be placed on a model when it is offered for sale to a dealer. This is hardly surprising bearing in mind that the dealer is carrying all the expense of offering a collecting service to his customers which costs money to maintain.

Collectors should therefore not be surprised when selling models to the trade to receive offers which may appear somewhat low in comparison with the figures shown in the catalogue.

Dealers are always keen to replenish their stocks with quality items and will, as a result, normally make perfectly fair and reasonable offers for models. Indeed, depending on the particular models offered to them, the actual offer made may well at times exceed the levels indicated in the catalogue which are only *guidelines* and not firm figures.

One last point when selling models to the trade do get quotations from two or three dealers especially if you have rare models to be sold.

HOW TO USE THE CATALOGUE

a. Identifying Models from their Lettering

All lettering shown in CAPITAL LETTERS indicates the actual lettering on the model itself. It may appear in either the Model Type or Model Features column. *Similarly lettering in Italics also indicates that it is shown on the model itself.*

b. Abbreviations

Where necessary abbreviations have been used. Whilst they are not difficult to use, an example of their use has been shown at the beginning of the Abbreviations section at the rear of the book.

DIE-CAST MODEL CODE REFERENCE SYSTEM

CODE 1

Applies to models which have been totally produced by a manufacturer.

CODE 2

Same as CODE 1 only model labelled outside the factory WITH the permission of the manufacturer.

CODE 3

Same as CODE 2 only model labelled WITHOUT permission of manufacturer.

OFFICIAL COMPANY ACKNOWLEDGEMENTS

The name 'MATCHBOX', 'MODELS OF YESTERYEAR', SUPERKINGS' and 'DINKY' are trademarks of the Matchbox Group of companies and are subject to extensive trademark registrations (Marca Registrada) 1987 and 1988.

'CORGI TOYS', 'CORGI CLASSIC', 'CARS OF THE FIFTIES', 'CORGITRONICS'
This catalogue acknowledges that these trademarks are the property of Corgi Toys Ltd.

'MODELS OF DAYS GONE'
The catalogue acknowledges that this trademark is the property of Lledo (London) Ltd.

'BUDGIE TOYS'
The catalogue acknowledges that this trademark is the property of Starcourt Ltd.

CATALOGUE OMISSIONS

Accurate birth records do not exist in respect of all the die-cast models issued. Therefore whilst every effort has been made to provide comprehensive information it is inevitable that collectors will have knowledge of models which have not been included. Consequently the compiler will be pleased to receive details of these models in order that they be included in any future editions. Naturally supporting evidence regarding authenticity will be required.

This catalogue has been prepared solely for use as a reference book and guide to the rarity and asking prices of die-cast model toys.

Whilst every care has been taken in compiling the catalogue, neither the compiler nor the publishers can accept any responsibility whatsoever for any financial loss which may occur as a result of its use.

TEN YEARS ON AND WE'RE STILL NUMBER ONE!

COLLECTORS' GAZETTE celebrates its first decade of publishing at the end of 1988 and there will be a suitably colourful issue to mark the event. Toy collecting was in its infancy in the late seventies when the Gazette first appeared, but within a couple of years we were flourishing . . . and so was the hobby with new shops opening and swapmeets being established up and down the country.

As the eighties have progressed toy collecting in all its branches has become a major leisure industry that the early pioneering collectors could hardly have dreamed about.

All along the way the Gazette has provided the main channel of communication in the hobby . . . and continues to do so. Because we're a NEWSPAPER we tackle the job seriously and give readers and advertisers an up-to-the-minute news and advertising service.

Not just in Great Britain but all over the world.

Small wonder that our circulation and readership figures are constantly on the increase. Well at 80p a copy on the news stand or from specialist shops, most collectors clearly know a bargain when they see one!

For the Gazette is packed with columns and pages of advertising and editorial news and features aimed specifically at the toy collector. It's published every month except January and includes, among other things, pages of events announcements PLUS detailed reports from the shows from our network of correspondents.

In short Collectors's Gazette neatly wraps up all your news, views and information needs in a bright monthly tabloid colour newspaper that'll keep you informed all year round about the hobby - the marketplace AND the people in the news.

Collectors Gazette

EDITORIAL & ADVERTISING: 0623 515574
92 KIRKBY ROAD, SUTTON-IN-ASHFIELD, NOTTS.   NG17 1GH
OVERSEAS: 0825 4951
THE ROSERY, NEW PLACE, UCKFIELD, EAST SUSSEX TN22 5DP.
SUBSCRIPTIONS: 0602 612747
17 ADBOLTON LODGE, WHIMSEY PARK, CARLTON, NOTTS NG4 1DR

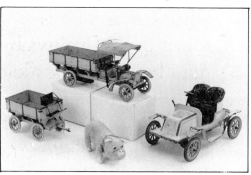
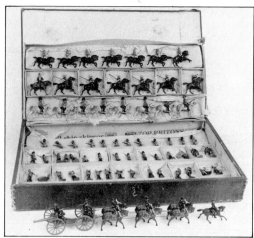

24

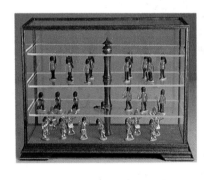

DINKY TOYS
Dinky Post-war Racing, Sports & Saloon Cars and their boxes

23a/220 Racing Cars with original trade box

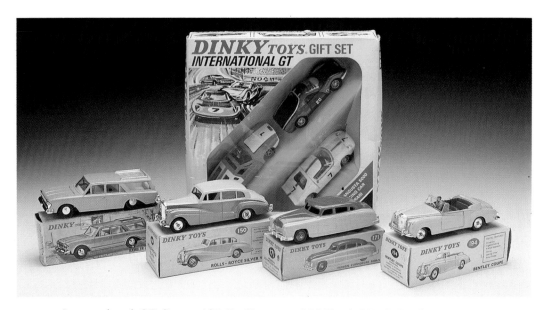

International GT Set — 187 De Tomaso, 215 Ford GT, 212 Dino Ferrari

Front Row: Hong Kong Issue, 006 Nash Rambler Wagon, 150 Rolls Royce Silver Wraith,
171 Hudson Commodore, 194 Bentley 'S' Series Coupé

DINKY TOYS

Police Vehicles
Gift Set 294 — 250 Mini Cooper 'S', 254 Range Rover
407 Ford Transit
Front Row — 269 Jaguar, 256 Humber Hawk

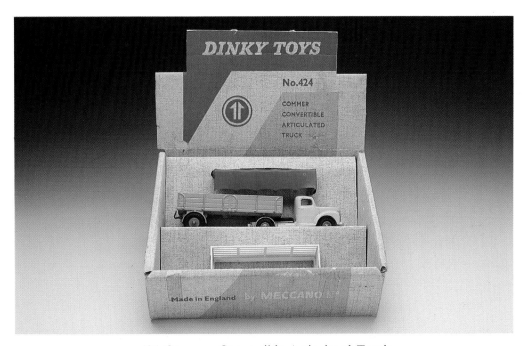

424 Commer Convertible Articulated Truck

DINKY TOYS
Commercial Vehicles and their boxes

Front Row: 504 Foden Tanker (1st Type)
944 Leyland Octopus 'SHELL BP' Tanker
943 Leyland Octopus 'ESSO' Tanker
on Boxes 941 Foden 'MOBILGAS' Tanker
942 Foden 'REGENT' Tanker

Bedford 'TK' Truck Models
425 Coal Wagon, 450 'CASTROL' Van
402 'COCA-COLA' Delivery Truck

DINKY TOYS

Special Aeroplane issue

No. 700 — The last aeroplane issued in 1979

Novelty and Film/TV link up models

102 Joe's Car
107 Stripey the Magic Mini
100 Lady Penelope's FAB 1

DINKY TOYS
Pre-war models

22b Sports Coupé, 28a Delivery Van

Three of a Kind — 22e Farm Tractors

DINKY TOYS

Pre-war No. 27 Tramcar and 29a Motor Bus

Model picture kindly supplied by John Watson of the Dinky Die-cast Club, Cheltenham

SPOT-ON MODELS
Models and common packaging for cars and commercials

Rear Row: 110/4 Mammoth Major & Shell BP Tanker
             106A/OC Austin Prime Mover displaying on the crate its 104 MGA load
Front Row: 102 Bentley Sports Saloon, 101 Armstrong Siddeley 236

SPOT-ON MODELS

Well-designed, detailed die-cast models; 1/42nd scale of the full-size vehicles. All models have steering wheels, number plates, seats, windows and detailed chassis. A number of models include independent suspension, plated grilles and bumpers. Special mention must be made of the model No. 100S/L Ford Zodiac, now fitted with front and rear electric lights.

All cars, roadways, pavements, traffic lights and road signs are to identical scale. The only complete scale highway system available.

126	156	Mulliner Coach with independent suspension. 14/6.
127	165	Vauxhall Cresta with independent suspension. 4/11.
128	157	Rover 3 Litre with independent suspension. 4/11.

129 No. 1 Presentation Set contains:—
1 No. 100 Ford Zodiac.
1 No. 101 Armstrong Siddeley Sapphire.
1 No. 103 Rolls Royce Silver Wraith.
1 No. 104 M.G.A. Sports Car.
1 No. L124/4 }
1 No. L125   } Road Signs
1 No. L127   }
1 No. L128
1 No. L129
2 No. L126 Belisha Beacon.
2 No. L132/2 7" Straight with dotted white line.
1 No. L132/3 7" Straight with Zebra Crossing.
4 No. L133/3 90° Curve with continuous white line. Box size 16" × 14½". 46/11.

130 158A/2 Bedford 10 Tonner with articulated 2,000 gallon tanker. 15/11.

131 100S/L Ford Zodiac with electric lights front and rear. Fitted with independent suspension.

132 191/1 Sunbeam Alpine with hardtop and independent suspension. 3/11.

133 No. 2 Presentation Set contains:—
1 No. 109/3 E.R.F. 68G Flat Float with Sides.
1 No. 102 Bentley 4-Door Saloon, Duo-tone.
1 No. 101 Armstrong Siddeley Sapphire.
1 No. 105 Austin Healey Sports Car.
4 No. L132/2 7" Straight with Dotted white line.
4 No. L133/3 90° Curve with Cont. white line.
1 No. L132/3 7" Straight with Zebra Crossing.
2 No. L126 Belisha Beacon.
1 No. L124/4 }   1 No. L129 } Road
1 No. L125   } Road Signs 1 No. L137 } Signs
1 No. L128/1 }
Box size 16" × 15½". 59/11.

SPOT-ON 1/42nd SCALE MODELS

SEE IMPORTANT NOTE ON PAGE 2.

Picture taken from the Christmas 1961 Tri-ang Toys Catalogue

MATCHBOX TOYS
MATCHBOX MINIATURES — 1-75 SERIES

Circa 1959 — 1st Type Gift Set PS3 (see Gift Sets listing)

Circa 1960/61 — 2nd Type Gift Set (see Gift Sets listing)

MATCHBOX TOYS
MATCHBOX MINIATURES — 1-75 SERIES

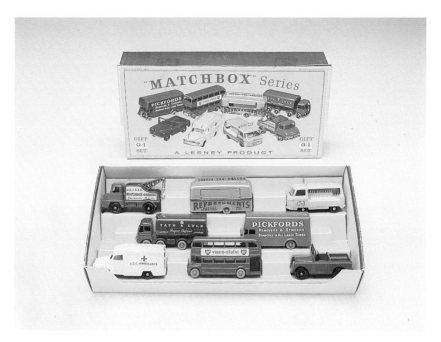

Circa 1962-63 — 3rd Type Gift Set G1

G6 Commercial Truck Gift Sets
Top Set — Superfast issue
Bottom Row: i) 1965 issue   ii) 1969 issue

MATCHBOX TOYS
MATCHBOX MINIATURES — 1-75 SERIES

Later Gift Sets
Top to bottom: G4 Team Matchbox Set 1973
G3 'Wild Ones' Set 1973
G11 Strike Force Set 1978
For further details see Gift Sets listing

MATCHBOX TOYS — MAJOR SERIES MODELS

Rear Row: M6 'PICKFORDS' Transporter
           M4 'FREUHOF' Hopper Train
           M86 'FARNBOROUGH-MEASHAM' Car Transporter
2nd Row: M8a 'MOBILGAS' Tanker
           M9 'COOPER-JARRETT' Freighter
           M2a 'WALLS ICE CREAM' Bedford Truck
           M2b 'DAVIES TYRES' York Freightmaster

MATCHBOX TOYS — KING SIZE MODELS

Gift Set G8 — Contains L-R Nos. 14, 13, 7, 1, 10 (see listings)

MATCHBOX TOYS   Models of Yesteryear

1st issues

Rear Row: Y16, Y11-1, Y9-1, Y3-1, Y15-1
Middle Row: Y13-1, Y5-1, Y8-1, Y4-1, Y2-1, Y12-1
Front Row: Y7-1, Y6-1, Y1-1, Y14-1, Y10-1

2nd issues

Y4-2 Shand Mason Horse Drawn Fire Engines
i) Kent Fire Brigade   ii) London Fire Brigade

MATCHBOX TOYS   Models of Yesteryear

1st, 2nd & 3rd issues in Picture Boxes 1960-68
Rear Row: Y15-1, Y9-2, Y6-3, Y12-2, Y14-2, Y16-1, Y2-2, Y4-3
Middle Row: Y3-2, Y13-2, Y10-2, Y7-2, Y5-2, Y11-2, Y1-2
Front Row: Y6-2, Y8-2

Later types of packaging
Rear Row: i) The 'Red' box 1984 onwards, ii) 'Red' Limited Edition Box issued 1987
iii) 'Straw' box 1979-1983
Front Row: i) 'Woodgrain' box 1974-1978, ii) Yellow Pink Window Box, issued 1968-70
iii) Yellow Mauve Window Box 1969-70

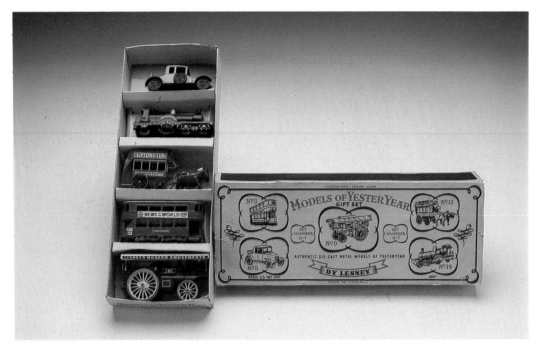

1st Type of Gift Set Pack G7

Gift Set — 'Golden Veterans' — Gift ware Gold plated models

MATCHBOX TOYS

Chester Toy Museum — Home of the Matchbox International Collectors Association (M.I.C.A.)

The Museum houses a remarkable collection of the complete range of Matchbox Toys' diecast products from 1947 onwards. In addition many other toys are on display including a fine Dinky Toy display.

Our picture shows just a few of the 'Early Lesney' toys on display and has been reproduced by the kind permission of Kevin Mcgimpsey and Stewart Orr.

Chester Toy Museum
Part of the tremendous 'Models of Yesteryear' display
Reproduced by kind permission of the museum

CORGI TOYS

Early Commercial Vehicles
i) 1966-67 1140 Bedford 'TK' Type Tanker
ii) 1962-65 1110 Bedford 'S' Type Tanker

Chipperfields Circus Commercial Vehicles
Rear Row: 1139 Scammell Handyman 'Menagerie Truck', 1121 Crane Truck
Front Row: 1144 Circus Crane & Cage, 1130 Horse Transporter

CORGI TOYS

Early Double Decker Buses and Taxi
Rear Row: London Gift Set No 35, 468 'Outspan', 418 Taxi plus a London Bobby on point duty
Front Row: 468 'Corgi Toys' and 468 'Visit the Design Centre'

Later Routemasters plus and A.E.C.
Rear Row: C469 'New Corgi Company', 477 'Woolworths' Silver Jubilee issue
C485 'Isle of Wight County Press'
Middle Row: Open Top '1984 Collectors Visit' one of just 12 issued
C469 'Manchester Lions Club', 409 Gloucester Toy Fair
Front Row: C523 'You can't afford to be without a British Diecast Model Toys Catalogue' — the Swapmeet
Bus. 592/2 A.E.C. 'Woodhams Scooters' — note the different radiator shell

Corgi Cars in early 'Blue' boxes
Top Row: 202, 207m, 211m, 303
Bottom Row: 210, 208m, 205, 204 (see listing for details)

2nd Type of packaging for small models

Rear Row: 153, *345 (later box), 224, 208S
Front Row: 216, 422, 304S, 222 (for details see listings)

CORGI TOYS

Models of U.S.A. Vehicles

i) 219 Plymouth Sports Suburban   ii) 439 Chevrolet Fire Chief   iii) 443 Plymouth — U.S. Mail
Original U.K. prices were 3s 11d, 5s and 4s 11d respectively.
Today's U.K. prices £35, £35 and £45!

Novelty Film and TV Tie-in Models and Packaging

261 — James Bond's Aston Martin DB5 — original 1965 'Goldfinger' issue
336 — 007's Toyota 2000GT from 'You Only Live Twice'

CORGI TOYS

Original Corgi Classic and packaging circa 1964-69

L-R: i) 9021 1910 Daimler, ii) 1915 Model 'T' Ford plus driver,
iii) 9001 1927 Bentley, iv) 9032 1910 12/16 Renault
N.B.: A line drawing of each model was enclosed in the box

Collector Club Model 1988

Classic Series Packaging — Morris Minor van C957/3

CORGI TOYS

Corgi Classics reintroduced 1985 onwards

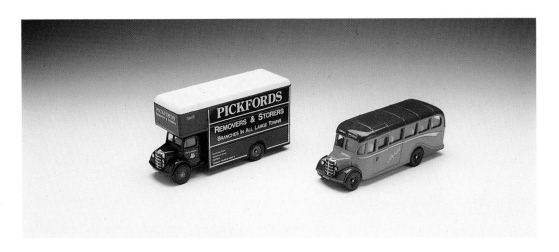

i) C953/1 Bedford 'O' Series Pantechnicon
ii) C949/1 Bedford Type 'OB' Coach

Rear Row: C859 Thorneycroft Van with roof rack, C858/1 Thorneycroft Bus, C906/1 Mack Truck
Middle Row: C867 Thorneycroft Beer Truck, 922 1926 Renault Van, 1929 Thorneycroft Box Van
Front Row: C865 Ford Model 'T' Van, C864 Ford Model 'T' Tanker

Tri-ang Ships

1 : 1200 Scale

REG'D TRADE MARK

First Edition 2d.

QUEEN ELIZABETH

Tri-ang Ships are an exciting new series. Scale Docks, an Ocean Convoy or Fleet Manoeuvres— all can be reproduced in thrilling miniature. Each model has a heavy diecast hull, bringing out in precise detail the lifeboats, bollards, portholes and anchors. Masts, cranes, and other projecting parts are moulded in resilient plastic for strength and safety. New models are continually being built and will be introduced at frequent intervals.

R.M.S. CARONIA
ACTUAL SIZE OF MODEL

First Edition Catalogue page circa 1960

Tri-ang Minic Ships

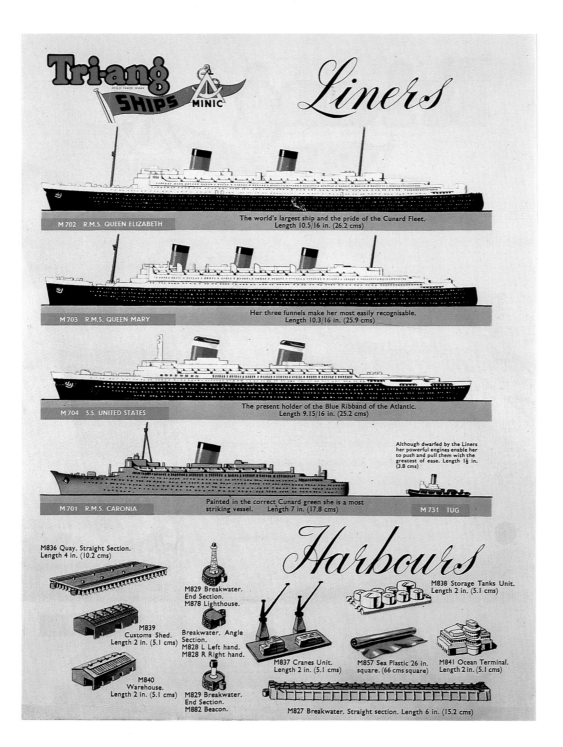

First Edition Catalogue page circa 1960

Tri-ang Minic Ships

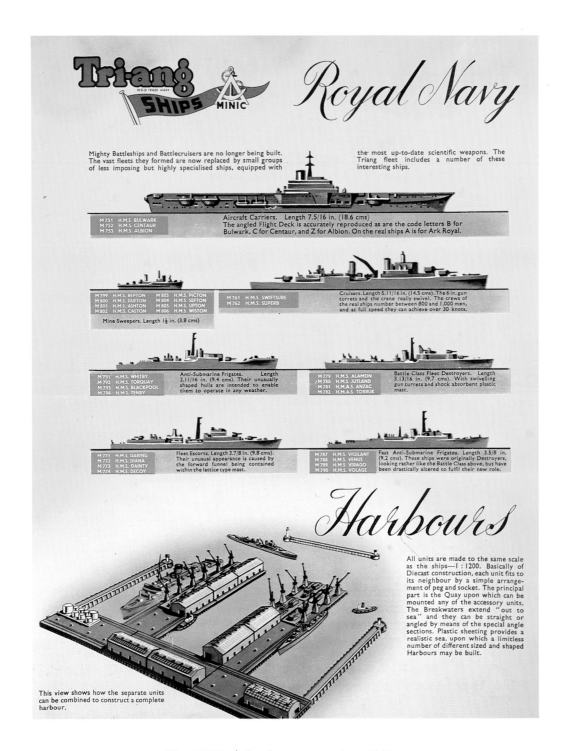

Tri-ang SHIPS MINIC

Royal Navy

Mighty Battleships and Battlecruisers are no longer being built. The vast fleets they formed are now replaced by small groups of less imposing but highly specialised ships, equipped with the most up-to-date scientific weapons. The Tri-ang fleet includes a number of these interesting ships.

M 751	H.M.S. BULWARK
M 752	H.M.S. CENTAUR
M 753	H.M.S. ALBION

Aircraft Carriers. Length 7.5/16 in. (18.6 cms) The angled Flight Deck is accurately reproduced as are the code letters B for Bulwark, C for Centaur, and Z for Albion. On the real ships A is for Ark Royal.

M 799	H.M.S. REPTON	M 803	H.M.S. PICTON
M 800	H.M.S. DUFTON	M 804	H.M.S. SEFTON
M 801	H.M.S. ASHTON	M 805	H.M.S. UPTON
M 802	H.M.S. CALTON	M 806	H.M.S. WISTON

Mine Sweepers. Length 1½ in. (3.8 cms)

| M 761 | H.M.S. SWIFTSURE |
| M 762 | H.M.S. SUPERB |

Cruisers. Length 5.11/16 in. (14.5 cms). The 6 in. gun turrets and the crane really swivel. The crews of the real ships number between 800 and 1,000 men, and at full speed they can achieve over 30 knots.

M 791	H.M.S. WHITBY
M 792	H.M.S. TORQUAY
M 793	H.M.S. BLACKPOOL
M 794	H.M.S. TENBY

Anti-Submarine Frigates. Length 3.11/16 in. (9.4 cms). Their unusually shaped hulls are intended to enable them to operate in any weather.

M 779	H.M.S. ALAMEIN
M 780	H.M.S. JUTLAND
M 781	H.M.A.S. ANZAC
M 782	H.M.A.S. TOBRUK

Battle Class Fleet Destroyers. Length 3.13/16 in. (9.7 cms). With swivelling gun turrets and shock absorbent plastic mast.

M 771	H.M.S. DARING
M 772	H.M.S. DIANA
M 773	H.M.S. DAINTY
M 774	H.M.S. DECOY

Fleet Escorts. Length 3.7/8 in. (9.8 cms). Their unusual appearance is caused by the forward funnel being contained within the lattice type mast.

M 787	H.M.S. VIGILANT
M 788	H.M.S. VENUS
M 789	H.M.S. VIRAGO
M 790	H.M.S. VOLAGE

Fast Anti-Submarine Frigates. Length 3.5/8 in. (9.2 cms). These ships were originally Destroyers, looking rather like the Battle Class above, but have been drastically altered to fulfil their new role.

Harbours

All units are made to the same scale as the ships—1 : 1200. Basically of Diecast construction, each unit fits to its neighbour by a simple arrangement of peg and socket. The principal part is the Quay upon which can be mounted any of the accessory units. The Breakwaters extend "out to sea" and they can be straight or angled by means of the special angle sections. Plastic sheeting provides a realistic sea, upon which a limitless number of different sized and shaped Harbours may be built.

This view shows how the separate units can be combined to construct a complete harbour.

First Edition Catalogue page circa 1960

First Edition Catalogue page circa 1960

BUDGIE AND MORESTONE MODELS

Models and Packaging — Major and Miniature Models

L–R: 238 Scammell Scarab 'BRITISH RAILWAYS'
PL6 Miniature Series Gift Set (see listings)
218 Seddon 'AA' Jumbo Traffic Control Unit
Morestone Guy Arab Double Decker Bus 'ESSO' plus box

CRESCENT TOYS

1809 Dextra Tractor

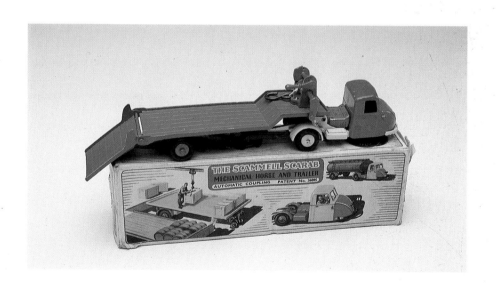

1274 Scammell Scarab and Low Loader Trailer

LLEDO 'MODELS OF DAYS GONE'

Rarities, Packaging and Plastic Figures

Rear Row: DG 005 003   Black boiler Guildford Fire Brigade
             DG 005 004   Red boiler Hong Kong Fire Brigade
             DG 004 001   Horse Drawn Omnibus
Front Row: DG 009 001   Two tone 'POLICE' Model 'A' Ford Open Car
             DG 005 004   Gold boiler Hong Kong Fire Brigade (not rare)

LLEDO 'MODELS OF DAYS GONE'

Special Set issued for 'HAMLEYS' of Regent Street, London

L-R: DG 004-006 Horse Drawn Omnibus   DG 007-005 1930 Ford Woody Wagon
       DG 010-006 Albion Single Decker Bus   DG 013-004 Ford Model 'A' Van
       DG 006-027 Model 'T' Van   DG 003-008 Horse Drawn Delivery Van

DINKY TOYS

293 Atlantean 'BP', 289 Routemaster 'TERN SHIRTS'
248 'CONTINENTAL TOURING COACH', 292 Atlantean 'REGENT'
289 Routemaster 'MADAME TUSSAUDS'
In front: 292 Atlantean 'RIBBLE'

DINKY TOYS

INTRODUCTION

Since the 1st Edition was published, Matchbox Toys Ltd have purchased the 'DINKY TOYS' trademark and intend to introduce a new range of classic cars to be called 'THE DINKY COLLECTION'. Christmas 1988 therefore will see the first new 'DINKIES' in the shops for 8 years — a sight that will gladden the heart of many a collector the world over.

HISTORY OF DINKY TOYS

Meccano Ltd introduced in 1931 a series of railway station and trackside accessories to accompany their famous 'HORNBY' train sets. These 'Modelled Miniatures' were in sets numbered 1-22 and included railwaymen, station staff, passengers and trains. Set number 22 was comprised of six vehicles which were representative rather than being replicas of actual vehicles. It was first seen advertised in the Meccano Magazine of December 1933.

At about this time 'Tootsie Toys' of America were importing model vehicles into the United Kingdom and they were proving to be very popular. Consequently Meccano Ltd decided to widen their range of products and issue a comprehensive series of models to include vehicles, ships and aircraft.

'Modelled Miniatures' therefore became 'Meccano Dinky Toys' and set number 22 the first set of 'Dinky Cars'. The first 'Dinky Toys' advertisement appeared in the April 1934 edition of the Meccano Magazine. The first actual Dinky car produced after the change of name, was 23a in April 1934. It was probably based on an early MG but was again more representative rather than being an actual replica.

Set 22 cost 4/- and consisted of 22a Sports Car, 22b Sports Coupe, 22c Motor Truck, 22d Delivery Van, 22e Tractor and 22f Tank and is today highly sought after.

The range of models produced quickly grew so that the Meccano Magazine of December 1935 was claiming that there were 200 varieties for sale.

Although the phrase 'Dinky Cars' became a household name, the actual range of models was of course far greater even including dolls house furniture.

Indeed by the time the famous Binns Road, Liverpool factory finally closed its doors in November 1979 over 1000 different designs had been produced, with a similar number emanating from the French factory outside Paris.

Today pre-war models are rare and fetch high prices which reflects how difficult it is to find a model in really good condition. This is because many pre-war models were made from an unstable alloy and have tended to crystallize and disintegrate.

Fortunately the post-war models do not suffer from the same problem and much of today's collecting interest in centred around the superb models produced in the fifties and sixties.

It has been said of Dinky Toys that if you love them you'll buy them. Nothing truer has ever been stated for in the eyes of all Dinky enthusiasts they really do seem to possess a delightful charm all of their own.

DINKY TOYS

MARKET SURVEY

The survey results reflected the following:-

i) With the exception of the 36 Series models the pre-war and immediate post-war issues have remained fairly static.

ii) Models issued 1953-1969 have moved ahead strongly — particularly the commercial vehicles.

iii) Aeroplane and train sets have increased considerably.

iv) At the time of going to print in mid-1988 prices for the rarer models appeared to be moving strongly ahead — possibly reflecting the increased investor interest in old toys following the October 1987 stockmarket crash.

PRICE AND RARITY CHANGES

			1981-83 Survey		1985 Survey		1988 Survey	
CARS	40b(151)	Triumph 1800 Saloon	£22-£27	MPR	£50	NC	£75	NC
	107	Sunbeam Alpine	£22	NC	£50	NC	£65	NC
	179	Studebaker President	£16	NC	£45	NC	£55	NC
COMMERCIALS	902	2nd Foden Flat Truck	£30	NC	£75	NC	£135	NC
	905	2nd Foden Chain Lorry	£55	NC	£85	NC	£150	NC
	908	Antar/Transformer	£75	NC	£175	GP	£300	GP
	942	Foden 'REGENT'	£100	GP	£175	GP	£350	GP
VANS	260	'ROYAL MAIL' Van	£32	NC	£60	NC	£90	NC
	451	Trojan 'DUNLOP' Van	£40	NC	£70	NC	£95	NC
	465	Morris 10 cwt						
		'CAPSTAN' Van	£55	NC	£125	GP	£175	GP
BUSES	292	Atlantean 'REGENT'	£30	NC	£55	NC	£70	NC
	949	Wayne 'SCHOOL						
		BUS'	£55	GP	£110	GP	£135	GP
FIRE VEHICLE	250	Fire Engine	£19-£25	MPR	£40	NC	£50	NC
POLICE	258	U.S.A. Police Car	£16-£20	MPR	£40	NC	£50	NC
AMBULANCES	30f	1947/48 Ambulance	£35	NC	£55	NC	£65	NC
	253	Daimler	£11-£16	MPR	£45	NC	£55	NC
ROADMAKING	960	Albion Lorry	£13-£16	MPR	£30	NC	£35	NC
FARM	27a	Massey Harris Tractor	£14-£17	MPR	£35	NC	£45	NC
MILITARY	642	R.A.F. Pressure						
		Refueller	£16-£22	MPR	£40	NC	£50	NC
AEROPLANES	708	Viscount 'BEA'	£28-£32	MPR	£65	NC	£75	GP
NOVELTY	485	Santa Special Model T						
		Ford	£22	NC	£55	NC	£65	NC
MISCELLANEOUS	071	Dinky Dublo						
		'HORNBY DUBLO'	£15	NC	£30	NC	£45	NC

Common Features

There are several common features which apply to the various groups of models and to avoid unnecessary repetition in the 'Features' column these have been shown below.

Dinky Toys, Meccano Ltd or Meccano Dinky Toys

These wordings are to be found stamped on all post-war models and virtually all pre-war models. They are either on the Base Plate or chassis or in the case of the early models cast into the model itself. On the very early 22 Series Van the words HORNBY SERIES are cast in.

Wheels

The Types of Wheels

It has been assumed that pre-war models have white tyres and post-war models black tyres unless otherwise described.

eg. MW   Metal Wheels
SWRW   Solid White Rubber Wheels
SBRW   Solid Black Rubber Wheels
PW   Plastic Wheels
SWS   Speedwheels
ATT   Arrow Tread Tyres

Wheel Hubs

Pre-war wheels have been assumed to have smooth wheel hubs and post-war ridged. This ridge or nave plate is clearly discernible on post-war models. A few of the smooth pre-war variety were issued in 1946, an example of this being 153A Jeep 1st issue.

Similarly it is generally accepted that a few ridged wheels may have been used pre-war.

Nevertheless smooth wheel hubs combined with the other identifying points given in the pre-war section should be sufficient to determine whether it is pre-war or not. One final point on smooth wheels is that if there is evidence of silver-plating on them the model is definitely pre-war.

Wheel Construction

It is assumed that all wheels were of a die-cast mazuk construction until 1958/59 when a shiny spun metal type was introduced. Models issued in both the old type and new type wheels included 131, 178, 179, 180, 181, 182 and the 290 bus.

The exceptions to the foregoing are the 1st type 28 Series Vans which were of a lead alloy construction.

The die-cast wheels on the 230-235 racing cars were replaced by plastic wheels as were the normal wheels on Model No 183, the Fiat 600. Where they are known to have been fitted this has been indicated by (PW) Plastic Wheels.

Speedwheels (SWS)

These were issued from the early seventies. Some models were issued with either Metal wheels or Speedwheels with the former being the more collectable.

Model Number and Name

It has been assumed that all post-war models have either the model number or name or both stamped on the base plate or chassis.

Pre-war models usually had neither although some did eg. the 38 Series and 39 Series had the Model name on the base plate.

Windscreens (WS)

Assumed to be Plastic unless otherwise described eg. celluloid Windscreen (CWS) Tinplate Windscreen (TPWS) Open or Solid Windscreen (Open/Solid WS) Open Windscreen (OWS) Solid Windscreen (SLWS).

Base Plate (BP) and Chassis (CH)

All assumed to be of Tinplate or metal construction unless otherwise indicated. eg. PCH Plastic Chassis.

Construction Materials

All models assumed to be constructed at last in part of a die-cast alloy. A few pre-war models were made of a lead alloy. eg. The 22 Series and 28 Series (Type 1) plus the odd models such as 23a Racing Car (1st casting) and 23m Thunderbolt Speed Car.

Windows (WDS)

All the first models to have plastic windows fitted have been given the above abbreviation. The later issues have been assumed to have them fitted anyway.

Hooks (H)

1947/8 Fodens had no hooks (NH).

Axles

Assumed that all pre-war models had crimped axles as did the following post-war issues:— 23, 25, 280, 29, 30, 34, 35, 36, 37, 38, 39 and 40 Series. Otherwise models had rivet ended axles until the advent of Speedwheels. Early Guy models had 'clip' type mountings.

Length of Models

The pre-war measurements shown may include slight inaccuracies due to the measurement of models which have expanded in the course of time.

'Supertoys' (ST)

These were first introduced in 1947 when six large lorries plus the Shetland Flying Boat were announced. These models are easily identified having DINKY SUPERTOYS on the chassis. The large commercials should also have treaded tyres.

Scale Sizes of Dinky Toys

The original Dinky models were made to an approximate 1/48 scale. In the late sixties and early seventies the 1/43 and 1/36 scale were introduced much to the annoyance of collectors who found the larger size models didn't match up with their existing collection too well!

PRE-WAR MODELS IDENTIFICATION FEATURES TO LOOK FOR:—

i)   The wheel hubs were smooth and not ridged (see section 2a on wheels).

ii)   Axles were crimped.

iii) Look for unpainted bare metal base plates.

iv)   Look for early chassis types.

v)   Only pre-war models had wing mounted spare wheels.

vi)   Whilst tyres can be changed only pre-war models had white tyres.

vii) Slots in the chassis for the driver and passengers indicates that the model is from the pre-war 36 series.

viii) Look for the early van and lorry front types.

ix)   Know your facts eg. only the pre-war Double Decker Bus of the 29 Series had stairs on the platform etc.

x)   Thinner axles used pre-war eg 22 Series Trucks.

NB. Model Numbers Reference System

Because of the Dinky habit of renumbering their models when they were re-issued some models have two or three numbers shown.

CLASSIFYING THE EARLY MODEL TYPES

In addition to the details given in the earlier sections, the age and category of a particular model is determined by features such as:—

 i) The type of chassis or Base Plate.

 ii) The type of Radiator Shell and Bumper.

iii) Body features such as the front of a Lorry, Van or Bus.

These features were first categorised into types by Cecil Gibson in his excellent book 'History of British Dinky Toys 1934-1964' and readers requiring detailed information should obtain a copy from MIKANSUE, 15 Bell Lane, Eton Wick, Windsor, Berks.

A basic understanding of these types is necessary as models described for sale often refer to Cecil Gibson's original 'Type 1' etc gradings.

The following diagrams show details of the differences between the types:—

A. The Chassis Types 1934-1950

1934-38 Criss Cross Chassis (CCCH)	1934-48 Open Chassis (OCH)	1938-50 Moulded Chassis (MCH)	1946-47 Plain Chassis (PLCH)

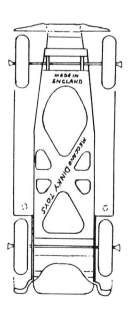 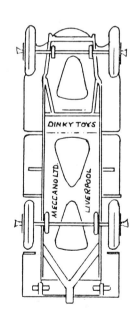 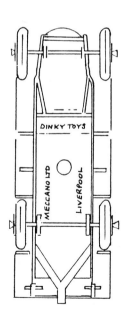 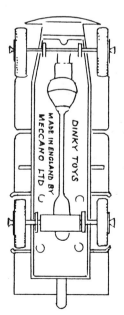

B. The Van Types 1934-1954
28 Series and 280 Series Castings.

1st Type 1934-36	2nd Type 1936-38	3rd Type 1938-54
	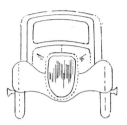	
2 Piece Lead Construction Metal Wheels Radiator not cast in. No Headlights.	One Piece Construction Rubber Tyres (White) Cast in Radiator Made of Poor Metal and liable to disintegrate.	One Piece Construction Rubber Tyres Cast in Radiator Front Bumper Made of Poor Metal and liable to disintegrate.

C. The Lorry Types 1934-50
25 Series Commercials

1st Type 1934-1938	2nd Type 1938-1940	3rd Type 1946-47	4th Type 1947-50
		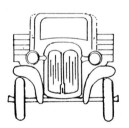	

1st Type No Headlights on a tinplate Radiator, Open Chassis.

2nd Type Headlights on a die-cast Radiator, Open Chassis.

3rd Type This model has the same lorry front as the 2nd Type but has a Plain Chassis.

4th Type Headlights on a die-cast Radiator plus the bumper.

D. The Heavy Commercial Types 1947-60

1st Type
Foden 1947-52

2nd Type
Foden 1952-55

1st Type
Guy 1947-54

2nd Type
Guy 1954-58

Warrior Type
1959-60

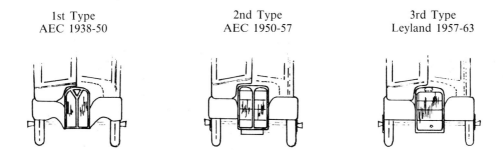

Note the slight difference in the casting around the area of the number plate between the 1st and 2nd Types of Guy Vehicles.

E. The Bus Types 1938-63

1st Type
AEC 1938-50

2nd Type
AEC 1950-57

3rd Type
Leyland 1957-63

There are three main types although many slight variations in the castings are thought to exist. Note the 2nd Type AEC is also referred to as a Guy at times.

Dinky Cars

Ref. No.		Model Type	Model Features and Size	Rarity and Price Grading		

Note. For a description and diagrams of the different Chassis Types see page 61.

Ref. No.		Model Type	Model Features and Size	Price	Grading	
22a	1933-35	Sports Car (Wolseley Hornet)	Orange/Cream body, Tinplate Radiator, Metal Wheels, No headlights. 82 mm.	£400	GP	☐
22b	1933-35	Sports Coupe (SS Jaguar)	Cream body, Red roof and wings, gold metal wheels, TPR with No Headlights or Yellow/Green body.	£400	GP	☐
22g	1935-40	Streamline tourer	Cream, Gold or Red body SSW and WS. 85 mm.	£135	NPE	☐
22h	1935-40	Streamlined Saloon	Red, Blue or Cream body, OPC. 85 mm.	£135	NPE	☐
23a	1934-35	Racing Car	Orange and Green body, No driver 4EX. 94 mm.	£100	NPE	☐
23a	1935-38	Racing Car	Blue and White body, driver, 6EX/RRD/RN. 94 mm.	£75	NPE	☐
23a	1938-40	Racing Car	Red body, Cream flash, D/6EX/RN. 94mm.	£65	GP	☐
23a	1946-48	Racing Car	Blue body, Silver flash DCI/No RN. 94 mm.	£50	NC	☐
23a	1949-52	Racing Car	Red body, Silver flash, Black circles RN '4' Driver cast in. 94 mm.	£35	NC	☐
23a	1953-54	Racing Car	Silver body, Red flash, Red circles RN '4', Driver cast in. 94 mm.	£35	NC	☐
23b	1935-40	Hotchkiss Racing Car	Blue body, white flash RN '5', OC. 100 mm.	£60	NC	☐
23b	1946-48	Hotchkiss Racing Car	Red or Silver body, Red RN '5'. 96 mm.	£30	NC	☐
23c	1936-40	Mercedes-Benz RC	Red or Blue body, Yellow circle, RN '2' MTB/DCI/ENR. 92 mm.	£65	GP	☐
23c	1947-50	Mercedes-Benz RC 'Large Open Racing Car'	Blue or Silver body, RN/MTB/DCI. 92 mm.	£30	NC	☐
23d	1936-40	Auto Union Racing Car	Red or Blue body, White or Yellow Circles, RN, DSI/ENR. 100 mm.	£55	GP	☐
23d	1947-50	Auto Union Racing Car	Silver body, Red RN '2', No D/MTPBP. 100 mm.	£35	NC	☐
23e	1936-40	'Speed of the Wind' Racing Car	Blue, Red or Yellow body RN '1', ENR/MTB/DCI. 104 mm.	£55	GP	☐
23e	1946-49	'Speed of the Wind' RC	Red (R) or Silver body MTB/DCI. 104 mm.	£35	NC	☐
23e (221)	1950-54	'Speed of the Wind' RC	Silver body, Plain base plate, DCI. 104 mm.	£25	NC	☐
23f (232)	1952-54	Alfa-Romeo Racing Car	Red body, White RN '8' on tail, D/SWCI. 100 mm.	£35	NC	☐
23g (233)	1952-54	Cooper Bristol Racing Car	Green body, White RN '6' on tail, D/SWCI. 89 mm.	£35	NC	☐
23h (234)	1953-54	Ferrari Racing Car	Blue body, Yellow nose & RN '5' on tail Driver and steering wheel cast in. 100 mm.	£35	NC	☐
23j (235)	1953-54	H.W.M. Racing Car	Green body, Yellow RN '7' on tail Driver and steering wheel cast in. 99 mm.	£35	NC	☐
23k (230)	1953-54	Talbot-Lago Racing Car	Blue body, Yellow RN '4' on tail Driver and steering wheel cast in. 103 mm.	£35	NC	☐
23m	1938-40	Thunderbolt Speed Car	Light or Dark Green body, Union Jacks on tailfin, DCI/LC/Boxed. 126 mm.	£100	GP	☐
23n (231)	1953-54	Maserati Racing Car	Red body, White flash, White RN '9' on tailfin, Driver and SW cast in. 94 mm.	£45	MPR	☐
23p	1939-40	Gardners MG Record Car	Green body, White flash, *MG Magnette* and UJS on sides, MG badge on nose DCI. 104 mm.	£100	GP	☐
23S	1938-40	Streamlined Racing Car	Silver body, DCI, Lead versions exist. 126 mm.	£50	GP	☐
23S (232)	1948-54	Streamlined Racing Car	Blue, Green or Silver body Green or Blue flashes. 128 mm.	£25	NC	☐
24a		See Ambulances				
24b	1934-38	Limousine	Maroon/Black or Maroon/Grey body, OC/SPWW/3SDW/CCCH/Plain R/3HBL/No SDL. 98 mm.	£145	GP	☐
24b	1938-40	Limousine	Blue body, yellow chassis, No SPW, OC, 3 SDW/CCCH/R badge/3 HBL/No SDL. 98 mm.	£120	GP	☐
24c	1934-38	Town Sedan	Blue or Cream Blue body, SPWW/1 SDW OC/Plain R/CCCH/VBL/No SDL. 97 mm.	£140	GP	☐
24c	1938-40	Town Sedan	Blue or Red/Black body No SPW/1 SDW/OC/R Badge/CCCH/VBL/No SDL. 97 mm.	£120	GP	☐
24d	1934-38	Vogue Saloon	Two tone Green or Green/Black body, OC/SPWW/1 SDW/CCCH/Plain R/VBL/No SDL. 107 mm.	£140	GP	☐
24d	1938-40	Vogue Saloon	Red/Grey or Brown/Green body OC/No SPW/1 SDW/R badge/VBL/No SDL/CCCH. 107 mm.	£120	GP	☐
24e	1934-38	Super Streamlined Saloon	Two tone Red or Green/Red body, OC/No SPW/1 SDW/CCCH/Plain R/VBL/No SDL. 97 mm.	£140	GP	☐
24e	1938-40	Super Streamlined Saloon	Red/Black or Green Blue body, OC/No SPW/1 SDW/CCCH/R Badge/VBL/No SDL. 97 mm.	£120	GP	☐
24f	1934-38	Sportsmans Coupe	White/Blue or Blue/Yellow body, OC/SPWW/1 SDW/CCCH/Plain R/VBL/No SDL. At Phillips Auction on June 1st 1983 a similar model fetched £180. 100 mm.	£140	GP	☐
24f	1938-40	Sportsmans Coupe	Two tone Brown or Two tone Blue body 1 SDW/No SPW/R badge/CCCH/VBL/No SDL. 100 mm.	£120	GP	☐
24g	1934-38	Sports Tourer 4 Seater	Yellow/Brown or Blue/Brown body, OC/SPWR/Plain R/CCCH/OWS/VBL/No SDL. 104 mm.	£140	GP	☐
24g	1938-40	Sports Tourer 4 Seater	Black/Cream or Yellow/Blue body, OC/No SPW/R badge/CCCH/SLWS/VBL/No SDL. 104 mm.	£120	GP	☐
24h	1934-38	Sports Tourer 2 Seater	Two tone Red or Two tone Green body, OC/SPWR/Plain R/CCCH/OWS/VBL/No SDL. 98 mm.	£140	GP	☐
24h	1938-40	Sports Tourer 2 Seater	Black/Cream or Cream/Green body, OC/No SPW/R badge/CCCH/SLWS/VBL/No SDL. 98 mm.	£120	GP	☐
			NB. The rarest models of the 24 Series have coloured tyres to match their body paintwork and can be expected to value higher.			
25j	1947-48	Jeep	Red or Green body LHD/SW/TPWS/SPWR Some issued with smooth pre-war hubs. 68 mm.	£45	GP	☐
25y	1952-54	Jeep	Red body, LHD/SW/TPWS/H/SPW on side. 83 mm.	£35	NC	☐
27d (340)	1950-54	Land Rover	Green/Orange body, D/SW/TPWS/SPW BD. 90 mm.	£35	NC	☐
27d (344)	1950-56	Estate Car	Brown/Fawn body, Rear axle pillars. 105 mm.	£45	NC	☐
30a (32)	1935-40	Chrysler 'Airflow' Saloon	Blue or Green body, No chassis 3 side windows, separate Bumper unit. 103 mm.	£135	NPE	☐
30a	1946-48	Chrysler 'Airflow' Saloon	Blue, Cream or Green body, No chassis 3 side windows, separate Bumper unit. 103 mm.	£110	GP	☐

Ref. No.		Model Type	Dinky Cars continued		Price	Grading
30b	1935-40	Rolls Royce	Grey body or Dark Blue body, OC/2 SDW/SBL/Open CH/No SDL. 101 mm.		£145	GP ☐
30b	1946-50	Rolls Royce	Blue/Black or Fawn/Black body, OC/2 SDW/SBL/Open or Plain CH/No SDL. 101 mm.		£55	NC ☐
30c	1935-40	Daimler	Fawn or Light Blue body OC/2 SDW/Open CH/No SDL. 98 mm.		£145	GP ☐
30c	1946-50	Daimler	Green/Black or Cream/Black body, OC/2 SDW/Open or Plain CH/No SDL. 98 mm.		£55	NC ☐
30d	1935-38	Vauxhall	Brown or Green body, OC/SPWW/CCR/Open CH/HBL/3 SDW/No SDL. 102 mm.		£145	NPE ☐
30d	1937-38	Vauxhall	Cream/Brown or Blue/Black body, OC/No SPWW/CCR/Open CH/HBL/3 SDW/No SDL. 102 mm.		£145	NPE ☐
30d	1938-40	Vauxhall	Maroon/Black or Yellow/Black body, OC/SPWW/SSR/Open CH/HBL/3 SDW/No SDL. 100 mm.		£120	GP ☐
30d	1946-48	Vauxhall	Brown/Black or GRN/BLK body, OC/3 SDW/No SPW/SSR/Open or Plain CH/HBL/No SDL. 98 mm.		£55	NC ☐
32 (30a)	1935	Chrysler 'Airflow' Saloon	See 30a for details. 103 mm.			
35a	1936-40	Austin 7 Ruby Saloon	Grey, Blue & TT, SWRW 51 mm.		£55	GP ☐
35a	1946-48	Austin 7 Ruby Saloon	Blue or TT Blue or TT grey body, SBRW		£50	GP ☐
35b	1936-39	Racer	Red body, Silver grille, No driver SWRW or SBRW. 61 mm.		£45	GP ☐
35b (200)	1939-40	Racer	Silver body, Brown D, Red grille, SBRW. 59 mm.		£40	GP ☐
35c	1936-40	MG Sports Car	Red, Green or Blue body, Silver Radiator, SWRW/SPW/WS/SW. 52 mm.		£55	GP ☐
35c	1946-48	MG Sports Car	Red or Green body, Silver R, SBRW. 52 mm.		£45	NC ☐
35d	1938-40	Austin 7 Tourer	Blue, Green or Yellow body, Silver grille, SWRW/WWS/SW. 50 mm.		£35	NC ☐
35d	1946-48	Austin 7 Tourer	Fawn or Grey body, SBRW/No WS. 50 mm.		£30	NC ☐
36a	1937-40	Armstrong-Siddeley	Blue or Brown/Black body, 3 SDW/ASR/MCH/SDL/VBL (3×4)/SBP. 97 mm.			
			With driver and footman		£500	NPE ☐
			Without		£180	GP ☐
36a	1946-48	Armstrong-Siddeley	Blue, Green, Grey or Maroon/Black body, AVI Red body 3 SDW/ASR/VBL (3×4)/ No figures. 97 mm.		£55	NC ☐
36b	1937-40	Bentley Two seater Sports Coupe	Green/Black or Cream/Black body, OC/SBL (3 + 9)/SBP/SDL/MCH/BR/1 SDW/S. 100 mm.			
			With driver and passenger		£500	NPE ☐
			Without		£180	GP ☐
36b	1946-48	Bentley Two seater Sports Coupe	Green, Grey or Cream body, OC/1 SDW/SBL (3 + 9)/SDL/MCH/BR No figures. 93 mm.		£55	NC ☐
36c	1937-40	Humber Vogue	Grey/Black or TT Green body, OC/1 SDW/SDL/MCH/HVR/5 SBL. 100 mm.			
			With driver and footman		£500	NPE ☐
			Without		£180	GP ☐
36c	1946-48	Humber Vogue	Grey/Black or Green/Black body OC/1 SDW/SDL/HVR/5 SBL/No figures. 97 mm.		£55	NC ☐
36d	1937-40	Rover Streamlined Saloon	Two tone Red or Green/Black body, 2 SDW/SDL/RVR/MCH/12 SBL. 99 mm.			
			With driver and passenger		£500	GP ☐
			Without		£180	GP ☐
36d	1946-48	Rover Saloon	Blue or Green body, black chassis, 2 SDW/SDL/MCH/RVR/12 SBL/ No figures. 94 mm.		£65	NC ☐
36e	1937-40	British Salmson (2 seater Sports)	Red/Black or Blue Black body, OC/SPWRS/MCH/BSR/13 VBL/SDL/SLWS. 98 mm.			
			With driver		£500	NPE ☐
			Without		£180	GP ☐
36e	1946-48	British Salmson (2 seater Sports)	Red or Blue body, Black chassis, OC/MCH/13 VBL/No SPW/SDL/BSR/No D/SLWS. 93 mm.		£55	NC ☐
36f	1938-40	British Salmson (4 seater Sports)	Red/Brown or Two Tone Green body, 13 VBL/SDL/MCH/No SPW/BSR/SLWS. 98 mm.			
			With driver		£500	NPE ☐
			Without		£180	GP ☐
36f	1946-48	British Salmson (4 seater Sports)	Green or Grey body, Black chassis, 13 VBL/SDL/MCH/SWCI/BSR/No D/SLWS. 96 mm.		£55	NC ☐
38a	1940	Fraser Nash (B.M.W.) Sports Car	Blue or Light Grey body, Blue or Fawn seats, Silver Trim, CWS/BMBP. 82 mm.		£100	GP ☐
38a	1946-49	Fraser Nash (B.M.W.) Sports Car	Blue or Green body, Matt Black or Khaki seats, SWOS/BPBP. 82 mm.		£55	NC ☐
38b	1940	Sunbeam Talbot Sports	Green/Brown body CWS/BMBP/OC. 92 mm.		£100	NPE ☐
38b	1946-49	Sunbeam Talbot Sports	Blue or Green body, Matt Blue or Maroon tonneau cover SWOS/BPBP. 92 mm. Yellow body version £30 more.		£55	NC ☐
38c	1946-50	Lagonda Sports Coupe	Green or Grey body, Matt black, dark green or grey seats, SWOS/BPBP, B/S/VSN. 102 mm.		£55	NC ☐
38d	1940	Alvis Sports Tourer	Green body, Brown seats and hood, OC/SW/BMBP/CWS. 95 mm.		£100	NPE ☐
38d	1946-49	Alvis Sports Tourer	Blue/Grey body OC/SWOS/BPBP. 95 mm.		£55	NC ☐
38e	1946-49	Armstrong Siddeley Coupe	Cream or Light Grey body, Blue seats, SW/BPBP/WS. 96 mm.		£55	NC ☐
38f	1940-46	Jaguar Sports Car	Khaki/Blue body, 2WS/BMBP. 80 mm.		£100	NPE ☐
38f	1946-49	Jaguar Sports Car	Red or Blue body, 2 WS/BPBP/OC. 80 mm.		£55	NC ☐
39a	1940-41	Packard Super 8 Tourer	Brown or Grey body, Silver Trim, Moulded Spare Wheel, OC/BMBP. 107 mm.		£140	GP ☐
39a	1946-50	Packard Super 8 Tourer	Brown or Green body, Silver Trim, Moulded Spare Wheel, OC/BPBP. 107 mm.		£60	NC ☐
39b	1940-41	Oldsmobile 6	Blue or Green body, Silver Trim Bare Metal Base Plate OC. 100 mm.		£140	GP ☐

Ref. No.		Model Type	Dinky Cars continued	Price	Grade	
39b	1946-50	Oldsmobile 6	Blue, Green or Brown body, Silver Trim OC/BPBP. 100 mm.	£80	NC	☐
39bu	1950-54	Oldsmobile Sedan US Issue	Two tone Blue or Two tone Sand body, BPBP. 100 mm.	£350	GP	☐
39c	1940-41	Lincoln Zephyr	Grey, Brown or Cream body Silver Trim, OC/BMBP. 106 mm.	£140	GP	☐
39c	1946-50	Lincoln Zephyr	Grey or Brown body, Black chassis, black painted base plate OC. 106 mm.	£80	NC	☐
39cu	1950-54	Lincoln Zephyr US Issue	Two tone Red or Two tone Tan body, Black painted base plate. 106 mm.	£350	GP	☐
39d	1940-41	Buick Viceroy	Grey or Maroon body, Silver trim, OC/BMBP/MSPW. 103 mm.	£140	GP	☐
39d	1946-49	Buick Viceroy	Brown, Green or Maroon body, Silver trim, OC/BPBP/MSPW. 103 mm.	£80	NC	☐
39e	1940-41	Chrysler Royal	Yellow or Green body, Silver trim, OC/BMBP/MSPW. 106 mm.	£140	GP	☐
39e	1946-49	Chrysler Royal	Blue or Cream body, Silver trim, OC/BPBP. 106 mm.	£80	NC	☐
39eu	1950-54	Chrysler Royal US Issue	Yellow/Red or Two tone Green body, Black painted base plate. 106 mm.	£350	GP	☐
39f	1940-41	Studebaker State Commander	Green or Dark Grey body, Silver trim, OC/BMBP. 103 mm.	£140	GP	☐
39f	1946-49	Studebaker State Commander	Brown or Green body, Silver Trim, OC/BPBP. 103 mm.	£80	NC	☐
40a	1947-55	Riley Saloon	Blue, Cream, Green or Grey body, BPBP/SPEV. 93 mm.	£75	NC	☐
40b	1948-49	Triumph 1800	Blue, Fawn or Grey body, RAP. 91 mm.	£75	NC	☐
40b	1949-55	Triumph 1800	Blue, Fawn or Grey body, RAHBP. 91 mm. (151)	£75	NC	☐
40d (152)	1949-54	Austin Devon	Lt or Dark green, Lt or Dk Blue or red body. 85 mm.	£75	NC	☐
40e	1948-50	Standard Vanguard	Brown or Maroon body, SPBP/ORWH. 91 mm.	£75	NC	☐
40e	1950-55	Standard Vanguard	Fawn or Maroon body, SPBP/CRWH. 91 mm. (153)	£75	NC	☐
40f (154)	1951-55	Hillman Minx	Lt or Dk Green or Lt or Dk Brown. 88 mm.	£75	NC	☐
40g (159)	1950-55	Morris Oxford	Dark Green or Fawn body. 93 mm.	£75	NC	☐
40j (161)	1949-55	Austin Somerset	Red or Light Blue body. 89 mm.	£75	NC	☐
101	1957-60	Sunbeam Alpine (TF)	Blue or Pink body, CD/SW/W/No RN. 94 mm.	£85	NC	☐
102	1957-60	MG Midget (TF)	Yellow or Orange body, CD/SW/WS/No RN. 83 mm.	£90	GP	☐
102	1957-60	MG Midget (TF)	Rare green version.	£175	GP	☐
103	1957-60	Austin Healey 100 (TF)	Red or Cream body, CD/SW/WS/No RN. 87 mm.	£65	NC	☐
104	1957-60	Aston Martin (TF)	Blue or Pink body, CD/SW/No RN. 87 mm.	£65	NC	☐
105	1957-60	Triumph TR2 SC (TF)	Grey body, CD/SW/WS/No RN. 84 mm.	£75	NC	☐
		Colour change	Yellow body version	£130	GP	☐
106	1954-58	Austin A90 Atlantic	Blue body, cream seats. 95 mm.	£70	NC	☐
		Colour variants	Blue body, red seats	£100	GP	☐
			Blue body, blue seats	£125	GP	☐
			Pink or black body	£95	GP	☐
			Red body	£500	NPE	
107	1955-59	Sunbeam Alpine (CF)	Blue body, RN '26', or Pink body RN '34', RCD/SW/WS. 94 mm.	£65	NC	☐
108	1955-59	MG Midget (CF)	Red body, RN '24', or White body RN '28', RCD/SW/WS. 83 mm.	£100	GP	☐
109	1955-59	Austin Healey 100 (CF)	Cream body, RN '23', or Yellow body RN '21', RCD/SW/WS. 85 mm.	£65	NC	☐
110	1966-70	Aston Martin DB5	Red/Black body, SS/SW/TS/OBN/WS. 111 mm.	£55	NC	☐
111	1956-59	Triumph TR2 (CF)	Pink body, RN '29', RCD. 84 mm.	£80	NC	☐
			Turquoise body RN '25'.	£75	NC	☐
112	1961-66	Austin Healey Sprite II	Red body, SS/SW/WS/FS/S. 78 mm.	£55	NC	☐
		South African Issues	Turquoise, light blue or dark blue body	£150	GP	☐
113	1962-68	M.G.B.	Cream body, CD/SW/SS/FS/WS/OD. 85 mm.	£55	NC	☐
		South African Issue	Red body version	£150	GP	☐
114	1963-71	Triumph Spitfire	Gold, Red, Grey or Purple body Lady driver SS/OD/WS/S/SW/SPKW. 88 mm.	£50	NC	☐
115	1967-68	Plymouth Fury Sports	Silver body D/PS/SW/SS/FS/SL/WS. 122 mm.	£80	GP	☐
116	1966-71	Volvo 1800 S	Red body, SS/TS/FS/SL/ODBB. 105 mm.	£40	NC	☐
120	1962-67	Jaguar 'E' Type	Red or Blue body, Black roof DHT. 91 mm.	£65	NC	☐
122	1977-79	Volvo 265 DL Estate	Blue or Orange body, SS/ORD/PW. 141 mm.	£20	NC	☐
123	1977-79	Princess 2200 HL	Bronze or White body, Black roof SS/PW. 128 mm.	£20	NC	☐
124	1977-79	Rolls Royce Phantom V	Met Light Blue body, SS/OD/PW/OBT/D. 141 mm.	£20	NC	☐
127	1964-66	RR Silver Cloud Mk 3	Gold body, SS/FS/SL/TS/WDS/ODBN. 125 mm.	£65	GP	☐
128	1964-73	Mercedes Benz 600	Met Red body, D/LHD/ODBB/LG/PW. 147 mm.	£25	NC	☐
128	1974-79	Mercedes Benz 600	Met Blue body, SW/SS/ODBB/PW. 147 mm.	£15	NC	☐
129	1968-74	1300 Volkswagen Sedan	Blue body, SS/FS/SL/OWDS/ODBB. 100 mm.	£30	NC	☐
130	1963-68	Ford Consul Corsair	Red body, OC/SS/FS/SL/OWDS/OBN. 108 mm.	£65	NC	☐
131	1956-62	Cadillac Eldorado	Pink or Yellow body, OBT/SPKW. 118 mm.	£55	NC	☐
132	1968-74	Jaguar 'E' Type 2 + 2	Met Red, Blue or Bronze body, OC/TS/SS/ODBB/SPKW. 112 mm.	£55	NC	☐
			Speedwheels version	£40	NC	☐
132	1955-60	Packard Convertible	Fawn or Green body, D/LHD/WS. 114 mm.	£75	NC	☐
132	1967-71	Ford 40 RV GT 40	Blue or White body, SL/SPKW/OBT. 100 mm.	£30	NC	☐
133	1955-60	Cunningham C5R	White/Blue body, D/LHD/SW/WS. 99 mm.	£55	NC	☐
133	1964-68	Ford Cortina	Met Yellow, SS/FS/SL/OD/WDS. 102 mm.	£40	NC	☐
134	1964-67	Triumph Vitesse	Met Green or Met Blue body SS/WDS/SW. 87 mm.	£45	NC	☐
135	1963-68	Triumph 2000	Blue/White body, OC/SS/FS/OD/LG/WDS. 107 mm.	£35	NC	☐
		Colour change	Also Black body, cactus roof version	£40	NC	☐
136	1964-72	Vauxhall Viva	Blue or White body, SS/FS/OD/WDS. 94 mm.	£30	NC	☐
137	1963-65	Plymouth Fury CV	Met Grey body, OC/LHD/FS/SW/WS/OBN. 122 mm.	£55	GP	☐
138	1963-72	Hillman Imp	Met Green or Blue body, SS/SL/ODBT/LG. 86 mm.	£30	NC	☐
139a	1949-54	Ford Fordor Sedan	Red or Brown body. 102 mm. (170)	£75	NC	☐
139b	1950-54	Hudson Commodore	Blue/Stone or Cream/Dark Red body. 111 mm.	£75	NC	☐
139	1963-64	Ford Cortina	Met Red body SS/FS/SL/OD/WDS. 102 mm.	£40	NC	☐
140	1963-68	Morris 1100	Blue body SS/OBT/WDS/FS. 87 mm.	£35	NC	☐
141	1963-67	Vauxhall Victor EC	Yellow body SS/FS/ORD/WDS. 92 mm.	£30	NC	☐
		South African Issue	With Pink Orange body	£150	GP	☐

66

Ref. No.		Model Type	Dinky Cars continued	Price	Grading	
142	1962-68	Jaguar Mark 10	Met Blue body SS/FS/OD/WDS. 106 mm.	£35	NC	☐
143	1962-66	Ford Capri	Green/White body SS/FS/WDS/LG. 90 mm.	£35	NC	☐
144	1963-66	Volkswagen 1500	White body, SS/FS/OBN/WDS/LG. 88 mm.	£35	NC	☐
145	1962-66	Singer Vogue	Met Green body SS/FS/WDS. 93 mm.	£35	NC	☐
146	1963-66	Daimler 2½ litre V8	Met Green body SS/FS/WDS. 95 mm.	£35	NC	☐
147	1962-68	Cadillac 62	Met Green body LHD/SS/FS/WDS. 113 mm.	£35	NC	☐
148	1962-65	Ford Fairlane	Met Green body LHD/SS/FS/WDS. 111 mm.	£35	NC	☐
		South African Issue	Bright Blue body	£150	GP	☐
149	1971-74	Citroen Dyane	Gold/Black body LHD/SS/ORDBT/WDS/SWS. 91 mm.	£15	NC	☐
150	1959-66	Rolls R Silver Wraith	Grey/Dark Grey body SS/WDS/CP. 117 mm.	£40	NC	☐
151 (40b)	1954-60	Triumph 1800	Blue or Brown body. 91 mm.	£75	NC	☐
151	1966-68	Vauxhall Victor 101	Yellow or Red body, OC/SS/FS/SL/OBB. 105 mm.	£35	NC	☐
152	1967-75	Rolls Royce Phantom V	Dark Blue body D/SS/ODBB/WDS. 141 mm.	£20	NC	☐
			Later Metallic Blue version	£12	NC	☐
152 (40d)	1954-56	Austin Devon	Maroon or Blue body. 86 mm.	£75	NC	☐
	1956-60	Colour changes	Blue/Yellow body or Grey/Pink body.	£150	GP	☐
		Rare colours	Green/Cerise body.	£225	GP	☐
153 (40e)	1954-60	Standard Vanguard	Blue, Cream or Fawn body, LPBP/RBT. 91 mm.	£75	GP	☐
153	1966-71	Aston Martin DB6	Blue or Green body, SS/FS/SL/TS/ODBB. 111 mm.	£30	NC	☐
154 (40f)	1954-56	Hillman Minx	Green or Brown body. 87 mm.	£75	NC	☐
154	1956-58	Hillman Minx	Green/Cream or Pink/Blue body. 87 mm.	£150	GP	☐
154	1966-68	Ford Taunus	Yellow/White body, LHD/SS/FS/TS/WDS. 110 mm.	£30	NC	☐
155	1961-64	Ford Anglia	Blue body, SS/WDS. 81 mm.	£30	NC	☐
		South African Issue	White body version	£150	GP	☐
156	1954-56	Rover 75	Cream body. AVI Maroon body. 101 mm. (140b)	£75	GP	☐
156	1956-60	Rover 75	Blue/Cream or Two tone Green body. 101 mm.	£100	GP	☐
156	1968-70	Saab 96	Red body SS/TS/OD. 98 mm.	£35	NC	☐
157	1954-56	Jaguar XK120	Green, White, or Red body. 97 mm.	£95	GP	☐
157	1960-62	Jaguar XK120	Cerise/Yellow or Grey/Yellow body. 97 mm.	£150	GP	☐
157	1968-71	BMW 2000 Tilux	Blue/White body SS/SL/WDS. '1st AGAIN! FLASHING INDICATORS'. 121 mm.	£35	NC	☐
158	1954-60	Riley Saloon	Blue or Cream body LPBP. 93 mm.	£75	NC	☐
158	1967-72	Rolls Royce Silver Shadow	Met Red body SS/ODBB/WDS. '1st AGAIN! 4 OPENING DOORS'. 125 mm.	£25	NC	☐
			Later Met Blue version	£15	NC	☐
159	1954-56	Morris Oxford	Fawn or Green body. 93 mm. (40g)	£75	NC	☐
159	1956-60	Morris Oxford	Green/Cream or White/Red body. 93 mm.	£125	GP	☐
159	1967-69	Ford Cortina Mk II	White body, SS/ODBB/WDS/FS/TS. 105 mm.	£30	NC	☐
160	1967-70	Mercedes Benz 250 SE	Met Blue body, LHD/FS/SS/SL/WDS. 117 mm.	£30	NC	☐
160	1958-62	Austin A30	Green or Brown body, plastic wheels.	£50	NC	☐
161	1954-56	Austin Somerset	Red or Lt Blue body (40j) 89 mm.	£75	NC	☐
161	1956-60	Austin Somerset	Black/Cream body. 89 mm.	£150	GP	☐
		Colour variant	Yellow/Red body.	£175	GP	☐
		Colour variant	Blue/Cerise body.	£225	GP	☐
161	1965-72	Ford Mustang	White or Yellow body SS/FS/SL/TS. 111 mm.	£20	NC	☐
162	1956-60	Ford Zephyr	Cream/Green or TT Blue body. 96 mm.	£55	GP	☐
162	1966-69	Triumph 1300	Blue body, SS/FS/SL/OBB. 92 mm.	£35	NC	☐
163	1956-60	Bristol 450	Green body, Black circle with RN. 98 mm.	£45	NC	☐
163	1966-69	Volkswagen 1600 TL	Red body, SS/SL/TS/ODBB. 102 mm.	£30	NC	☐
164	1957-60	Vauxhall Cresta	Maroon/Cream or Green/Grey body. 96 mm.	£60	GP	☐
164	1967-71	Ford Zodiac Mk IV	Silver body, SS/FS/SL/ODBB. '1st AGAIN! 4 OPENING DOORS'. 114 mm.	£30	NC	☐
165	1959-63	Humber Hawk	Maroon/Fawn or Green/Black body, WDS. 102 mm.	£55	NC	☐
165	1969-74	Ford Capri	Green or Met Purple body SS/OD/SWS. 102 mm.	£25	NC	☐
166	1958-63	Sunbeam Rapier	Cream/Orange or TT Blue body or Blue/TQ. 89 mm.	£45	NC	☐
166	1967-69	Renault R16	Blue body SS/OD/FS/TS/OD. 86 mm.	£25	NC	☐
167	1958-63	A.C. Aceca	Red/Grey or Cream/Brown body WDS. 89 mm.	£55	NC	☐
168	1959-63	Singer Gazelle	Cream/Brown or Grey/Green body. 92 mm.	£55	NC	☐
168	1968-76	Ford Escort	Blue or Red body, OD/TS/PW later/BUP. 97 mm.	£20	NC	☐
169	1958-63	Studebaker Golden Hawk	Green/Fawn or Fawn/Red body. 106 mm.	£45	NC	☐
169	1967-69	Ford Corsair 2000E	Silver/Black body SS/FS/SL/OD. 108 mm.	£50	NC	☐
170	1954-56	Ford Fordor	Yellow or Red body. 102 mm.	£75	NC	☐
170 (139a)	1956-59	Ford Fordor	Cream/Red or Pink/Blue body. 102 mm.	£100	GP	☐
170	1964-69	Lincoln Continental	Blue body, White roof, OC/OC/SL/LHD/SS/FS/OBN/WDS/CP. 127 mm.	£35	NC	☐
170	1979	Granada Ghia	Never issued on general release. 127 mm.	—		☐
171 (139b)	1954-56	Hudson Commodore	Blue/Stone or Cream, Dark Red body. 111 mm.	£75	NC	☐
171	1956-58	Hudson Commodore	Cream/Maroon or Dark Blue/Fawn body.	£75	NC	☐
171	1966-69	Austin 1800	Blue body, SS/FS/SL/OBB. 101 mm.	£40	NC	☐
172	1954-56	Studebaker Land Cruiser	Green or Blue body. 107 mm.	£65	NC	☐
		Colour change	Beige/Cream body.	£95	NC	☐
		Colour change	White/Pink body.	£95	NC	☐
172	1965-68	Fiat 2300 Station Wagon	Blue body, SS/FS/SL/TS/OBRD. 108 mm.	£35	NC	☐
173	1958-62	Nash Rambler	Green/Cerise or Pink/Blue body, WDS. 101 mm.	£40	NC	☐
173	1968-73	Pontiac Parisienne	Maroon body, FS/SS/SWS/2A. '1st AGAIN! RETRACTABLE AERIALS'. 132 mm.	£25	NC	☐
174	1958-63	Hudson Hornet	Red/Cream or Yel/Grey body, WDS. 111 mm.	£55	NC	☐
174	1969-72	Ford Mercury Cougar	Blue body, SS/OD/SWS/2A. 122 mm.	£25	NC	☐
175	1958-61	Hillman Minx	Beige/Green, Grey/Blue or Blue/TQ. body. 88 mm.	£55	GP	☐
175	1969-72	Cadillac Eldorado	Purple/Black body, OC/SS/OD/SWS. 133 mm.	£45	NC	☐
176	1958-63	Austin A 105	Grey/Red, Cream/Blue or Black/Cream body. 102 mm.	£45	NC	☐
176	1969-73	N.S.U. R 080	Maroon or Green body, LVS/SS/SL. 90 mm.	£25	NC	☐
177	1961-67	Opel Kapitan	Blue body, LHD/FS/SS/WDS. 100 mm.	£25	NC	☐
		South African Issue	Dark Blue version	£150	GP	☐

Ref. No.		Model Type	**Dinky Cars continued**		Rarity and Price Grading		
178	1959-63	Plymouth Plaza	Pink/Green body, WDS. 108 mm.	£80	GP	
		Colour change	Light Blue body, Dark Blue roof and flash	£60	NC	
178	1974-80	Mini Clubman	Bronze body, OD/WDS. 75 mm.	£15	NC	
179	1958-63	Studebaker President	Blue body, Blue FL, or Yel body, BL FL. 108 mm.	£65	NC	
179	1971-74	Opel Commodore	Blue/Black body, OC/SS/ODB/SWS. 107 mm.	£20	NC	
180	1958-63	Packard Clipper	Fawn/Pink body, OC/WDS. 112 mm.	£55	NC	
180	1978-79	Rover 3500	White body, OC/OD/PCH/PW. 131 mm.	£15	NC	
180	1979-80	Volvo Estate Car	Orange body. Made in Italy. (Polistil)	£15	NC	
181	1956-69	Volkswagen Saloon	Dark Blue body or Grey body or Green body.	£45	NC	
		South African Issue	Cream, Light Green or Light Blue body	£150	GP	
182	1958-66	Porsche 356A Coupe	Blue, Cream or Red body. 89 mm.	£65	NC	
			Dusty Pink version	£250	GP	
183	1958-60	Fiat 600	Green or Red body, PW seen. 71 mm.	£45	NC	
183	1967-74	Morris Mini Minor	Blue/Black or Red/Black, OD/TS/SL. 75 mm.	£35	NC	
		South African Issue	Red body version	£150	GP	
184	1961-64	Volvo 122S	Red, SS/WDS/SS/S/SW. 97 mm.	£40	NC	
185	1961-63	Alfa Romeo 1900	Red or Yellow body, LHD/SS/FS/S/WDS. 102 mm.	£30	GP	
186	1961-66	Mercedes Benz 220SE	Blue body, LHD/SS/FS/WDS/CP. 102 mm.	£35	NC	
187	1959-63	VW Karmann Ghia Coupe	Red/Black or Cream/Green body, SS/WDS. 96 mm.	£40	NC	
187	1969-77	De Tomaso Mangusta 5000	Red/White body, RN '7', 102 mm.	£20	NC	
188	1968-74	Jensen FF	Yellow or Green body, ODBN/SS/FS/SL/TS. 121 mm.	£30	NC	
189	1959-63	Triumph Herald	Green/White or Blue/White body. 86 mm.	£45	NC	
189	1969-77	Lamborghini Marzal	Red or Green body, DD/SWS. 108 mm.	£20	NC	
190	1971-73	Monteverdi 375L	Red body, OD/SWS. 116 mm.	£20	NC	
191	1959-64	Dodge Royal Sedan	Cream body, Light Brown flash, WDS. 111 mm.	£55	NC	
192	1958-63	De Soto Fireflite	Grey body, Red flash or Green with Fawn flash.	£60	NC	
192	1971-79	Range Rover	Bronze or Yellow body, OD/SWS. 109 mm.	£18	NC	
193	1961-68	Rambler Cross Country	Yellow/White body, SS/FS/WDS/CP. 102 mm.	£35	NC	
		South African Issues	TT Cream and Mauve, Mauve or Green body	£150	GP	
			NB. With all South African issues be wary of fakes.			
194	1961-66	Bentley 'S' Coupe	Grey body, Red seats, Brown DB, Grey D, or Gold body, Cream seats, SS/FS/CP. 113 mm.	£55	NC	
		South African Issue	Cream body version	£150	GP	
195	1960-66	Jaguar 3.4 Mk II	Maroon, Cream or Grey body, SS/FS. 97 mm.	£50	NC	
196	1963-69	Holden Special Sedan	Bronze/White body, SS/FS/ODBN/WDS. 108 mm.	£45	NC	
		South African Issue	Two tone White and Turquoise	£150	GP	
197	1961-70	Morris Mini Traveller	Cream or Green body, SS/FS/WDS. 73 mm.	£30	NC	
198	1962-68	Rolls Royce Phantom V	Green/Cream or Two tone Grey body, D. 125 mm.	£45	NC	
199	1961-70	Austin 7 Countryman	Blue body, Wood TR, SS/FS/WDS. 73 mm.	£30	NC	
200	1954-57	Midget Racer	Red or Silver body. 57 mm. (356)	£35	NC	
200	1971-74	Matra 630 Le Mans	Blue body, RN '5' or '36'. 105 mm	£20	NC	
201	1979	Plymouth Stock Car	Blue body, RN '34' PW. 134 mm.	£15	NC	
202	1971-74	Fiat Abarth	Red/White body, OD/SWS. 91 mm.	£20	NC	
202	1979-80	Customised Land Rover	Black/Yellow body, PCH/PB. 115 mm.	£15	NC	
202	1978-79	Customised Land Rover	Black body, Yel Labels/LRW/PCH. 110 mm.	£15	NC	
203	1978-79	Customised Range Rover	Black body, PCH/LRW. 109 mm.	£15	NC	
204	1971-74	Ferrari 312P	Red body, OD/SWS RN '60'. 99 mm.	£20	NC	
205	1962-64	Talbot Lago	Blue body, BUP/PW. 103 mm.	£40	NC	
205	1968-71	Lotus Cortina Rally	White/Red body, RN '7' ODBB/SS/FS/TS. 105 mm.	£35	NC	
206	1962-64	Maserati	Red/White body, BUP/PW. 94 mm.	£40	NC	
206	1978-79	Customised Sting Ray	Red/Yellow body, PCH/PW. 113 mm.	£15	NC	
207	1962-64	Alfa Romeo	Red body, BUP/PW. 100 mm.	£40	NC	
207	1977-79	Triumph TRT Rally	White/Red/Blue body RN '8' PW/PCH. 98 mm.	£15	NC	
208	1962-64	Cooper Bristol	Green body, BUP/PW. 89 mm.	£40	NC	
208	1971-74	V.W. Porsche 914	Yellow or Blue body. 89 mm.	£15	NC	
209	1962-64	Ferrari	Blue/Yellow body, BUP/PW. 101 mm.	£40	NC	
210	1962-64	Vanwall	Green body, BUP/PW. 95 mm.	£40	NC	
210	1971-73	Alfa-Romeo 33	Blue body RN '36', SWS. 107 mm.	£25	NC	
211	1972-79	Triumph TR7	Red body, OC/OD/PW. 98 mm.	£15	NC	
212	1967-69	Ford Cortina Rally	White/Black body, *Castrol* RN '8' SS/FS/SL. 102 mm.	£35	NC	
213	1971-74	Ford Capri Rally	Red/Black body RN '20', OD/SWS. 102 mm.	£35	NC	
214	1967-68	Hillman Imp Rally	Blue body RN '35', SS/FS/SC/OBB. 86 mm.	£35	NC	
215	1967-74	Ford GT Racer	White body RN '7', OBN/SL/DE. 96 mm.	£20	NC	
216	1967-74	Dino Ferrari	Blue or Red body, SPW. 98 mm.	£20	NC	
217	1968-73	Alfa Romeo Searabeo OSI	Red body, OD/SWS/OEC. 90 mm.	£20	NC	
218	1970-74	Lotus Europa	Yellow/Blue/Black body, SWS. 90 mm.	£20	NC	
219	1978	'Leyland' Jaguar XJ5-3	Purple/White/Red body, RN '2'. 127 mm.		NGPP	
219	1978-79	Jaguar XJ5 3 litre	White body, Cat decal, No BX. 137 mm.	£15	NC	
220 (23a)	1954-55	Small Open Racing Car	Silver/Red body, RN '4'. 94 mm.	£40	NC	
220	1970-74	Ferrari P5	Red body, OD/SWS. 96 mm.	£15	NC	
221(23e)	1954-57	Speed of the Wind R.C.	Silver body Plain BP. 104 mm.	£40	NC	
221	1970-78	Corvette Stingray	Brown/Orange body, OD/SWS. 113 mm.	£15	NC	
222 (23s)	1955-57	Streamlined Racing Car	Silver or Green body, Red or Blue trim. 126 mm.	£35	NC	
222	1978-79	Hesketh 308E	Blue body, RN '2', PCH/SWS. 132 mm.	£5-£10	MPR	
223	1971-74	McLaren M8A Can-Am	White/Green body, RN '5', SWS, OC. 94 mm.	£10-£15	MPR	
224	1970-73	Mercedes Benz C111	Met Dark Red body, ODBT/SWS. 102 mm.	£10-£15	MPR	
225	1971-77	Lotus F1	Red or Blue body, RN '7'. 127 mm.	£10-£15	MPR	
226	1978-79	Ferrari 312/B2	Red or Gold body RN '5'. 121 mm.	£5-£10	MPR	
227	1975-77	Beach Buggy	Yellow body, White detachable roof. 105 mm.	£10-£15	MPR	
228	1970-72	Super Sprinter	Blue/Silver body, SWS/SS. 113 mm.	£10-£15	MPR	
230 (23k)	1954-64	Talbot Lago RC	Blue body, Yellow RN '4', DCI. 102 mm.	£30	NC	
231 (23n)	1954-64	Maserati RC	Red body, White flash, RN '9', DCI. 92 mm.	£30	NC	
232 (23p)	1954-64	Alfa Romeo RC	Red body, White flash, RN '8', DCI. 102 mm.	£30	NC	
233 (23q)	1954-64	Cooper Bristol RC	Green body, White flash, RN '6', DCI. 89 mm.	£30	NC	

Ref. No.		Model Type	Dinky Cars continued	Rarity and Price Grading		
234 (23h)	1954-64	Ferrari RC	Blue body, Yellow RN '7', DCI, LV had Yellow triangle OL nose. 99 mm.	£30	NC	☐
235 (23j)	1954-60	H.W.M. Racing Car	Green body, Yellow RN '7', DCI. 99 mm.	£30	NC	☐
236	1956-59	Connaught RC	Green body, RN '32', White RCD. 96 mm.	£50	NC	☐
237	1957-68	Mercedes Benz RC	White body RN '30', Blue RCD. 96 mm.	£45	NC	☐
238	1957-64	D-type Jaguar	Turquoise body, White RCD. 87 mm.	£65	NC	☐
239	1958-66	'Vanwall' RC	Green body, White RN '35', RCD. 95 mm.	£35	NC	☐
240	1963-69	Cooper Racing Car	Blue/Green body, RN '20', SS/WS/OEC/DE. 80 mm.	£30	NC	☐
241	1963-69	Lotus Racing Car	Green body, RN '24', SS/WS/OEC/DE. 80 mm.	£30	NC	☐
242	1963-69	Ferrari Racing Car	Red body, RN '36', SS/WS/OEC/DE. 89 mm.	£30	NC	☐
243	1964-71	B.R.M. Racing Car	Green/Yellow body, RN '7', SS/WS/OEC/DE. 83 mm.	£30	NC	☐
262	1966-75	VW Swiss Post	Yellow/Black body plus emblem with cross	£200	GP	☐
			2nd type with opening doors	£35	NC	☐
342	1967-74	Austin Mini-Moke	Green/Fawn body, BVP/WS/OD/PW. 73 mm.	£15	NC	☐
344	1970-77	Land Rover (Pick Up)	Blue/Silver body, SWS/BVP. 108 mm.	£10-£15	MPR	☐
405	1955-66	Universal Jeep	Red/Green body, LHD/TPWS. 83 mm.	£45	NC	☐
518	1962-65	Renault	Brown body, FI/LHD/SS/FS/WDS. 85 mm.	£45	NC	☐
535	1962-65	2CV Citroen	Blue body, FI/LHD/SS/FS/WDS. 88 mm.	£45	NC	☐
550	1962-65	Chrysler Saratoga	Pink/White body, FI/LHD/SS/FS/WDS. 129 mm.	£45	NC	☐
553	1962-65	Peugeot 404	Green body, FI/LHD/SS/FS/WDS. 102 mm.	£45	NC	☐
555	1962-65	Ford Thunderbird CV	White body, FI/LHD/SS/CD/WS/FS. 121 mm.	£45	NC	☐

Gift Sets — Dinky Cars

Ref. No.		Model Type	Model Features and Size	Rarity and Price Grading		
	1933-40	22 Series Set	Contains 22a, 22b, 22c Motor Truck, 22d, Delivery Van, 22e Tractor, 22f Tank	£225	NPE	☐
	1936-40	23 Series Set	Contains 23c, d, e,	£300	NPE	☐
	1934-40	24 Series Set	Contains 24a Ambulance 24b, c, d, e, f, g, h	£2500	NPE	☐
	1935-40	30 Series Set	Contains 30a, b, c, d, 30e Breakdown Van, 30f AMB	£2000	NPE	☐
	1935-40	35 Series Set	Contains 35a, b, c	£400	GP	☐
	1938-40	36 Series Set	Contains 36a, b, c, d, e, f, plus figures	£2500	NPE	☐
	1938-40	38 Series Set	Contains 38a, b, c, d, e, f	£1500	NPE	☐
	1940-41	39 Series Set	Contains 39a, b, c, d, e, f	£1500	NPE	☐
No 3	1952-55	Passenger Cars	Contains 27f, 30h, 40c, 40g, 40h, 140b	£350	GP	☐
No 4	1953-55	Racing Cars Set	Contains 23f, g, h, j, k, n	£350	GP	☐
118	1965-66	Towaway Glider Set	Contains 135 and trailer	£130	GP	☐
121	1964-67	Goodwood Racing Set	Contains 112, 113, 120, 182 (9 figs)	£400	NPE	☐
122	1963-65	Touring Gift Set	Contains 188, 193, 195, 270, 295	£400	NPE	☐
123	1963-65	Mayfair Gift Set	Contains 142, 150, 186, 194, 198, 199 (4 figs)	£600	NPE	☐
124	1964-66	Holiday Gift Set	Contains 952, 137, 142, 796	£175	GP	☐
125	1964-66	Fun-A-Hoy Set	Contains 130, 796	£145	GP	☐
126	1967-68	Motor Show Set	Contains 127, 133, 151, 171	£350	NPE	☐
149	1958-61	Sports Cars Set	Contains 107, 108, 110, 111	£450	GP	☐
201	1966-68	Racing Cars Set	Contains 240, 241, 242, 243	£350	GP	☐
245	1969-73	Superfast Gift Set	Contains 131, 153, 188	£100	GP	☐
246	1969-73	International Gift Set	Contains 187, 215, 216	£100	GP	☐
950	1969-70	Car Transporter Set	Contains 974 Transporter 136, 138, 162, 168, 342	£250	NPE	☐
990	1956-58	Car Transporter Set	Contains 992 Pullmore Car Transporter 154 Hillman Minx (Lt Green/Cream) 156 Rover 75 (Cream/Blue), 161 Austin Somerset (Red/Yellow), 162 Ford Zephyr (Dark Green/White)	£500	NPE	☐

Auction Prices Results
At Phillips, New Bond Street, London. Sale 23.1.88.
23p — £120, Set 990 — £600, Set 149 — £480
At Lacey Scotts, Bury St. Edmunds Sale 27.2.88
105 — £80, Set 245 — £130

THE DINKY COLLECTION

Matchbox bought the Dinky trademark in early 1987 and will use the famous name for a completely new range of classic cars of the 1950's and 1960's to be called 'The Dinky Collection'. It is intended that the models will be of a very high quality in terms of design and finish. They will be packaged in perspex boxes. The outer box sleeves will be given a nostalgic design of blue and white stripes and will be highly reminiscent of past Dinky boxes. There will be a DY reference number system and the scale will be a constant 1.43. The models will be priced the same as the normal 'Models of yesteryear' range and the first three issues will be:-
DY 'E' Type Jaguar Series 1½
    British Racing Green body with a black hard top.
DY 1957 Chevrolet Belair
    Red and White/Cream body.
DY 1966 MGB GT Teal Blue body.
    The models should be in the shops ready for Christmas 1988 and will be the first new Dinky Toys as such for eight years. Undoubtedly their reintroduction marks an exciting new chapter in the history of Dinky Toys which first started in 1933. Collectors the world over will be wishing them every success in the years to come.

Dinky Commercial and Utility Vehicles

Ref. No.		Model Type	Model Features and Size	Rarity and Price Grading		

For descriptions of the different commercial Types and Chassis see pages 62-63.

Ref. No.		Model Type	Model Features and Size	Price	Grade	
14a (400)	1949-60	B.E.V. Truck	Blue or Grey body. 85 mm.	£20	NC	☐
14c (401)	1949-64	Coventry Climax Fork Lift	Green/Orange body. 108 mm.	£15	NC	☐
22c	1933-35	Motor Truck	Red/Blue body. No HL on TPR. 90 mm.	£300	GP	☐
22c	1935-40	Motor Truck	Red, Green or Blue body, Rear Window. 84 mm.	£75	GP	☐
22c	1946-50	Motor Truck	Red, Green or Brown body, No Window. 84 mm.	£55	GP	☐
25a	1934-38	Wagon	Red, Blue body, Type 1, OCH/No HL or TPR. 108 mm.	£75	GP	☐
25a	1938-40	Wagon	Blue, Red body, Type 2, OCH/HL or DCR. 105 mm.	£55	GP	☐
25a	1946-47	Wagon	Grey body, Type 3, Plain CH/DCR with HL. 105 mm.	£55	NC	☐
25a	1947-50	Wagon	Red body, Type 4, OC/MCH/DCR with HL and B. 110 mm.	£45	NC	☐
25b	1934-38	Covered Wagon	Blue or Cream body, Type 1/OCH/TPR/NoL. 105 mm.	£85	GP	☐
25b	1938-40	Covered Wagon 'HORNBY TRAINS'	Grey/Cream body, Type 2, OCH/DCR/L/H, Gold Logo. 105 mm.	£150	GP	☐
25b	1938-40	Covered Wagon 'MECCANO'	Green/Cream body, Type 2, OCH/DCR/L/H, Red/Black logo, *Engineering For Boys*. 105 mm.	£150	GP	☐
25b	1938-40	Covered Wagon 'CARTER PATERSON'	Green/Red body, Type 2, OCH/DCR/H, White logo *Express Carriers London*. 105 mm.	£150	GP	☐
25b	1946-47	Covered Wagon	Green or Grey body, Type 3/Plain CH/DCR/L/H. 105 mm.	£55	NC	☐
25b	1947-50	Covered Wagon	Yellow/Blue body, OC/Type 4/MCH/DCR/L/BM/H. 105 mm.	£55	NC	☐
25c	1934-38	Flat Truck	Grey or Red body, OC/Type 1/OCH/TPR/No L/H. 105 mm.	£75	GP	☐
25c	1938-40	Flat Truck	Grey or Blue body, OC/Type 2/OCH/H. 105 mm.	£65	GP	☐
25c	1947-50	Flat Truck	Green or Orange body, Type 4/MCH/DCR/L/BM/H. 105 mm.	£55	NC	☐
25a	1934-38	Petrol Tank Wagon	Red or Green body, Type 1/OCH/TPR/No L. 108 mm.	£125	GP	☐
25a	1936-38	'SHELL BP' Wagon	Red body, Type 1/OCH/TPR/No L. 108 mm.	£125	GP	☐
25d	1938-40	'PETROL' Wagon	Red or Green body, Type 2/OCH/DCR/L. 104 mm.	£125	GP	☐
25d	1939-40	'SHELL BP' Wagon	Red body, Type 2/OCH/DCR/L. 107 mm.	£125	GP	☐
25d	1936-40	'TEXACO' Wagon	Red body, Type 2/OCH/DCR/L. 107 mm.	£125	GP	☐
25d	1939-40	'POWER' Wagon	Green body, Type 2/OCH/DCR/L. 107 mm.	£125	GP	☐
25d	1939-40	'ESSO' Wagon	Red body, Type 2/OCH/DCR/L. 107 mm.	£125	GP	☐
25d	1939-40	'MOBIL OIL' Wagon	Red body, Type 2/OCH/DCR/L. 107 mm.	£125	GP	☐
25d	1939-40	'CASTROL' Petrol Wagon	Green body, Type 2, OCH/DCR/L, Red logo. 107 mm.	£125	GP	☐
25d	1939-40	'POWER' Petrol Wagon	Green body, Type 2, OCH/DCR/L, Gold logo. 107 mm.	£125	GP	☐
25d	1939-40	'REDLINE GLICO' Petrol Wagon	Blue/Red body, Type 2, OCH/DCR/L, Gold logo. 107 mm.	£125	GP	☐
25d	1939-40	'SHELL BP' Petrol Wagon	Red body, Type 2, OCH/DCR/L, Gold logo. 107 mm.	£125	GP	☐
25d	1939-40	'TEXACO' Petrol Wagon	Red body, Type 2, OCH/DCR/L, White logo. 107 mm.	£125	GP	☐
25d	1939-40	'MOBIL OIL' Petrol Wagon	Orange body, Type 2, OCH/DCR/L, Bl/Wh logo. 107 mm.	£125	GP	☐
25d	1940-41	'POOL' Petrol Wagon	Grey body, Type 2, OCH/DCR/L, White logo. 107 mm.	£125	GP	☐
25d	1946-47	'PETROL' Wagon	Green body, Type 3, Plain CH/DCR/L. 107 mm.	£65	GP	☐
25d	1947-50	'PETROL' Wagon	Red body, Type 4, MCH/DCR/L/BM. 107 mm.	£45	GP	☐
25e	1934-38	Tipping Wagon	Maroon/Yellow body, Type 1/TPR/No L/H	£75	GP	☐
25e	1938-40	Tipping Wagon	Fawn body, Type 2, OCH/DCR/L/H. 105 mm.	£65	GP	☐
25e	1946-47	Tipping Wagon	Grey body, Type 3, Plain CH/DCR/L/H. 105 mm.	£55	NC	☐
25e	1947-50	Tipping Wagon	Brown body, Type 4, OC/MCH/DCR/L/BM/H. 110 mm.	£45	NC	☐
25f	1934-38	Market Gardeners Lorry	Green body, Type 1, OCH/TPR/No L/H. 107 mm.	£85	GP	☐
25f	1938-40	Market Gardeners Lorry	Green body, Type 2, OCH/DCR/L/H. 105 mm.	£75	GP	☐
25f	1946-47	Market Gardeners Lorry	Green body, Type 3, Plain CH/DCR/L/H. 105 mm.	£65	NC	☐
25f	1947-50	Market Gardeners Lorry	Yellow body, Type 4, MCH/DCR/L/BM/H. 140 mm.	£65	NC	☐
25g	1935-40	Trailer	Green body, Tinplate Towbar H. 69 mm.	£10-£15	MPR	☐
25g	1947-54	Trailer	Green or Red body, Wire Towbar H. 69 mm.	£10-£15	MPR	☐
25m (410)	1948-54	Bedford End Tipper	Orange body, OC/handle crank tipper. 98 mm.	£50	NC	☐
25r (450)	1948-50	Forward Control Lorry	Red, Green or Grey body. 107 mm.	£45	NC	☐
25s	1937-40	Six Wheeled Wagon	Brown body, SWC1/H/holes in seat. 101 mm.	£75	GP	☐
25s	1946-48	Six Wheeled Wagon	Green body, SWC1/H/holes in seat. 101 mm.	£65	NC	☐
25v	1948-54	Bedford Refuse Wagon	Fawn and Grey body OD. 107 mm.	£55	NC	☐
25w (411)	1949-54	Bedford Truck	Green body, Hook. 104 mm.	£55	NC	☐
25x (430)	1949-54	Commer Breakdown Lorry 'DINKY SERVICE'	Grey/Blue or Light Brown/Green body Cream/Blue or Red/Grey body, Mid Brown/Green	£45 £65	NC GP	☐
30j (343)	1950-54	Austin Wagon	Blue or Brown body, Hook. 104 mm.	£50	NC	☐
30e	1936-40	Breakdown Lorry	Red or Green body, Blk Wings, RWD/WH. 92 mm.	£75	GP	☐
30e	1946-48	Breakdown Lorry	Red or Green body, Blk Wings, No RWD/WH. 92 mm.	£45	NC	☐
30m (414)	1950-54	Rear Tipping Wagon	Orange body, *Dodge* on BP. 99 mm.	£45	NC	☐
30n	1950-60	Farm Produce Wagon	Green/Yellow or Blue/Red body, H. 107 mm.	£55	NC	☐
30p	1952-54	'PETROL' Tanker	Red body or Green body. 112 mm.	£65	GP	☐
30p (440)	1952-54	Studebaker Petrol Tanker	Red body. 112 mm. *'Mobilgas'*	£75	GP	☐
30pa (441)	1952-54	Studebaker Petrol Tanker	Green body. 112 mm. *'Castrol'*	£75	GP	☐
30pb (442)	1952-54	Studebaker Petrol Tanker	Red body *Esso Motor Oil Petrol*. 112 mm.	£75	GP	☐
30r (422)	1951-54	Fordson Thames Flat Truck	Red or Green body, Hook. 112 mm.	£45	NC	☐
30s (413)	1950-54	Austin Covered Wagon	Maroon/Fawn or two tone Blue, H. 104 mm.	£65	NC	☐
30w (421)	1952-54	Electric Articulated Vehicle	Maroon body *British Railways* TV/H. 85 mm.	£75	NC	☐
33a	1935-40	Mechanical Horse	Green or Blue body, Silver trim. 65 mm.	£125	GP	☐
33b	1935-40	Flat Truck Trailer	Grey or Green body, no sides. 64 mm.	£20	NC	☐
33c	1935-40	Open Truck Trailer	Blue or Green body, with sides. 64 mm.	£20	NC	☐
33d	1935-40	Box Van 'Trailer MECCANO'	Green body, Red and Black logo *Engineering For Boys*. 70 mm.	£95	GP	☐
33d	1935-40	Box Van Trailer 'HORNBY TRAINS'	Dark Blue body, Gold logo.	£95	GP	☐
33e	1935-40	Refuse Wagon Trailer	Blue/Yellow body. 64 mm.	£35	NC	☐
33e	1946-47	Refuse Wagon Trailer	Grey or Red/Blue body. 64 mm.	£25	NC	☐

70

Ref. No.		Model Type	**Dinky Vehicles continued**	Rarity and Price Grading		
33f	1937-40	Petrol Tank Trailer	Green/Red body, no logo. 61 mm.	£45	GP	☐
33f	1937-40	Petrol Trailer and Tug 'ESSO'	Green/Red body, Gold logo. 61 mm.	£135	GP	☐
33f	1937-40	Petrol Trailer and Tug 'WAKEFIELD CASTROL MOTOR OIL'	Dark Green and Red body. 61 mm.	£135	GP	☐
33w (415)	1947-50	Mechanical Horse and Open Wagon	Blue/Cream body, Two tone Green, OC. 102 mm.	£50	NC	☐
60y	1938-40	Thompson Aircraft Tender	Red body, *Shell Aviation Services* in Gold.	£250	GP	☐
107a (385)	1949-54	Sack Truck	Blue body. 65 mm.	£15	NC	☐
151b	1938-40	Six W Covered Transport	Green body, holes for PS, SPW. 100 mm.	£65	NC	☐
252 (25v)	1954-64	Bedford Refuse Wagon	Fawn/Green body, body tips, OD. 107 mm.	£55	NC	☐
252	1960-65	Refuse Wagon	Fawn/Green body, OC/WDS. 107 mm.	£35	NC	☐
402	1966-69	Bedford TK Lorry	Red/White body, *Coca Cola* Crate load (6). 121 mm.	£135	GP	☐
404	1968-79	Climax Fork Lift	Red/Yellow body, *CG4 Conveyancer.* 97 mm.	£15	NC	☐
408 (922)	1956-63	Big Bedford Lorry	Maroon/Fawn or Blue/Yellow body, H. 146 mm.	£75	GP	☐
409 (921)	1956-63	Bedford AV	Yellow body, SPW/H. 166 mm.	£95	GP	☐
410 (25m)	1955-63	Bedford End Tipper	Brown/Yellow or Blue/Yellow. 97 mm.	£55	NC	☐
410	1962-63	Bedford End Tipper	Red/Cream body, WDS. 97 mm.	£50	NC	☐
411 (25w)	1954-60	Bedford Truck	Green body. Does not tip but has hinged tailboard and handle hole. 104 mm.	£55	NC	☐
412 (30j)	1954-60	Austin Wagon	Blue/Mrn or Yel/Blue body. 104 mm.	£50	NC	☐
413 (30s)	1954-60	Austin Covered Wagon	Blue or Maroon body. 104 mm.	£65	GP	☐
414 (30m)	1954-64	Dodge Rear Tipping Wagon	Green/Orange or Grey/Blue body. 99 mm.	£45	NC	☐
415 (33w)	1954-59	Mechanical Horse and Wagon	Blue/Cream body, open wagon. 102 mm.	£50	NC	☐
417	1956-59	Leyland Comet Lorry	Blue/Yellow body, Hook. 144 mm.	£75	GP	☐
418 (532/932)	1956-59	Leyland Comet with Hinged Tailboard	Green/Orange body. 142 mm.	£75	NC	☐
419 (533/933)	1956-59	Leyland Comet Cement Lorry	Yellow body, *Ferrocrete* and *Portland Cement,* ST/SPW. 142 mm.	£85	NC	☐
420 (25r)	1954-61	Leyland Forward Control Lorry	Red, Grey or Blue body, Hook. 107 mm.	£35	NC	☐
421 (30w)	1955-59	Electric Articulated Vehicle	Maroon *British Railways,* Hook. 135 mm.	£75	GP	☐
422 (30r)	1954-60	Thames Flat Truck	Green or Red body, WDS/Hook. 112 mm.	£45	NC	☐
424	1963-66	Commer Convertible Articulated Vehicle	Yellow body, Blue detachable cover, 2 White plastic TRL fittings, SPW. 171 mm.	£150	GP	☐
425	1964-67	Bedford TK Coal Wagon	Red body, *Hall & Co* etc, coal bags/scales. 121 mm.	£95	GP	☐
428 (551/951)	1955-64	Large Trailer	Grey body, front axle swivels, Hook. 105 mm.	£15	NC	☐
430 (25x)	1954-64	Commer Breakdown Lorry 'DINKY SERVICE'	Grey/Blue or Light Brown/Green body, 123 mm / Cream/Blue, Red/Grey or Mid Brown/Green body	£45 / £65	NC / GP	☐ ☐
431 (911/511)	1956-58	Guy 4 ton Lorry	Two tone Blue, 2nd type SPW/H. 132 mm.	£85	NC	☐
431	1958-64	Guy Warrior 4 ton Lorry	Green/Fawn body, *Warrior* type, WDS/SPW/H. 136 mm.	£300	GP	☐
432 (912/512)	1956-58	Guy Flat Truck	Blue/Red body, 2nd type, SPW/H. 132 mm.	£85	NC	☐
432	1955-58	Guy Warrior Flat Truck	Red/Cream, *Warrior* type, WDS/SPW/H. 136 mm.	£250	GP	☐
432	1977-79	Foden Tipping Lorry	White/Red/Yellow body. 175 mm.	£15	NC	☐
433 (913/513)	1955-58	Guy Flat Truck with Tailboard	Green/Yellow body, 2nd type, H. 132 mm.	£85	NC	☐
434	1964-68	Bedford TK Crash Truck	White body, Green flash, winch, gong design, *Top Rank Motorway Services*	£40	NC	☐
	1966-70	Colour/Logo change	Red cab, White rear, *Auto Services*	£30	NC	☐
435	1964-68	Bedford TK Tipper	Grey/Blue/Orange body, OC/WDS. 120 mm.	£35	NC	☐
438	1970-74	Ford D800 Tipper Truck	Red/Black body, Yellow tipper. 132 mm.	£20	NC	☐
439	1971-74	Ford D800 Snow Plough/Tipper	Blue body, Yellow plough, OC. 194 mm.	£25	NC	☐
440	1977-79	Ford D800 Tipper Truck	Red body, Yellow tipper. 132 mm.	£10-£15	MPR	☐
440 (30p)	1956-61	Studebaker Petrol Tanker	Red body. 112 mm. *Mobil Gas*	£95	GP	☐
441 (30pa)	1954-60	Studebaker Petrol Tanker	Green body. 112 mm. *Castrol*	£95	GP	☐
442	1973-79	Land Rover Breakdown Crane	Red/White body, *Motorway Rescue,* WO.	£10-£15	MPR	☐
442 (30pb)	1954-60	Studebaker Petrol Tanker	Red body and Hubs, Blue, White and Red Logo, Silver trim. 112 mm. *Esso Motor Oil Petrol*	£95	GP	☐
443	1957-58	Studebaker Petrol Tanker	Yellow body and Hubs, Black Logo, Silver Trim. 112 mm. *National Benzole Mixture*	£135	GP	☐
448	1963-67	Chevrolet El Camino Pick-Up and 2 Trailers	TQ/WH/Red B, CEM on BOX TRL *Acme Trailer Hire* (3 parts). 256 mm.	£70	NC	☐
449	1963-67	Chevrolet El Camino PU	GR/WH or Red/Yel, LHD/SS/FS/SW/WDS. 111 mm.	£38	NC	☐
449	1977-79	Johnston Road Sweeper	All Yellow body	£19	NC	☐
451	1971-77	Johnston Road Sweeper	Orange body with metallic Green back	£27	NC	☐
501	1947-52	Foden 8 Wheel Diesel Wagon	Red/Fawn or Brown body. 1st type cab, OC/ST/SPW/H. ATT/NH. 188 mm.	£275	GP	☐
501 (901)	1952-55	Foden 8 Wheel Diesel Wagon	Brown or Blue 2nd type, OC/ST/SPW/H. 188 mm.	£165	GP	☐
502	1947-52	Foden Flat Truck	Red/Blue 1st type, OC/ST/SPW/H. ATT/NH. 188 mm.	£135	GP	☐
502 (902)	1952-55	Foden Flat Truck	Orange/Green 2nd type, OC/ST/SPW/H. 188 mm.	£135	GP	☐
503	1947-52	Foden Flat Truck with Tailboard	Red/Blue body, 1st type/ST/H. ATT/NH.	£145	GP	☐
503 (903)	1952-55	Foden Flat Truck with Tailboard	Blue/Orange body, 2nd type/ST/H. 188 mm.	£145	GP	☐
504	1948-52	Foden 14 ton Tanker	Grey/Red body, or Blue 1st Type, ST/SPW/H. ATT. 188 mm.	£125	GP	☐
504	1953-54	Foden 14 ton Tanker	Two tone blue 2nd Type, ST/SPW/H. 188 mm.	£200	GP	☐
504 (941)	1953-54	Foden 14 ton Tanker	Red body, *Mobilgas,* CEM/ST/SPW/H. 188 mm. 2nd Type	£350	GP	☐
505 (905)	1952-55	Foden Chain Lorry	Green or Maroon body, 1st type, SPW/H. 188 mm.	£750	GP	☐
		New Casting	with 2nd type cab	£150	NC	☐
511 (911/431)	1947-55	Guy 4 ton Lorry	Two tone Blue body, 1st type, OC/ST/SPW/H. 132 mm. EAX.	£85	GP	☐

Ref. No.		Model Type	Dinky Vehicles continued	Price	Grade
512 (912/432)	1947-54	Guy flat Truck	Maroon body, 1st type, ST/SPW/H. 132 mm. EAX.	£85	GP ☐
513 (913/433)	1947-54`	Guy Flat Truck with Tailboard	2 tone Green, 1st type, OC/ST/SPW/H. 132 mm. EAX.	£85	GP ☐
521	1948-54	Bedford AV	Maroon/Fawn body, ST/H. 166 mm.	£95	GP ☐
522 (922/408)	1952-54	Big Bedford	Blue/Yellow or Maroon/Fawn, SPW/H. 146 mm.	£75	NC ☐
531 (931/417)	1949-54	Leyland Comet with slatted sides	Blue/Yellow body, ST/H. 144 mm.	£75	GP ☐
532 (932/418)	1953-54	Leyland Comet with hinged tailboard	Green/Orange body, ST/HTBD. 142 mm.	£75	NC ☐
533 (933/419)	1953-54	Leyland Comet Cement	Details as for Model 419. 142 mm.	£85	GP ☐
551	1948-54	Trailer	Grey, front axle swivels, H. 105 mm. (951/428)	£10-£15	MPR ☐
571 (971)	1949-55	Coles Mobile Crane	Yellow/Black body, ST/CO. 160 mm.	£35	NC ☐
579	1961-63	Simca Glaziers Lorry 'SAINT-GOBAIN'	Grey/Green body, Mirror load FI 'MIROITEUR'	£85	GP ☐
			Yellow/Green body (UK issue)	£65	NC ☐
581	1962-64	Berliot Flat Truck	Red/Grey body, FI/6W/SPW/H/C. 130 mm.	£50	NC ☐
581	1953-54	Racehorse Transport	Maroon body, British Railways 2 DDR. 175 mm.	£70	NC ☐
581	1953-54	US Issue changed decals	No 'British Railways'. Maroon body with Hire Service & Express Horse Van on sides, Express on roof. 2DDR 175 mm	£2000	GP ☐
582 (982)	1953-54	Pullmore Car Transporter	Lt or Dk Blue cab, Lt Blue TRL, Brown decks, Dinky Toys Delivery Service. 250 mm. AV/DDR Model 794 (ramp) accompanies this model	£40	NC ☐
591	1952-54	A.E.C. Tanker	Red/Yellow body, Shell Chemicals Ltd. 151 mm.	£125	NC ☐
893	1962-64	Unic Pipe Line TPTR	Sand body, FI/AV/SPW/6 Pipes. 215 mm.	£100	NC ☐
894	1962-64	Unic Boilet Car TPTR	Grey body, Dinky Toys Service, FI/AV. 325 mm.	£100	NPE ☐
901 (501)	1955-57	Foden Diesel Wagon	Red/Grey body, 2nd type, ST/SPW/H. 188 mm.	£150	GP ☐
		Colour change	Red/Fawn body, 2nd type	£175	NC ☐
902 (502)	1955-60	Foden Flat Truck	Orange/Green body, 2nd type, ST/SPW/H. 188 mm.	£135	NC ☐
903 (503)	1955-60	Foden Flat Truck with Tailboard	Blue/Orange body, 2nd type, ST/SPW/H.	£145	NC ☐
			Also Blue/Cream version. 188 mm.	£750	GP ☐
905 (505)	1955-64	Foden Chain Lorry	Green body, 2nd type, ST/SPW/H. 188 mm.	£130	NC ☐
		Colour change	Red/Grey body, 2nd type	£180	GP ☐
908	1962-66	Mighty Antar with Transformer	Yellow cab, Red/Grey Trailer, ST/DDR/AV/CD/WDS/SPW. 337 mm.	£300	GP ☐
911 (511/431)	1954-56	Guy 4 ton Lorry	Two tone Blue body, 2nd type, ST/SPW/H. 132 mm.	£85	NC ☐
912 (512/432)	1954-56	Guy Flat Truck	Blue/Orange body, 2nd type, ST/SPW/H. 132 mm.	£85	NC ☐
913 (513/433)	1954-56	Guy Flat Truck with Tailboard	Blue/Orange body, 2nd type, ST/SPW/H. 132 mm.	£85	NC ☐
914	1967-70	A.E.C. A.V. Lorry	Red/White body, British Road Services SL. 210 mm.	£65	NC ☐
915	1973-74	A.E.C. with Flat TRL	Orange/White body, Truck Hire Co Liverpool. 210 mm.	£30	NC ☐
915	1973-74	A.E.C. with Flat TRL	Orange/White body Thames Board Mills BUP. 210 mm.		NGPP ☐
917	1968-74	Mercedes Truck and TRL	Blue/Yellow/White body, IS/SL/ODB. 397 mm.	£35	NC ☐
921 (521/409)	1954-60	Bedford Articulated Vehicle	Yellow body, ST/ODB/SPW/H. 166 mm.	£95	NC ☐
922	1954-56	Big Bedford Lorry	Maroon/Fawn, SPW/H. 146 mm.	£75	NC ☐
925	1967-69	Leyland Dump Truck	White Cab, Red back, Cab Tilts, Sand Ballast Gravel on Tipper flap. 192 mm.	£135	GP ☐
931 (531/417)	1955-56	Leyland Comet Lorry	Blue/Yellow body, ST/H. 144 mm.	£75	NC ☐
932 (532/418)	1954-56	Leyland Comet with Hinged Tailboard	Green/Orange body, ST. 142 mm.	£75	NC ☐
933 (533/419)	1954-56	Leyland Comet Cement Wagon	Details as for Model 419. 142 mm.	£95	NC ☐
934	1954-64	Leyland Octopus Wagon	Yellow/Green body, ST/SPW/H. 194 mm.	£135	GP ☐
		Rare Variant	Blue/Cream Body	£1200	GP ☐
935	1964-66	Leyland Octopus with Chains	Green/Grey body, ST/SPW/H. 192 mm.	£750	GP ☐
936	1964-69	Leyland 8 Wheel Chassis	Red/Silver body Another Leyland on Test 3 × 5 ton weights. 197 mm.	£60	NC ☐
940	1977-79	Mercedes Benz Truck	White body, Grey tarpaulin. 200 mm.	£20	NC ☐
941 (504)	1955-57	Foden Tanker 'MOBILGAS'	Red body, Mobilgas 2nd type, CEM/ST/SPW/H. 188 mm.	£350	GP ☐
942	1955-57	Foden Tanker 'REGENT'	Red/Blue/White body, CEM Regent in Gold, 2nd type, ST/SPW/H. 188 mm.	£350	GP ☐
943	1958-64	Leyland Octopus Tanker 'ESSO PETROLEUM'	Red/White body, Esso Petroleum, CEM/ST/SPW/H. 192 mm.	£250	GP ☐
944	1963-65	4000 gallon Tanker 'SHELL BP'	Yellow/White body, ST/SPW/H Shell BP & CEMS on sides. 192 mm. Leyland Octopus. 8W.	£180	GP ☐
944	1963-65	Leyland Octopus	White cab/tank, Sweeteners for Industry. PRM.		NVPP ☐
945	1966-67	A.E.C. Fuel Tanker 'ESSO'	White body, Esso tiger on tank AV/TV. 266 mm.	£55	NC ☐
			Later version with no tiger. BW red or black.	£30	NC ☐
945	1978	A.E.C. Fuel Tanker 'LUCAS'	Green body, Black CH, White Lucas Oil Company, AV/PRM. 266 mm.	£55	NC ☐
948	1961-67	Tractor TRL 'McLEAN'	Red/Grey body, McLean Winston, ST/AV/TV. 290 mm.	£185	GP ☐
950	1978-79	Foden Tanker 'BURMAH'	Red/White/Black body, Burmah AV/TV, LV has Cream wheels and Silver PFC. 266 mm.	£35	NC ☐
950	1978	Foden Tanker 'SHELL'	Red/White/Black body, Shell AV/TV. 266 mm.	£75	GP ☐
951	1954-55	Trailer	Grey body, Hook. 105 mm. (551/428)	£10-£15	MPR ☐
958	1961-66	Guy Warrior Snow Plough	Yellow/Black body, ST/SPW. 195 mm.	£110	GP ☐
967	1959-64	BBC TV Control Room	Green body, BBC Television Service, ST/WDS. 149 mm.	£90	NC ☐

Ref. No.		Model Type	Dinky Vehicles continued	Rarity and Price Grading	
968	1959-64	BBC TV Roving Eye V	Green body, B.B.C. crest, camera/ST/WDS. 110 mm.	£85	NC ☐
969	1959-64	BBC TV Extending Mast V	Green body, B.B.C. crest, ST/WDS/A. 165 mm.	£85	NC ☐
970	1967-74	Jones Cantilever Crane	Yellow body, *Jones Fleetmaster* Co. 174 mm.	£35	NC ☐
971	1955-66	Coles Mobile Crane	Yellow/Black body, ST/D/CO. 162 mm. Also on Red	£35	NC ☐
972	1955-69	Coles 20 ton Crane	Yellow/Orange/Black body, ST/2D/CO. 240 mm.	£35	NC ☐
974	1969-74	A.E.C. Hoynor TPTR	Blue/Yellow body, *Silcock & Colling Ltd*. 322 mm.	£35	NC ☐
977	1960-64	Servicing Platform Vehicle	Red/Cream body, platform operates, SPW. 130 mm.	£175	GP ☐
978	1964-79	Bedford Refuse Wagon	Green/Grey body, Bins/OD/Tips. RMV cab box LV Met Green or Lime Green WW/RMV box.	£30 £20	NC ☐ NC ☐
979	1961-64	Racehorse Transport (Maudsley)	Grey/Yellow body, *Newmarket Racehorse Transport Service Ltd,* 2 HS/ST/ODB. 175 mm.	£250	GP ☐
980 (581)	1955-61	Racehorse Transport (Maudsley) U.S. Issue	Maroon Body, *Hire Service & Express Horse Van* on sides with *Express* on roof. 2 DDR 175 mm.	£2000	GP ☐
980	1974-79	Coles Hydra Truck	Yellow/Black body, crane elevates. 210 mm.	£25	NC ☐
981 (581)	1955-61	'EXPRESS' Horse Box	Maroon body *British Railways*. 175 mm.	£70	NC ☐
982 (582)	1954-63	Pullmore Car Transporter	LT or DK Blue cab, LT Blue TRL, Brown decks, *Dinky Toys Delivery Service* AV/DDR. 280 mm.	£40	NC ☐
983	1958-63	Car Carrier and Trailer	Red/Grey body, *Dinky Toys Delivery Service* (984 and 985), ST. 196/240 mm.	£175	GP ☐
984	1958-63	Car Carrier	Red/Grey body, *Dinky Auto Service*, ST. 240 mm.	£120	GP ☐
985	1958-63	Car Trailer	Red/Grey body, *Dinky Auto Service*, ST. 196 mm.	£55	GP ☐
986	1959-64	Mighty Antar with Propellor Load	Red/Grey body, Driver, ST/AV. 305 mm.	£185	GP ☐
987	1962-69	TV Control Room 'A-B-C TELEVISION SERVICE'	Blue/Grey body, Red stripe, CEM/ST, white logo, camera and operator. 151 mm.	£95	NC ☐
988	1962-69	TV Transmitter Van 'A-B-C TV'	Blue/Grey body, Red stripe, CEM/ST, revolving dish, white logo. 113 mm.	£145	NC ☐
989	1963-69	Car Transporter 'AUTO TRANSPORTERS'	Yellow cab, Grey body, Blue tier, Red hubs and logo, DDR/ST. 240 mm.	£2000	GP ☐
991 (591)	1955-58	A.E.C. Tanker	Red/Yellow body, *Shell Chemicals Ltd*, ST. 151 mm.	£125	NC ☐

Dinky Commercial and Utility Vehicles Gift Sets

25 Series	1934-40	Type 1 Gift Set	Contains 25a, b, c, d, e, f	NGPP ☐
33 Series	1935-40	33 Series Gift Set	Contains 33a, b, c, d, e, f	NGPP ☐
No 2	1952-53	Commercial Vehicles Set	Contains 25m, 27d Land Rover 30n, 30p, 30s	NGPP ☐

Auction Price Results
Lacy Scotts, Bury St. Edmunds Sale 27.2.88.
979 — £300, 936 — £42, 983 — £80, 925 — £60, 413 — £85, 934 — £70
Lacey Scotts Sale 13.6.87
591/991 — £95, 905 green — £90
All models mint boxed

Dinky Vans

Ref. No.		Model Type	Model Features and Size	Rarity and Price Grading		

Note for descriptions of Types 1, 2 and 3 see page 62.

Ref. No.		Model Type	Model Features and Size	Price	Grade	
22d (28n)	1934-36	Delivery Van	Orange/Blue body, *Hornby Series* or *LV*, *Dinky Toys* cast in.			
			Type 1. 83 mm.	£350	GP	☐
22d	1934-36	Delivery Van 'MECCANO'	Yellow body, Red/Gold letters *Meccano Engineering for Boys*			
			Type 1. 83 mm.	£500	GP	☐
28a	1936-40	Delivery Van 'HORNBY TRAINS'	Yellow body, Gold letters, *Hornby Trains British and Guaranteed.*			
			Type 1. 83 mm.	£500	GP	☐
			Type 2. 81 mm.	£250	GP	☐
28a	1936-40	Delivery Van 'GOLDEN SHRED'	Cream body *Golden Shred* in Red/Blue.			
			Type 2. 81 mm.	£250	GP	☐
			Type 3. 83 mm.	£175	GP	☐
28b	1934-36	Delivery Van 'PICKFORDS'	Blue body, Gold letters, *Pickfords Removals and Storage Over 100 Branches.*			
			Type 1. 83 mm.	£500	GP	☐
			Type 2. 81 mm.	£250	GP	☐
28b	1936-40	Delivery Van 'SECCOTINE'	Blue body, Gold letters *Seccotine Sticks Everything*			
			Type 2. 81 mm.	£250	GP	☐
			Type 3. 83 mm.	£175	GP	☐
28c	1934-40	Delivery Van 'MANCHESTER GUARDIAN'	Blue body, Gold letters *The Manchester Guardian.*			
			Type 1. 83 mm.	£500	GP	☐
			Type 2. 81 mm.	£250	GP	☐
28d	1934-40	Delivery Van 'OXO'	Blue body, Gold letters, *Oxo Beef in Brief* and *Oxo Beef at its Best.*			
			Type 1. 83 mm.	£500	GP	☐
			Type 2. 81 mm.	£250	GP	☐
			Type 3. 83 mm.	£175	GP	☐
28e	1934 only	Delivery Van 'ENSIGN'	Orange body, Gold letters, *Ensign Lukos Film* and *Ensign Cameras* Type 1.	£500	GP	☐
28e	1934-40	Delivery Van 'FIRESTONE'	White body, Gold letters, *Firestone Tyres.*			
			Type 1. 83 mm.	£500	GP	☐
			Type 2. 81 mm.	£250	GP	☐
			Type 3. 83 mm.	£175	GP	☐
28f	1934-37	Delivery Van 'PALETHORPES'	Light Grey body, Blue and Red letters, Pink sausage decal *Palethorpes Royal Cambridge.*			
			Type 1. 83 mm.	£500	GP	☐
			Type 2. 81 mm.	£250	GP	☐
28f	1937-40	Delivery Van 'VIROL'	Yellow body, Black letters *Give Your Child a Virol Constitution.*			
			Type 2. 81 mm.	£250	GP	☐
28g	1934-40	Delivery Van 'KODAK'	Yellow body, Red letters, *Use Kodak Film* and *To Be Sure.*			
			Type 1. 83 mm.	£500	GP	☐
			Type 2. 81 mm.	£250	GP	☐
			Type 3. 83 mm.	£175	GP	☐
28h	1934-36	Delivery Van 'SHARPS'	Red/Black body, Gold letters, Yellow *Sharps Toffees Maidstone.*			
			Type 1. 83 mm.	£500	GP	☐
28h	1935-40	Delivery Van 'DUNLOP'	Red body, Gold letters *Dunlop Tyres.*			
			Type 2. 81 mm.	£250	GP	☐
			Type 3. 83 mm.	£175	GP	☐
28k	1935-40	Delivery Van 'MARSH'S'	Green body, Gold letters, Pink *Marsh's Sausages* and design, MW on Type 1.			
			Type 1. 83 mm.	£500	GP	☐
			Type 2. 81 mm.	£250	GP	☐
			Type 3. 83 mm.	£175	GP	☐
28l	1934-35	Delivery Van 'CRAWFORDS'	Red body, gold letters, *Crawfords Biscuits.* 83 mm. Type 1	£500	GP	☐
28m	1934-40	Delivery Van 'WAKEFIELD'	Green body, Red letters, *Wakefield Castrol Motor Oil.*			
			Type 1. 83 mm.	£500	GP	☐
			Type 2. 81 mm.	£250	GP	☐
			Type 3. 83 mm.	£175	GP	☐
28n (22d)	1934-35	Delivery Van 'MECCANO'	Yellow body, Red/Gold letters, *Meccano Engineering for Boys*			
			Type 1. 83 mm.	£500	GP	☐
			Type 2. 81 mm.	£250	GP	☐
28n	1935-41	Delivery Van 'ATCO'	Green body, Gold letters, *Atco Sales and Service* and *Motor Mowers.*			
			Type 2. 81 mm.	£250	GP	☐
			Type 3. 83 mm.	£175	GP	☐
28p	1935-36	Delivery Van 'CRAWFORDS'	Red body, Gold letters *Crawfords Biscuits.*			
			Type 2. 81 mm.	£250	GP	☐
			Type 3. 83 mm.	£175	GP	☐
28r	1936-41	Delivery Van 'SWANS'	Black body, Gold letters *Swans Pens.*			
			Type 2. 81 mm.	£250	GP	☐
			Type 3. 83 mm.	£175	GP	☐
28s	1936-41	Delivery Van 'FRYS'	Chocolate body, Gold letters *Frys Chocolate.*			
			Type 2. 81 mm.	£250	GP	☐
			Type 3. 83 mm.	£175	GP	☐
28t	1936-41	Delivery Van 'OVALTINE'	Red body, Gold letters *Drink Ovaltine for Health.*			
			Type 2. 81 mm.	£250	GP	☐
			Type 3. 83 mm.	£175	GP	☐
28w	1936-41	Delivery Van 'OSRAM'	Yellow body, Gold letters, *Osram Lamps A G.E.C. Product.*			
			Type 2. 81 mm.	£250	GP	☐
			Type 3. 83 mm.	£175	GP	☐

Ref. No.		Model Type	Dinky Vans continued	Rarity and Price Grading		
28x	1936-41	Delivery Van 'HOVIS'	White body *Hovis* in Gold.			
			Type 2. 81 mm.	£250	GP	☐
			Type 3. 83 mm.	£175	GP	☐
28y	1936-41	Delivery Van 'EXIDE'	Red body, Gold letters *Exide Batteries, Drydex Batteries.*			
			Type 2. 81 mm.	£250	GP	☐
			Type 3. 83 mm.	£175	GP	☐
			Further issues in this series were numbered 280 onwards as the alphabet ran out!			
280	1948-54	Delivery Van	Red or Blue body, Type 3, No RWD. 83 mm.	£24	NC	☐
280a	1937-41	Delivery Van 'VIYELLA'	Blue body, White/Black letters *Viyella for the Nursery.*			
			Type 2. 81 mm.	£250	GP	☐
			Type 3. 83 mm.	£175	GP	☐
280b	1937-41	Delivery Van 'LYONS'	Dark Blue body, Red/White letters *Lyons Tea Always the Best.* 81 mm.			
			Type 2. 81 mm.	£250	GP	☐
			Type 3. 83 mm.	£175	GP	☐
280b	1939-40	Delivery Van 'HARTLEYS'	Cream body, Red/Green letters, *Hartleys is Real Jam.*			
			Type 2. 81 mm.	£250	GP	☐
			Type 3. 83 mm.	£175	GP	☐
280c	1937-41	Delivery Van 'SHREDDED WHEAT'	Cream body, Red/Black letters, *Shredded Wheat.*			
			Type 2. 81 mm.	£250	GP	☐
			Type 3. 83 mm.	£175	GP	☐
280d	1937-38	Delivery Van 'BISTO'	Yellow body, MLCD letters/design *Ah Bisto.* Type 2. 81 mm.	£350	NPE	☐
280d	1938-41	Delivery Van 'BISTO'	Yellow body, MLCD letters/design *Bisto.*			
			Type 2. 81 mm.	£250	GP	☐
			Type 3. 83 mm.	£175	GP	☐
280e	1937-41	Delivery Van 'EKCO'	Green body, Gold letters *Ekco Radio.* Type 2. 81 mm.	£250	GP	☐
280e	1938-39	Delivery Van 'EVENING POST'	Cream body, Gold letters *Yorkshire Evening Post.*			
			Type 2. 81 mm.	£250	GP	☐
			Type 3. 83 mm.	£175	GP	☐
280f	1937-41	Delivery Van 'MACKINTOSH'S	Red body, gold letters *Mackintosh's Toffee* pro.			
			Type 2. 81 mm.	£250	GP	☐
			Type 3. 83 mm.	£175	GP	☐
280f	1939-40	Delivery Van 'BENTALL'S'	Green/Yellow body, Green letters *Bentalls Kingston on Thames* Phone Kin 1001, Type 2.		NGPP	☐
NB Normal numbering resumed						
30e	1935-40	Bedford Breakdown Van	Red, Green or Grey body, RWD in cab. 92 mm.	£75	GP	☐
30e	1946-47	Bedford Breakdown Van	Red, Green or Grey body, No RWD in cab. 92 mm.	£55	NC	☐
30v (491)	1949-54	Electric Dairy Van	Cream/Red body, *N.C.B.* 85 mm.	£45	NC	☐
			AVI grey body with blue N.C.B.	£45	NC	☐
30v (490)	1951-54	Electric Dairy Van	Grey/Blue body *Express Dairy.* 85 mm.	£65	NC	☐
			AVI Cream/Red body	£55	NC	☐
30v	1953-4	Electric Dairy Van	Cream/Red, *Job's Dairy* PRM. 85 mm.	£85	NC	☐
31	1935-40	Holland Coachcraft Van	Blue or Green *Holland Coachcraft Registered Design* in gild. 88 mm.	£175	GP	☐
31a (450)	1951-54	Trojan 15 cwt Van	Red body, *Esso.* 85 mm.	£115	NC	☐
31b (451)	1952-54	Trojan 15 cwt Van	Red body, *Dunlop the Worlds Master Tyre.* 85 mm.	£125	NC	☐
31c (452)	1953-54	Trojan 15 cwt Van	Green body, *Chivers Jellies* and design. 85 mm.	£125	NC	☐
31d	1953-54	Trojan 15 cwt Van	Blue body, *Beefy Oxo* issued without box. 85 mm.	£175	GP	☐
33d	1936-38	Box Van Trailer and Tug	Green body, *Hornby Trains British and Guaranteed.* 70 mm.	£135	GP	☐
33d	1938-39	Box Van Trailer and Tug	Green body, *Meccano Engineering* for boys in Black etc. 70 mm.	£125	GP	☐
33r	1935-40	Mechanical Horse L.N.E.R.	Blue/Black body, *L.N.E.R. 901.*	£55	GP	☐
33r	1935-40	Trailer Van and Horse 'L.N.E.R.'	Blue/Black body, *L.N.E.R., Express Parcels Traffic.*	£125	GP	☐
33r	1935-40	Mechanical Horse 'L.M.S.'	Brown/Black body, *L.M.S. 2246.*	£65	GP	☐
33r	1935-40	Trailer Van and Horse 'L.M.S.'	Brown/Black body, *L.M.S., Express Parcel Service.*	£125	GP	☐
33r	1935-40	Mechanical Horse 'G.W.R.'	Brown/Cream body, *G.W.R. 2742.*	£65	GP	☐
33r	1935-40	Trailer Van and Horse 'G.W.R.'	Brown/Cream body, *G.W.R., Express Cartage Service.*	£125	GP	☐
33r	1935-40	Mechanical Horse 'S.R.'	Green with Black or White roof *3016 M.*	£65	GP	☐
33r	1935-40	Trailer Van and Horse 'S.R.'	Green/Black *Southern Railway, Express Parcels Service.*	£125	GP	☐
34a	1935-38	'ROYAL AIR MAIL SERVICE' Car	Blue body. 83 mm.	£225	GP	☐
34b	1938-40	'ROYAL MAIL' Van	Red/Black body, Rear WDS, *GR* and crown. 83 mm.	£85	NC	☐
34b	1948-52	'ROYAL MAIL' Van	Red/Black body, No rear WDS, *GR* and crest. 83 mm.	£65	NC	☐
34c (492)	1948-55	Loudspeaker Van	Brown body, Blk OC/Type 3. 81 mm. AVI Silver LS.	£50	NC	☐
260	1955-61	'ROYAL MAIL' Van	Red/Black body, crest. 78 mm.	£90	NC	☐
261	1956-61	'POST OFFICE TELEPHONES' Van	Green and Black body, crest. 73 mm.	£90	NC	☐
262	1956-59	VW Swiss Postal Van	Yellow/Black *P.T.T.*/crest. 90 mm.	£75	NC	☐
273	1965-70	'R.A.C.' Mini Minor Van	Blue body, *Road Service* CEM/SS/FS/OD. 78 mm.	£50	NC	☐
			LV Blue/White	£35	NC	☐
274	1967-71	'A.A.' Mini Minor Van	Yellow body, *Patrol Service* CEM/SS/FS/OD. 78 mm.	£40	NC	☐
			LV Yellow/Black body		GP	☐
274	1967-71	Mini Minor Van	Red body *Joseph Mason Paints* PRM	£100	GP	☐
275	1964-69	Brinks Armoured Car	Grey/Blue body, *Brinks Security Since 1859,* with 2 drivers & 2 bullion crates.	£95	GP	☐
	1979	2nd Issue	With no drivers or bullion, US packaging.	£35	GP	☐
		Mexican Issue	Blue body, Grey doors & Red, White and Blue crest on sides	£1000	GP	☐
280	1948-54	Delivery Van	Red or Blue body, Type 3, No RWD. 83 mm.	£45	NC	☐
280	1967-68	Mobile Midland Bank	Sil/Cream/Blue body, *Midland Bank Ltd.* 124 mm.	£55	NC	☐
390	1979-80	Transit Van	Metallic Blue body. Type III, *Vampire.*	£15	NC	☐
407	1966-69	Ford Transit Van	Blue White, *Kenwood* Pro. 129 mm. Type I.	£55	NC	☐
407	1970-71	Ford Transit Van	White body, *Colour TV, Telefusion* Pro. 129 mm.	NOT ISSUED		☐
407	1970-73	Ford Transit Van	Yel body, *Hertz Truck Rentals* Pro. 129 mm. Type I.	£45	NC	☐

Ref. No.		Model Type	Dinky Vans continued	Rarity and Price Grading	
407	1970-73	Ford Transit Van	White body *Rediffusion Colour TV* Pro. 129 mm.	NOT ISSUED	☐
407	1970-73	Ford Transit Van	Red body, *Avis Truck Rentals*. 129 mm. (Kit only).	NOT ISSUED	☐
410	1972-76	Bedford CF Van	Black/Red, *Simpsons* and CEM. 90 mm.	£25	GP ☐
410	1974	Bedford CF Van	Yellow body, *Danish Post* emblem	£10-£15	MPR ☐
410	1974-75	Bedford CF Van	Blue body, *John Menzies*. 90 mm.	£10-£15	MPR ☐
410	1974-75	Bedford CF Van	Orange/Black body, *Belaco Brake and Clutch Parts*. 90 mm.	£25	GP ☐
410	1975-76	Bedford CF Van	White body *MJ Hire Service*. 90 mm.	£10-£15	MPR ☐
410	1975-77	Bedford CF Van	White body *Modellers World*. 90 mm. Code 2 Model.	£35	GP ☐
410	1975-77	Bedford CF Van	Red body *Marley Building* etc. 90 mm.	£15	NC ☐
410	1979	Bedford CF Van	White body *Collectors Gazette*. 90 mm. Code 2. Model.	£25	GP ☐
410	1972-80	Bedford 'ROYAL MAIL' Van (CF)	Red body *EIIR* PW. 90 mm.	£10-15	MPR ☐
412	1974-80	Bedford 'AA SERVICE' Van (CF)	Yellow/Black body PW. 90 mm.	£10-£15	MPR ☐
416	1975-78	Ford Transit Van	Yellow body, '1,000,000 TRANSITS' Type II	£15	NC ☐
416	1975-78	Ford Transit Van	Yellow body *Motorway Services* SL/2OD. 129 mm. Type II.	£15	NC ☐
417	1978-79	Ford Transit Van	Yellow body, *Motorway Services* SL/OD. 129 mm. Type III.	£10-15	MPR ☐
450 (31a)	1955-57	Trojan Van 'ESSO'	Red/White body *Esso* decals. 85 mm.	£115	NC ☐
450	1965-70	Bedford TK Van	Metallic Green and White body, *Castrol The Masterpiece in Oils* OD. 143 mm.	£125	GP ☐
451 (31b)	1955-57	Trojan Van 'DUNLOP'	Red body *Dunlop The Worlds Master Tyre*. 85 mm.	£95	NC ☐
452 (31c)	1954-57	Trojan Van 'CHIVERS'	Green body *Chivers Jellies* and design. 85 mm.	£95	NC ☐
454	1957-59	Trojan Van 'CYDRAX'	Green body *Drink Cydrax* and design. 85 mm.	£115	NC ☐
455	1957-61	Trojan Van 'BROOKE BOND'	Red body *Brooke Bond Tea* and design. 85 mm.	£95	GP ☐
465	1957-59	Morris 10 cwt Van 'CAPSTAN'	Blue/Dark Blue body, cigarette design *Have a Capstan*. 78 mm.	£175	GP ☐
470	1954-56	Austin Van 'SHELL BP'	Red/Green body *Shell, BP* decals. 89 mm. A40 type.	£75	NC ☐
471	1955-60	Austin Van 'NESTLÉS'	Red body *Nestlés* decals. 89 mm. A40 type.	£75	NC ☐
472	1957-60	Austin Van 'RALEIGH CYCLES'	Green body *Raleigh Cycles* decals. 89 mm. A40 type.	£75	NC ☐
480	1954-56	Bedford Van 'KODAK'	Yellow body, *Kodak Cameras and Films*. 83 mm.	£70	NC ☐
481	1955-60	Bedford Van 'OVALTINE'	Blue body *Ovaltine* decals. 83 mm.	£70	NC ☐
482	1956-60	Bedford Van 'DINKY TOYS'	Yellow body *Dinky Toys* decals. 83 mm.	£85	NC ☐
490 (30v)	1954-56	Electric Dairy Van	Grey/Blue or Cream/Red body *Express Dairy*. 85 mm.	£55	NC ☐
491 (30v)	1956-60	Electric Dairy Van	Cream/Red body *N.C.B.* on front. 85 mm.	£65	NC ☐
491	1960	Electric Dairy Van	Cream/Red body, *Jobs Dairy*, PRM. 85 mm.	£85	NC ☐
492 (34c)	1954-57	Loudspeaker Van	Brown body, Type 3, OC, Black LS. 81 mm. AVI Blue.	£45	NC ☐
492	1964-65	Election Mini Van	White body *Vote for Somebody* Fig/OD. 78 mm.	£50	GP ☐
514	1949-52	Guy Van 'SLUMBERLAND'	Red *Slumberland Spring Interior Mattresses* and crest. 1st type ST/OD/SPW. 134 mm.	£250	NC ☐
514	1951-54	Guy Van 'LYONS'	Blue *Lyons Swiss Rolls* 1st type ST/OD/SPW. 134 mm.	£600	GP ☐
514	1952-54	Guy Van 'WEETABIX'	Yellow body 1st type ST/OD/SPW. 134 mm.	£600	GP ☐
514	1953-54	Guy Van 'SPRATTS'	Red/Cream body, 1st type *Bonio Ovals & Dog Cakes* ST/OD/SPW. 134 mm.	£275	GP ☐
561	1962-64	Citroen Delivery Van	Metallic Blue *Cibie* sliding doors. 90 mm.	£55	NC ☐
917	1955-56	Guy Van 'SPRATTS'	Red/Cream body — details as for 514. 134 mm.	£275	GP ☐
918	1955-58	Guy Van 'EVER READY'	Blue body, 2nd type ST/OD/SPW *Ever Ready Batteries for Life*. 134 mm.	£175	GP ☐
919	1957-58	Guy Van 'GOLDEN SHRED'	Red body, 2nd type ST/OD/SPW *Robertson's Golden Shred* plus CEM. 134 mm.	£500	GP ☐
920	1960-61	Guy Warrior Van 'HEINZ' Tomato Ketchup Bottle decal	Red and Yellow body, Warrior front *Heinz 57 Varieties* ST/OD/SPW. 137 mm.	£750	GP ☐
923	1955-58	Big Bedford Van 'HEINZ'	Red/Yellow *Heinz 57 Varieties* plus Baked Beans tin ST/SPW. 146 mm.	£175	GP ☐
923	1958-59	Big Bedford Van 'HEINZ' `	Red/Yellow *Heinz 57 Varieties* plus Tomato Ketchup bottle ST/SPW. 146 mm.	£400	GP ☐
930	1960-64	Bedford Pallet — Jekta Van	Orange/Yellow body, *Dinky Toys, Meccano* ST/OD/WPEM. 177 mm.	£175	GP ☐

ADDENDUM — FORD TRANSIT VANS

Type I	1966-74	Has a sliding drivers door and an opening side door together with opening side hinged twin rear doors.
Type II	1975-78	Does NOT have sliding drivers door. Has one side hinged door and a top hinged rear door.
Type III	1978-80	Model same as Type II but has slightly longer bonnet. (18 mm).

Gift Sets Dinky Vans

Ref. No.		Model Type	Model Features and Size	Rarity and Price Grading		
28 Series	1934-40	28/1 Delivery Vans All 1st Type	Contains 28a Hornby, 28b Pickfords, 28c Manchester Guardian, 28d Oxo, 28e Ensign, 28f Palethorpes	£3000	GP	☐
28 Series	1934-40	28/2 Delivery Vans All 1st Type	28g Kodak, 28h Sharps, 28k Marsh's, 28l Crawfords, 28m Wakefield, 28n Meccano	£3000	GP	☐
28 Series		Revised Set 28/1 Delivery Vans	Contains 28a Hornby, 28b Pickfords, 28c Manchester Guardian, 28e Firestone, 28f Palethorpes	£3000	GP	☐
28 Series		Revised Set 28/2 Delivery Vans	Contains 28d Oxo, 28g Kodak, 28h Dunlop Van, 28k Marsh's, 28m Wakefield, 28h Crawfords	£2000	GP	☐
28 Series	1936-40	28/3 Delivery Vans (2nd Type)	Contains 28r Swans, 28s Frys, 28t Ovaltine, 28w Osram, 28x Hovis, 28y Exide	£2000	GP	☐
280 Series	1936-40	280 Series Delivery Vans (2nd Type)	Contains 280a Viyella, 280b Lyons, 280c Shredded Wheat, 280d Bisto, 280e Ekco, 280f Mackintosh's	£2000	GP	☐
299	1958	Post Office Services	Contains 260, 261, plus Telephone Box Messenger and Postman	£250	GP	☐

Auction Price Results
Lacey Scotts, Bury St. Edmunds Sale 27.2.88
930 — £135, 482 — £65, 261 — £48, 470 — £70
Lacey Scotts Sale 12.12.87
465 — £140, 918 — £130 (All mint boxed)
Lacey Scotts Sale 13.6.87
514 'Slumberland' (MB) — £205
514 'Lyons Swiss Rolls' (boxed good) — £330
Phillips, Son & Neale, 7 Blenheim Street, New Bond Street, London Sale 27.1.88.
A set of six mint Austin 'Nestle' Vans (471) in a trade box realised £260
A set of six Trojan 'Chivers' Vans (452), all individually mint boxed and in a trade box realised £300

Auction price results
Christies, 85 Old Brompton Road, London SW7 3LD.
Sale dated 28.1.88.
28 Series, 3rd type 'Hovis' — £300
28 Series, 2nd type 'Kodak' — £600 (believed to be a world record price at auction)
514 'Ever Ready' — £260

Sale dated 8.10.87:
923 'Heinz beans' — £160
514 'Slumberland' — £170
28 Series, 3rd type 'Crawfords' — £400

Sale dated 20.1.87:
28 Series 1st type 'Ensign Cameras' — £580

Sale dated 28.5.87:
514 'Lyons Swiss Rolls' — £300
514 'Weetabix' — £260
514 'Golden Shred' — £300

Sotheby Parke Bernet, 34 New Bond Street, London W1
Sale dated 29.9.87:
28 Series Delivery Vans
1st type 'Pickfords' — £400
1st type 'Meccano' — £380
1st type 'Hornby trains' — £550

Lacey Scott, Bury St Edmunds
Sale dated 13.8.88
Set No. 299 realised £240

Dinky Fire, Police and Ambulance Vehicles

Ref. No.		Model Type	Model Features and Size	Rarity and Price Grading		

Note: For description of the different chassis types see page 61.
      For description of the different Transit Van types see page 76.

Ref. No.		Model Type	Model Features and Size			
24a	1934-38	Ambulance (No crosses)	Grey/Red or Cream/Red body, CCCH/PLR/open windows. 102 mm.	£125	GP	☐
24a	1938-40	Ambulance (No crosses)	Green/Red or Grey/Red body, CCCH/RB/open windows. 102 mm.	£100	GP	☐
25h	1936-40	Streamline Fire Engine	Red/Silver body, No CH/TPLD/bell/WT. 101 mm.	£125	GP	☐
25h (250)	1948-54	Streamline Fire Engine	Red/Silver body, No CH/TPLD/bell. 101 mm.	£55	NC	☐
25k	1938-40	Streamline Fire Engine	Red/Sil body, No CH/6 TP FM/TPLD/bell. 101 mm.	£150	GP	☐
30f	1935-38	Ambulance (Red crosses)	Red/Grey body, MCH/PLR/open WDS. 99 mm.	£125	GP	☐
30f	1938-40	Ambulance (Red crosses)	Black/Grey body, MCH/RB/open WDS. 99 mm.	£100	GP	☐
30f	1946-47	Ambulance (Red crosses)	Grey body, Black, MCH, open WDS. 99 mm.	£85	NC	☐
30f	1947-48	Ambulance (Red crosses)	Cream body, Black, MCH, No WDS. 99 mm.	£85	NC	☐
30h	1950-54	Daimler Ambulance	Cream body, Red crosses. 96 mm also white body.	£55	NC	☐
195	1971-74	Fire Chiefs Land Rover	Red, *Fire Service*, FLL/OD/SWS/BUP. 109 mm.	£18	NC	☐
243	1978-79	Volvo Police Car	White/Red, *Police*, FLL/PCH/PW. 141 mm.	£15	NC	☐
244	1978-79	Plymouth Fury Police Car	Black/White body, *Police* PCH/PW/A. 134 mm.	£15	NC	☐
250 (25h)	1954-62	Fire Engine	Red/Silver body, TPL/bell. 99 mm.	£50	NC	☐
250	1968-74	Police Mini Cooper S	White *Police* cones/sign/FLL/TS. 75 mm RT/SWS.	£15	NC	☐
251	1971-74	U.S.A. 'POLICE' Car	Black body, D/FLL/SWS/A. 132 mm. Also on Black/White	£30	NC	☐
252	1971-74	R.C.M.P. Chevrolet	Blue/White body, D/FLL/SWS/2A/crest. 132 mm.	£30	NC	☐
253 (30h)	1954-64	Daimler Ambulance	Cream body, Red crosses, some have WDS. 95 mm.	£55	NC	☐
254	1977-79	Police Range Rover	White body, *Police*, FLL/OD/SWS. 109 mm. WWA.	£18	NC	☐
255	1955-61	Mersey Tunnel Police	Red body, *Mersey Tunnel* and *Police* H. 77 mm.	£65	NC	☐
255	1968-71	Ford Zodiac Police Car	White body, *Police* D/FLL/ODB/SS/FS/A. '1st AGAIN! 4 OPENING DOORS'. 114 mm.	£45	NC	☐
256	1960-64	Humber Hawk Police Car	Black body, *Police* D/PM/SS/WDS/A.	£65	NC	☐
255	1977-79	Police Mini Clubman	Blue/White body, *Police*, FLL/ODB/PW. 82 mm.	£15	NC	☐
257	1961-68	Canadian 'FIRE CHIEF'	Red body, ST/FLL/SS/WDS, Nash Rambler. 102 mm.	£35	NC	☐
258	1960-61	U.S.A. 'POLICE' Car	Black/White body, LHD/FLL/WDS, De Soto Fireflite. 114 mm.	£50	NC	☐
258	1961-62	U.S.A. 'POLICE' Car	Black body, LHD/A/WDS, Dodge Royal, Sedan. 111 mm.	£50	NC	☐
258	1962-67	U.S.A. 'POLICE' Car	Black/White body, LHD/FLL/FS/A, Ford Fairlane. 111 mm.	£40	NC	☐
258	1967-68	Cadillac	Black/White body *Police*, LHD/SS/FS/FLL/A. 111 mm.	£50	NC	☐
261	1967-77	Ford Taunus German issue	White/Green *'Polizei'* body.	£25	NC	☐
263	1962-68	Superior Criterion	Cream body *Ambulance* on WDS. 127 mm.	£30	NC	☐
263	1978-79	Fire Tender	Yellow body *Airport Rescue*, PL/FLL. 177 mm.	£15	NC	☐
264	1967-68	R.C.M.P. Cadillac	Blue/White body, SS/FS/FLL/A/crest. 111 mm.	£50	NC	☐
264	1978-79	Rover 3500	White/Yellow body, *Police*, FLL/ODB. 131 mm.	£5-£10	MPR	☐
266	1977-79	E.R.F. Fire Tender	Red body *Fire Service*, white PLD. 223 mm.	£15	NC	☐
267	1978-79	Paramedic Truck	Red body, 5 yellow cylinders, PW. 119 mm.	£10-£15	MPR	☐
268	1974-77	Range Rover	White body *Ambulance*, FLL/OD/BUP/SR. 109 mm.	£10-£15	MPR	☐
269	1962-66	Jaguar 'POLICE' Car	White body, FLL/SS/FS/WDS/A/2PM. 95 mm.	£65	NC	☐
269	1978-79	Ford Transit	White/Red body SR/PM etc. 129 mm. Type III.	£10-£15	MPR	☐
270	1971-74	Ford Panda	Blue/White body, *Police* SWS/BUP. 97 mm.	£20	NC	☐
271	1975-76	Ford Transit 'FIRE'	Red body, hose/axe/bells/PLD/BUP. 129 mm. Type II.	£35	NC	☐
272	1975-77	Police Accident Unit	White body, *Police* OD FLL/A/cones/signs. 129 mm. Type II.	£20	NC	☐
274	1978-79	Ford Transit Ambulance	White body, *Ambulance*, SR/FLL/RCS. 129 mm. Type III.	£15	NC	☐
276	1962-69	'AIRPORT FIRE CONTROL' Tender	Red body, FLL/SS/FS/WDS/bell. 117 mm.	£45	NC	☐
277	1962-68	Superior Criterion Ambulance	Blue/White/Red, D/LHD/SR/ODB/FLL. 127 mm.	£40	NC	☐
277	1977-79	Land Rover	Blue/White body *Police*, FLL. 110 mm.	£10-£15	MPR	☐
278	1964-68	Vauxhall Victor	White body *Ambulance*, SR/SL/SS/FS/ODB. 87 mm.	£45	NC	☐
282	1974-79	Land Rover Appliance	Red body *Fire Service*, FLL/Metal LD/BUP.	£12-£17	MPR	☐
285	1970-79	Merryweather Marquis	Red/White body *Fire Service*, PL/FLL. 177 mm.	£35	NC	☐
286	1969-74	Ford Transit	Red body *Fire Service*, hose/FLL/BUP. 112 mm. Type I.	£35	NC	☐
287	1967-74	Police Accident Unit	Cream/Orange body *Police Accident Unit*. 122 mm. Type I.	£35	NC	☐
288	1974-79	Superior Cadillac	Red/White body *Ambulance*, SR/FLL. 152 mm.	£10-£15	MPR	☐
555	1952-69	Fire Engine	Red/Silver body, ST/ladder. 140 mm.	£45	NC	☐
956	1958-71	Turntable Fire Escape	Red body, small cab/ST LV. 200 mm.	£85	NC	☐
			LV *Berliot* large cab.	£85	NC	☐
2253	1974-76	Ford Capri Police Car	White/Red body *Police/Accident*. 175 mm.	£30	NC	☐

NB. Details of the Ford Transit Van different types are shown at the end of the Dinky Van section.

DINKY MODELS ISSUED IN DENMARK
The following models were issued with the Danish 'FALCK' labels.
    271   Ford Transit Fire Appliance (Type II).
    282   Land Rover Fire Appliance.
    285   Merryweather Marquis Fire Engine.
    286   Ford Transit Fire Appliance (Type II).
    288   Superior Cadillac Ambulance.
NB Models are not common. Asking prices 25% higher than U.K. issues.

Gift Sets

Ref. No.		Model Type	Model Features and Size	Rarity and Price Grading		
294	1973-76	Police Vehicles Gift Set	Contains 250, 254, 287	£65	NC	☐
297	1967-72	Police Vehicles Gift Set	Contains 250, 255, 287	£95	NC	☐
298	1963-64	Emergency Services Set	Contains 258, 276, 263, 277 (9 figures)	£225	GV	☐
299	1963-66	Motorway Services Set	Contains 257, 276, 263, 277	£225	GP	☐
299	1978-79	Crash Squad Gift Set	Contains 244, 732 helicopter	£20	NC	☐
302	1978-79	Emergency Squad Gift Set	Contains Paramedic Truck and 288	£20	NC	☐
304	1978-79	Fire Rescue Gift Set	Contains 195, 282, 384	£35	NC	☐
957	1959-64	Fire Services Gift Set	Contains 257, 955, 956	£400	GP	☐

NB Set 298 realised £200 at Phillips New Bond Street Auction on 20.8.86.

Dinky Farm and Garden Models

Ref. No.		Model Type	Model Features and Size	Rarity and Price Grading		
22c	1933-40	Fram Tractor 'Modelled Miniature'	Yellow/Blue/Red body, metal wheels, SW cast in. 70mm. Also Blue/White/Red and Green/Yellow/Red.	£150	GP	☐
27a (300)	1948-54	Massey Harris Tractor	Red/Yellow body, D/SW/H. 89 mm.	£45	NC	☐
27ak (310)	1948-54	Tractor and Hay Rake	Red/Yellow body	£55	NC	☐
27b	1949-54	Halesowen Harvest Trailer	Brown/Red body. 121 mm.	£25	NC	☐
27c	1949-54	M.H. Manure Spreader	Red body, towbar, hook. 113 mm.	£20	NC	☐
27g (342)	1949-56	Moto-Cart	Brown/Green body. 110 mm.	£25	NC	☐
27m	1950-55	Land Rover Trailer	Orange/Green body, TB/H. 79 mm.	£8-£11	MPR	☐
27n (301)	1950-60	Field Marshall Tractor	Orange body, D/SW/H/FAS. 79 mm.	£65	NC	☐
30n	1950-60	Farm Produce Wagon	Green/Yellow or Blue/Red body, H. 107 mm.	£55	NC	☐
105a (381)	1949-54	Garden Roller	Green/Red body. 67 mm.	£15	NC	☐
105b (382)	1949-54	Wheelbarrow	Brown body. 82 mm.	£15	NC	☐
105c (383)	1949-54	4 Wheeled Hand Truck	Green body. 126 mm.	£5-£10	MPR	☐
105e (384)	1949-54	Grass Cutter	Red/Green/Yellow body. 73 mm.	£20	NC	☐
107a (385)	1949-54	Sack Truck	Blue body. 65 mm.	£11-£15	MPR	☐
300	1954-75	'MASSEY HARRIS' Tractor	Red body, driver, SW/H. 89 mm.	£50	NC	☐
300	1960-65	'MASSEY FERGUSON' Tractor	Red/Orange body, driver, SW/H. 89 mm.	£50	NC	☐
301 (27n)	1954-61	Field Marshall Tractor	Orange body, D/SW/H/FAS. 79 mm.	£65	NC	☐
301	1962-67	Field Marshall Tractor	Red body, D/SW/H. 76 mm.	£45	NC	☐
305	1965-70	'DAVID BROWN' Tractor	Red/Yellow body, detachable cab, D. 83 mm.	£30	NC	☐
305	1971-75	David Brown Tractor	White body, detachable cab, D/BUP. 83 mm.	£20	NC	☐
308	1971-75	'LEYLAND 384' Tractor	Met Red body, D/SW/H/BUP. 86 mm.	£30	NC	☐
308	1976-79	'LEYLAND 384' Tractor	Blue body, D/SW/H/BUP. 86 mm.	£20	NC	☐
310	1954-60	Tractor with Hay Rake	Red/Yellow body. 157 mm.	£45	NC	☐
319	1961-68	Weeks Tipping Trailer	Red/Yellow body. 105 mm.	£15	NC	☐
320	1954-60	Halesowen Trailer	Red/Brown body, tow bar, hook. 120 mm.	£15	NC	☐
321	1954-60	Massey Harris Manure Spreader	Red/Silver body. 113 mm.	£10-£15	MPR	☐
322	1954-60	Disc Harrow	Red/Yellow body. 86 mm.	£10-£15	MPR	☐
323	1954-63	Triple Gang Mower	Red/Yellow/Green body. 114 mm.	£20	NC	☐
324	1954-64	Hayrake	Red/Yellow body. 77 mm.	£10-£15	MPR	☐
325	1967-73	'DAVID BROWN' Tractor	White/Red Body. 83 mm.	£25	NC	☐
342	1955-60	Moto-Cart	Green/Brown body. 110 mm.	£25	NC	☐
343 (30)	1954-64	Farm Produce Wagon	Green/Yellow (Dodge BP). 107 mm. Red/Blue body	£55 £55	NC NC	☐ ☐
381	1977-80	Convoy Farm Truck	Yellow/Black body. 110 mm.	£10-£15	MPR	☐
399	1969-75	Tractor and Trailer Set	Red/Orange body, *Massey Ferguson*. 188 mm.	£45	NC	☐
428	1967-71	Trailer	Red or Grey body. 105 mm.	£5-£10	MPR	☐
564	1952-68	Elevator Loader	Yellow/Blue body.	£45	NC	☐
751 (386)	1954-58	Lawn Mower	Green or Red body, separate box, 140 mm.	£40	NC	☐

Gift Sets

Ref. No.		Model Type	Model Features and Size	Rarity and Price Grading		
	1952-54	Set No 1	Contains 27a, b, c, g, h	£300	NPE	☐
	1960-69	Set No 387	Contains 300, 320, 321, 322, 324	£200	NPE	☐

Dinky Military Models

Ref. No.		Model Type	Model Features and Size	Rarity and Price Grading	
22f	1933-40	Army tank	Green/Orange body turret rotates. 87 mm.	£150	GP ☐
22s	1933-38	Searchlight Lorry	Green body. 99 mm	£200	GP ☐
25wm	1950-54	Bedford Military Truck	Military Green body (U.S. issue)	£165	GP ☐
30hm	1950-54	Daimler Ambulance	Green body, Red crosses (US issue).	£185	GP ☐
30sm	1950-54	Austin Covered Lorry	Green body. (US issue)	£185	GP ☐
37c	1938-40	Signals Dispatch Rider	Green body, Blue/White arms 46 mm.	£40	GP ☐
139am	1950	US Army Staff Car	Green body, White star (FORD FORDOR)	£175	GP ☐
150a	1938-40	Royal Tank Corps Officer	Khaki, binoculars in hand	£10	NC ☐
150b	1938-40	Royal Tank Corps Private	Khaki uniform (sitting) DC	£10	NC ☐
150c	1938-40	Royal Tank Corps Private	Khaki uniform (standing) DC	£10	NC ☐
150d	1938-40	Army Driver	Khaki uniform DC (sitting)	£10	NC ☐
150e	1938-40	Royal Corps NCO	Khaki uniform DC (walking)	£10	NC ☐
151a	1937-40	Medium Tank	MG body White SQM/TRR/CHT/A. 92 mm.	£65	GP ☐
151b	1938-40	6 W Transport Wagon	MG body, SPW/H/holes/TP cover. 99 mm.	£60	GP ☐
151b	1946-48	6 W Transport Wagon	MG body, SPW/H/holes/TP cover. 99 mm.	£50	NC ☐
151c	1938-40	Cooker Trailer	MG (with stand). 60 mm.	£40	NC ☐
151c	1946-48	Cooker Trailer	MG (with stand). 60 mm.	£40	NC ☐
151d	1938-40	Water Tank Trailer	Military green. 52 mm.	£30	NC ☐
151d	1946-48	Water Tank Trailer	Military green. 52 mm.	£30	NC ☐
152a	1937-40	Light Tank	MG body, White, SQM/TRR/CHT/A. 68 mm.	£45	GP ☐
152a	1946-48	Light Tank	MG body, White, SQM/TRR/CHT/A. 68 mm.	£45	GP ☐
152b	1938-40	Reconnaissance Car	Military Green body, Green BP, 6 wheels. 89 mm.	£40	GP ☐
152b	1946-48	Reconnaissance Car	Military Green body, 6 wheels. 89 mm.	£35	NC ☐
			Brown version 6 wheels	£45	NC ☐
152c	1938-40	Austin Seven	Military Green body, Royal Tank Corps	£60	GP ☐
153a	1946-48	Jeep (U.S. Market)	MG body, White star, SW/LHD/SPW at rear. 69 mm.	£45	GP ☐
160a	1939-40	Royal Artillery NCO	Khaki uniform	£10	NC ☐
160b	1939-40	Royal Artillery Gunner	Khaki uniform (seated)	£10	NC ☐
160c	1939-40	Royal Artillery Gunlayer	Khaki uniform	£10	NC ☐
160d	1939-40	Royal Artillery Gunner	Khaki uniform (standing)	£10	NC ☐
161a	1939-40	Searchlight on Lorry	Military Green body. 99 mm.	£160	GP ☐
161b	1939-40	A.A. Gun on Trailer	MG body, H/gun elevates/holes/TB. 115 mm.	£35	GP ☐
161b	1946-48	A.A. Gun on Trailer	MG body, H/gun elevates/holes/TB. 115 mm.	£30	NC ☐
162a	1939-40	Light Dragon Tractor	MG body, chain track. 89 mm.	£45	GP ☐
162a	1946-48	Light Dragon Tractor	MG body, chain track/holes. 65 mm.	£45	NC ☐
162b	1939-40	Trailer	MG body towbar and hook. 43 mm.	£15	NC ☐
162b	1946-48	Trailer	MG body towbar and hook. 54 mm.	£15	NC ☐
162c	1939-40	18-pdr Gun	MG body towbar. 78 mm.	£15	NC ☐
162c	1946-48	18-pdr Gun	MG body towbar. 78 mm.	£15	NC ☐
170	1957-58	Ford Fordor	MG body, White star on nose. 102 mm.	£175	GP ☐
281	1973-75	Military Hovercraft	MG body, Black start *Army* 139 mm	£15	NC ☐
601	1974-78	Austin Paramoke	MG/Grey body, PW/BUP. 76 mm.	£10-£15	MPR ☐
602	1977-80	Armoured Car Command	MG body, White star/fires sparks. 57 mm.	£10-£15	MPR ☐
603	1950-68	Army Private	Khaki (seated)	£2 each	MPR ☐
603a	1950-68	Army Personnel Set	Khaki 6 figures	£5-£10	MPR ☐
604	1960-72	Army Personnel	Khaki 6 drivers	£5-£10	MPR ☐
604	1976-79	Land Rover Bomb Disposal	MG/Orange body, *Explosive Disposal*. 110 mm.	£25	NC ☐
609	1976-79	105 mm with Crew	MG body, 3 soldiers, BUP. 160 mm.	£10-£15	MPR ☐
612	1976-79	Commando Jeep	MG/D/2 guns/A. 108 mm.	£10-£15	MPR ☐
612a	1974-79	Commando Jeep	MG or camouflage. 108 mm.	£10-£15	MPR ☐
615	1968-78	US Jeep and 105 mm	MG US Army markings/D. 199 mm.	£20-£25	MPR ☐
616	1968-78	AEC with Chieftain	MG *Army* AVTU/SQM/CM/PT/UJ. 318 mm.	£35	NC ☐
617	1969-78	VW KDF and 50 mm	German MG and crosses	£25	NC ☐
618	1976-78	AEC with Helicopter	MG body *Rescue* etc. AVTU/SQM/CM/UJ. 318 mm.	£35	NC ☐
619	1976-78	Bren Gun Carrier and Anti Tank Gun	MG, WS/D/PS/SQM/SPW/PT/A/H/SH/BUP. 125 mm. 159 mm.	£15-£20	MPR ☐
620	1967-71	Berliot Missile Launcher	MG Body, Black/White missile. 150 mm.	£75	GP ☐
621	1954-63	3 ton Army Wagon	MG, SQM/SPW/H. 113 mm. WW driver	£35	NC ☐
622	1954-63	10 ton Army Truck	MG body, ST/D/SQM/SPW/holes/6 W. 137 mm.	£45	NC ☐
622	1975-78	Bren Gun Carrier	MG body, Star/D/PS/SQM/PT/SPW. 125 mm.	£10-£15	MPR ☐
623	1954-63	Army Covered Wagon	MG Body, D/SQM/SPW. 105 mm.	£35	NC ☐
624	1954-60	Daimler Ambulance	MG body, Red crosses (US market). 105 mm.	£185	GP ☐
625	1954-60	Austin Covered Lorry	Green body. (30 mm US issue)	£185	GP ☐
625	1975-78	Six Pounder Gun	MG body. 159 mm.	£10-£15	MPR ☐
626	1956-62	Military Ambulance	MG Body, Red crosses, ODB/SPW. 110 mm.	£35	NC ☐
630	1973-78	Ferret Armoured Car	MG body. 80 mm.	£10-£13	MPR ☐
640	1954	Bedford Truck	MG body. (25 mm US issue)	£165	GP ☐
641	1954-62	Army 1 ton Cargo Truck	MG body, D/SQM/holes for PS. 79 mm.	£35	NC ☐
642	1957-62	R.A.F. Pressure Refueller	RAF Blue body, *roundel*, ST/D/H/6 W. 142 mm.	£50	NC ☐
643	1958-64	Army Water Tanker	MG body, D/SQM. 89 mm.	£35	NC ☐
650	1954	Light Tank	Green body (see 152a)	£35	NC ☐
651	1954-70	Centurion Tank	MG body, ST/SQM/rubber tracks. 149 mm.	£35	NC ☐
654	1974-76	155 mm Mobile Gun	MG body, star/PT/shells. 151 mm.	£10-£15	MPR ☐
656	1975-79	88 mm Gun	MG body. 218 mm.	£10-£15	MPR ☐
660	1956-64	Tank Transporter	MG body, 6×6 W/folding ramps/SPW. 335 mm.	£50	NC ☐
660a	1978-80	AA Gun with Crew	MG body, 3 soldiers, BUP. 218 mm.	£10-£15	MPR ☐
661	1957-64	Recovery Tractor	MG body, ST/D/SQM/CO. 134 mm.	£45	NC ☐
662	1975-77	88 mm Gun with Crew	MG body, 3 Germans/shells/BUP. 185 mm.	£10-£15	MPR ☐
665	1964-69	Honest John M.L.	MG, Black/White missile/10 W/SPW. 188 mm.	£45	NC ☐
666	1959-64	Missile Erector Vehicle and Corporal Missile	MG body, Black/White missile erector elevates, ST/D/WDS/SPW/H. 240 mm.	£125	NC ☐

Ref. No.		Model Type	**Military Models continued**	Rarity and Price Grading	
667	1960-61	Missile Servicing P.V.	MG body, ST/WDS/SPW/platform lifts. 197 mm.	£95	NC ☐
667	1954-64	Armoured Patrol Car	MG body. 80 mm aerial SPW	£10-£15	MPR ☐
668	1977-79	Foden Army Truck	MG body, SQM/WDS. 197 mm.	£20	NC ☐
669	1956-58	U.S.A. Universal Jeep	MG body, star (U.S. market issue). 83 mm.	£250	GP ☐
670	1954-64	Armoured Car	MG body, SQM/turret rotates. 73 mm.	£10-£15	MPR ☐
673	1953-61	Scout Car	MG body, holes/SQM. 68 mm.	£10-£15	MPR ☐
674	1954-62	Austin Champ	MG body, D/TPWS/SW/SPW. 69 mm.	£20	NC ☐
674	1958	'U.N.' Austin Champ	White body, D/TPWS/SW/SPW. 69 mm.	£200	GP ☐
674	1965-71	Austin Champ	MG body, D/SPW. 70 mm.	£15-£20	MPR ☐
675	1966-67	Ford Fordor	MG body, star (U.S. market issue). 102 mm.	£185	GP ☐
676	1955-62	Saracen A.P.C.	MG body, SQM/turret rotates. 82 mm.	£25	NC ☐
676a	1960-66	Daimler Armoured Car	MG body, rubber tracks. 72 mm.	£40	GP ☐
677	1973-76	Daimler Armoured Car	MG body, plastic wheels. 72 mm.	£5-£10	MPR ☐
677	1957-62	Armoured Command Vehicle	MG body, SQM/6 wheels. 134 mm.	£60	NC ☐
680	1972-75	Ferret Armoured Car	MG body, PW/BUP. 80 mm.	£5-£10	MPR ☐
681	1972-75	D.U.K.W.	MG or Blue body, PW/BUP. 127 mm.	£5-£10	MPR ☐
682	1972-77	Stalwart Load Carrier	MG body, PW/BUP. 103 mm.	£5-£10	MPR ☐
683	1972-79	Chieftain Tank	MG body, SQM/PT/shells/BUP. 117 mm.	£35	NC ☐
686	1978-79	Convoy Army Truck	Green/Black body. 110 mm.	£5-£10	MPR ☐
686	1957-67	25 pdr Field Gun	MG body. 90 mm.	£5-£7	MPR ☐
687	1957-67	25 pdr Trailer	MG body, towbar, hook. 58 mm.	£5-£7	MPR ☐
688	1957-70	Field Artillery Tractor	MG body, SQM/SPW. 79 mm.	£20	NC ☐
689	1957-66	Medium Artillery Tractor	MG body, ST/SQM/D/H/6 W. 140 mm.	£55	NC ☐
690	—	Mobile AA Gun	See 161b	£20	NC ☐
690	1975-79	Scorpion Tank	MG body, SQM/PT/2A/CN/BUP. 120 mm.	£18	NC ☐
691	—	Field Gun Unit	See 162	£100	GP ☐
691	1976-79	Striker Anti Tank	Camouflaged 5 firing rockets. 122 mm.	£10-£15	MPR ☐
692	1955-62	5.5 Medium Gun	MG body, towbar. 131 mm.	£10-£15	MPR ☐
692	1974-79	Leopard Tank	MG body, SQM/PT/2A/CN/BC/BUP. 198 mm.	£15-£20	MPR ☐
693	1958-67	7.2" Howitzer Gun	MG body, gun elevates. 130 mm.	£10-£15	MPR ☐
694	1974-80	Hanomag Destroyer	MG body, SQM/PT/PW/BC/BUP. 171 mm.	£10-£15	MPR ☐
696	1976-78	Leopard Anti-Aircraft Tank	MG body, SQM/PT/2A/BC/BUP. 147 mm.	£20	MPR ☐
699	1976-78	Leopard Recovery Tank	MG body, SQM/PT/A/jib/black cross/BUP. 147 mm.	£25	NC ☐
815	1962-64	Panhard Armoured Tank	Green body, French flag/FI. 104 mm.	£40	GP ☐
817	1962-64	AMX 13 ton Tank	Green body, French flag/FI. 107 mm.	£40	GP ☐
822	1962-64	Half Track M3	Green body, rubber tracks/FI. 121 mm.	£55	GP ☐
884	1962-64	Brockway Bridge Truck	Green body, pontoons/FI. 181 mm.	£100	GP ☐

Dinky Military Models Gift Sets

Ref. No.		Model Type	Model Features and Size	Rarity and Price Grading	
	1938-40	150 Series Royal Tank Corp Set	Contains 150a, 2xb, 2xc, 150d	£80	GP ☐
	1937-40	151 Series Royal Tank Corps Medium Tank Set	Contains 151a, b, c, d and 150d	£300	GP ☐
	1937-40	152 Series Light Tank Set	Contains 152a, b, c, d	£275	NPE ☐
	1939-40	156 Series Mechanised Army Set	Contains 151, 152, 161, 162	£950	GP ☐
	1939-40	160 Series Royal Artillery Set	Contains 160, a, b, c, d	£45	NC ☐
	1939-40	161 Series Anti Aircraft Unit	Contains 161a, 161b	£300	GP ☐
	1939-40	162 Series Field Gun Set	Contains 162a, b, c	£75	GP ☐
303	1978-80	Commando Squad Set	Contains Truck/AC/HC	£75	GP ☐
606	1954	Royal Artillery Personnel	Contains 6 figures	£65	GP ☐
677	1975	Task Force Set	3 Models in Green	£10-£15	MPR ☐
695	1963-66	Howitzer/Tractor Set	Contains 689 and 693	£50	GP ☐
697	1963-66	25 pdr Field Gun Set	Contains 686, 687, 688	£50	GP ☐
698	1958-62	Tank Transporter Set	Contains 651 and 660	£70	GP ☐
699	1956-67	Military Vehicles Set	Contains 621, 641, 674, 676	£175	GP ☐

Auction Price Results
Phillips Son & Neal, 7 Blenheim Street, New Bond Street, London. Sale 30.4.86.
Model Set 151 — sold for £360, Model Set 152 — sold for £260

Dinky Aeroplanes

Ref. No.		Model Type	Model Features and Size	Rarity and Price Grading	
60a	1934-41	Imperial Airways Liner	Gold/Blue body, OC, 4×2, PB, DC/TP. 125 mm.	£200	GP ☐
60a	1937-40	Imperial Airways Liner	Gold body, OC, DC/TP, 4×2 PB. 125 mm.	£200	GP ☐
60b	1934-36	D. H. Leopard Moth	Blue body, Orange wing tips OC/DC, 1×2 PB. 75 mm.	£65	GP ☐
60b	1936-40	D. H. Leopard Moth	Silver body, 1×2, PB. 75 mm.	£55	GP ☐
60c	1934-37	'Percival Gull'	White/Blue body, 1×2 PB. 75 mm.	£55	GP ☐
60c	1937-40	Percival Gull	White body, OC G-ADZO, 1×2 PB. 75 mm.		GP ☐
			Note for the purposes of continuity all the Percival Gull aircraft are together.		
60k	1936	Percival Gull (Amy Mollinson's)	Blue/Silver body, G-ADZO in blue, BX, 1×2 PB. 75 mm.	£250	GP ☐
60k	1937-	Percival Gull (H. L. Brook's)	Blue/Silver body, 1×2 PB, G-ADZO in black, BX. 75 mm.	£250	NPE ☐
60k	1946-48	Percival Gull Light Tourer	Various single colours, 1×2 PB. 75 mm.	£40	GP ☐
60d	1934-36	Low Wing Monoplane	Red/Cream body, OC/no pilot, 1×2 PB. 75 mm.	£60	GP ☐
60d	1936-40	Low Wing Monoplane	Orange body, 1×2 PB, OC/pilot G-AVYP. 75 mm.	£60	GP ☐
60e	1934-36	General Monospar Plane	Gold body, 2×2 PB. 80 mm.	£100	GP ☐
60e	1936-40	General Monospan Plane	Silver body 2×2 PB. 80 mm.	£100	GP ☐
60f	1934-36	Cierva Autogiro	Gold/Blue no pilot, 3 vanes. 50 mm.	£175	GP ☐
60f	1937-40	Cierva Autogiro	Gold/Blue with pilot, 3 vanes. 50 mm.	£175	GP ☐
60g	1935-37	D. H. Comet	Red/Gold body, 2×2 PB. 85 mm.	£65	GP ☐
	1937-40	D. H. Comet	Silver body, OC, 2×2 PB. 85 mm.	£65	GP ☐
	1946-49	Light Racer (D. H. Comet)	Silver body, OC, G-RACE, 2×2 PB. 85mm.	£50	GP ☐
60h	1936-40	'Singapore' Flying Boat	Silver body, RAF RDLS, 2×2 PB. 125 mm.	£150	NPE ☐
60m	1939-40	Four Engined Flying Boat	Silver, OC/DRGN/BX/4×2 PRB. 125 mm.	£150	NPE ☐
60n	1937-39	Fairy 'Battle' Bomber	Silver body, RAF roundels 1×3 PB. 75 mm.	£75	GP ☐
60s	1939-40	Fairy 'Battle' Bomber	Camouflage body, 1×3 PB. 55 mm.	£55	GP ☐
60p	1936-40	Gloucester Gladiator	Silver body, RAF roundels, Red 1×2 PB. 45 mm.	£130	GP ☐
60r	1937-40	Empire Flying Boat	Silver/Red body, 12 different types eg Caledonia Red 4×3 PB. 125 mm.	£130	GP ☐
60t	1938-40	Douglas DC3	Silver/Black body, Red, 2×3 PB. 130 mm.	£125	GP ☐
60v	1937-40	Armstrong Whitworth Bomber	Silver body, RAF roundels, Red, 2×3 PB. 86 mm.	£100	GP ☐
60w	1938-40	Flying Boat 'Clipper III'	Silver body, Red 4×3 PB. 125 mm.	£110	GP ☐
60w	1946-48	Flying Boat	Silver body, with no markings 4×3 PB. 125 mm.	£60	GP ☐
60x	1937-41	Atlantic Flying Boat	Blue/White body, Red 4×3 PB.	£200	GP ☐
62a	1938-40	Vickers-Supermarine 'Spitfire'	Silver body, RAF roundels 1×3 PB. 80 mm.	£65	GP ☐
62b	1938-40	'Bristol' Blenheim	Silver body, RAF roundels Red 2×3 PB.	£75	GP ☐
62c		No record of model with this number in Meccano Magazine.		—	
62d	1940-41	'Bristol Blenheim'	Camouflaged body, RAF RDLS, 2×3 PB. 75 mm.	£75	GP ☐
62e	1940-41	Supermarine Spitfire	Camouflaged body, RAF RDLS, 1×3 PB. 80 mm.	£65	GP ☐
62f	1939-40	DH Flamingo Airliner	Not issued	—	—
62g	1939-41	Flying Fortress	Silver body, 4×3 PB.	£100	GP ☐
62g	1945-48	'Long Range Bomber'	Silver body, Red 4×3 PB.	£55	GP ☐
62h	1938-40	Hawker Hurricane	Camouflaged body, RAF RDLS, 1×2 PB.	£65	GP ☐
62k	1938-41	Kings Aeroplane	Silver/Red body, Red 2×2 PB. 125 mm.	£175	GP ☐
62m	1938-41	Airspeed Envoy Monoplane	Green/Silver body, Red 2×2 PB. 125 mm.	£75	GP ☐
62m	1946-48	Light Transport	Red or Silver body, G-ATMH, Red 2×2 PB. 125 mm.	£35	NC ☐
62n	1939-41	Junkers JU90 Air Liner	Silver/Red body, D-AALV etc. Red 4×3 PB. 125 mm.	£150	GP ☐
62p	1938-41	Ensign Air Liner	Silver body, Ensign G-ADSR, Red 4×3 PB. 125 mm.	£95	GP ☐
			Also issued in 5 other names and reg nos.		
62p	1946-49	Armstrong Whitworth Air Liner	Silver body, OC 4×3 PB. 86 mm.	£100	GP ☐
62r	1939-41	D. H. Albatross Mail Liner	Silver body, G-AEVV, Red 4×3 PB. 140 mm.	£175	GP ☐
62r	1946-49	Four Engined Liner	Blue body, G-ATPV OC and reg nos. Red 4×3 PB. 140 mm.	£55	GP ☐
62s	1939-41	Hawker Hurricane	Silver body RAF roundels 1×2 PB. 88 mm.	£65	GP ☐
62s	1946-49	Hawker Hurricane	Silver body RAF roundels 1×2 PB. 88 mm.	£30	GP ☐
62t	1939-41	Armstrong Whitworth Bomber (Whitley)	Camouflaged body RAF roundels 4×3 PB. 86 mm.	£100	GP ☐
62w	1939-41	'Frobisher' Clan Air Liner	Silver body G-AFDI, 4×3 PB.	£175	GP ☐
62x	1939-41	40 Seat Airliner	Two tone Green/G-AZCA/OC 4×3 PB. 140 mm.	£85	GP ☐
62y	1946-49	Giant High Speed Monoplane	Silver body, OC/G-ATBK 4×3 PB. 125 mm.	£75	GP ☐
63	1939-41	Mayo Composite Aircraft	Sil/Red body, G-ADHJ/G-ADHK, Red 2×4×3 PB. Models 63a and 63b combined PBF. 125 mm. 102 mm.	£200	GP ☐
63a	1939-41	Flying Boat 'MAIA'	Sil/Red body, G-ADHK, Red 4×3 PB. 125 mm.	£160	GP ☐
63b	1939-41	Seaplane 'MERCURY'	Sil/Red body, G-ADHJ, 4×3 PB. 102 mm.	£40	GP ☐
66a	1940-41	Heavy Bomber	Camouflaged body, RAF RDLS, 4×2 PB (60a). 125 mm.	£350	GP ☐
66b	1940-41	Dive Bomber	Camouflaged body, RAF RDLS, 1×2 PB (60b). 75 mm.	£250	GP ☐
66c	1940-41	Two Seater Fighter	Camouflaged body, RAF RDLS, 1×2 PB (60c). 75 mm.	£250	GP ☐
66d	1940-41	Torpedo Dive Bomber	Camouflaged body, RAF, RDLS, 1×2 PB. 75 mm.	£250	GP ☐
66e	1940-41	Medium Bomber	Camouflaged body, RAF RDLS, 2×2 PB (60e). 75 mm.	£350	GP ☐
66f	1940-41	Army Co-operation Autogiro	Gold or Silver, 3 vanes, (60f).	£350	NPE ☐
67a	1940-41	Junkers Heavy Bomber JU89	Black/Blue body, swastikas, BX, 4×3 PB. 190 mm.	£200	NPE ☐
68a	1940-41	'ENSIGN' Air Liner	Camouflaged body, RAF RDLS, 4×3 PB. 140 mm.	£350	NPE ☐
68b	1940-41	'FROBISHER' Air Liner	Camouflaged body, RAF RDLS, 4×3 PB. 125 mm.	£350	NPE ☐
70a (704)	1946-59	Avro York Airliner	Silver body, G-A, GJC Red 4×3 PB. 102 mm.	£45	NC ☐
70b (730)	1946-55	Tempest II Fighter (Hawker)	Silver body, RAF RDLS, Red 1×4 PB. 51 mm.	£25	NC ☐
70c (705)	1947-62	Viking Air Liner	Silver body, G-A, GOL Red 2×4 PB. 140 mm.	£25	NC ☐
70d (731)	1946-55	Twin Engined Fighter	Silver body, no markings, Red 2×3 PB. 51 mm.	£15	NC ☐
70e	1946-62	Gloster Meteor	Silver body, RAF roundels. 66 mm.	£10	NC ☐
70f	1947-62	Shooting Star	Silver body, US markings on wings. 60 mm.	£10	NC ☐

Ref. No.		Model Type	Dinky Aeroplanes continued		Rarity and Price Grading	
700 (63b)	1979	Spitfire Mark II	Plated body, Onyx stand, 1×3 PB *Diamond Jubilee of the RAF.* 135 mm.	£50	GP	☐
701	1947-49	Shetland Flying Boat	Silver body, G-AGVD, BX, Black 4×4 PB.	£200	GP	☐
702 (999)	1954-65	DH Comet Airliner	Silver body, *B.O.A.C.* decals. 184 mm.	£45	NC	☐
706	1956-57	Vickers Viscount Airliner	Sil/Red/White body, *Air France*, Red 4×4 PB. 150 mm.	£75	GP	☐
708	1957-65	Vickers Viscount Airliner	Silver/White/Red body, Red 4×4 PB *British European Airways.* 150 mm.	£75	NC	☐
710	1965-76	Beechcraft Bonanza S35	Red/White or Bronze/Yel body, 1×2 PB. 133 mm.	£25	NC	☐
712	1972-77	U.S. Army T.42A	Military Green body, 2×2 PB. 153 mm.	£25	NC	☐
715	1956-62	Bristol 173 Helicopter	Blue body/Red Body, FL, G-AVXR 2×3 Red vanes. 127 mm.	£25	NC	☐
715	1968-76	Beechcraft C55 Baron	White or Red body, with Yellow 2×2 PB. 150 mm.	£25	NC	☐
716	1957-62	Westland Sikorsky HLC	Red/Cream/Silver body, 2×3 vanes. 89 mm.	£30	NC	☐
717	1970-75	Boeing 737 'LUFTHANSA'	White/Blue body, ARV a Dinky first. 152 mm.	£35	NC	☐
718	1972-75	Hawker Hurricane Mk II	Camouflaged body, RAF RDLS, 1×3 PB. 188 mm.	£15-£20	MPR	☐
719	1969-78	Spitfire Mk II	Camouflaged body, RAF RDLS, Black 1×3 PB. 173 mm.	£30	NC	☐
721	1969-80	Junkers JU876 Stuka	MG body, Black crosses, DCFB/1×3. 191 mm.	£25	NC	☐
722	1970-80	Hawker Harrier	Camouflaged body, RAF markings. 125 mm.	£45	NC	☐
723	1970-75	Hawker Siddeley HS 125	Yellow/White or Blue/White body. 133 mm.	£25	NC	☐
724	1971-79	Seaking Helicopter	White/Blue body, RAF RDLS, 5 vanes, BOF. 179 mm.	£17	NC	☐
725	1972-78	Royal Navy Phantom II	Dark Blue body, RAF nose, RAF RDLS. 132 mm.	£35	NC	☐
726	1972-76	Messerschmitt BF 109E	Desert CM, BC, Brown 1×3 PB/A. 165 mm.	£25	NC	☐
727	1976-77	German Phantom II	TT Grey CM body, BC, RTW/FMS. 132 mm.	£35	NC	☐
727	1976-77	F-4K Phantom	CM body, US Air Force, RTW/FMS. 132 mm.	£35	NC	☐
728	1972-75	R.A.F. Dominic	Blue/Green body, CM body, RTW, RAF RDLS. 132 mm.	£27	MPR	☐
729	1974-76	Multi-Role Aircraft	Camouflage Grey/Green RTW. 164 mm.	£25	NC	☐
730	1972-76	US 'NAVY' Phantom II	Grey/Red body, *USS Saratoga* RTW/FMS. 132 mm.	£25	NC	☐
731	1973-76	S.E.P.E.C.A.T.	Blue/Green body, CM body, Orange pilot, OCP, RTW. 106 mm.	£25	NC	☐
732	1974-80	Bell's Helicopter	Orange/Blue/White body, 2 vanes. 211 mm. AVI Red.	£10-£15	MPR	☐
734	1955-62	Supermarine Spitfire	Camouflaged body, RAF markings 1×3 PB. 51 mm.	£50	NC	☐
734	1975-78	P47 Thunderbolt	Metallic Silver body, Red 1×4 PB, RTW. 190 mm.	£25	NC	☐
735	1956-66	Gloster Javelin	Camouflaged body, RAF markings. 82 mm.	£25	NC	☐
736	1973-78	Bundesmarine Seaking HC	Grey body, Black crosses. 179 mm.	£10-£15	MPR	☐
736	1959-63	Hawker Hunter	Camouflaged body, RAF markings. 54 mm.	£25	NC	☐
737	1959-68	PIB Lightning Fighter	Silver body, RAF markings. 55 mm.	£20	NC	☐
738	1960-65	DH 110 Sea Vixen	Grey/White body, Black nose, RAF RDLS. 81 mm.	£20	NC	☐
739	1975-78	A6M5 Zero Sen	Metallic Green body, Japanese markings 1×3 PB. 184 mm.	£10-£15	MPR	☐
741	1978-80	Spitfire Mk II	Camouflaged body, RAF RDLS, RTW. 1×3PB. 173 mm.	£50	NC	☐
749 (992)	1955-56	Avro Vulcan Delta Wing Bomber	Silver body, RAF RDLS and tail markings, only 500 models made so —	£700	NPE	☐
997	1962-65	Caravelle SE 210	White/Blue/Sil body, *Air France.* 126 mm.	£100	GP	☐
998	1959-65	Bristol Britannia	White/Blue/Sil body, *Canadian Pacific.* 225 mm.	£150	GP	☐

MECCANO SPITFIRE FUND

Model 62a sold in special souvenir boxes. Model has brass ring through the fin so that it could be worn as a lapel badge. All proceeds went to the Meccano Spitfire Fund. Available in Red, Green, Blue, Yellow, Black, Silver and in camouflage at 2/6 each. Also in Chromium plate at 10/6. Lettering under wing reads '*Meccano Spitfire Fund*'.

Prices — Red and Colours £450 (MB) Chromium £1000+ (MB)

Gift Sets

60	1935-41	Gift Set	Contains 60a, b, c, d, e, f	£2000	GP	☐
61	1937-41	R.A.F. Aeroplanes Set	Contains 60h, 60n×2, 60p×2	£500	GP	☐
64	1939-41	Wartime Aircraft Set	Contains 60g, 62h, k, m, s, 63b	£750	GP	☐
65	1939-41	Passenger Aircraft Set	Contains 60r, t, v, m, 62n, p, v, m	£1500	GP	☐
66	1940-41	Wartime Camouflage Set	Contains 66a, b, c, d, e	£2000	GP	☐
68	1940-41	Wartime Aircraft Set	Contains 60s×2, 62d×2, 62e×3, 62h×3, 62t, 68a, 68b	£1750	GP	☐

Auction Price Results

Phillips, 7 Blenheim Street, New Bond Street, London. Sale dated 30.4.86.

60h Singapore Flying Boat boxed £150, 60k Amy Mollison's Percival Gull boxed £280, 60r Empire Flying Boats — *Ceres* £170 *Corsair, Corinna* and *Cambria*, £140 each and *Challenger* £130 — all boxed. 60t Douglas DC 3 boxed — £120

60x *Enterprise* Atlantic Flying Boat unboxed — £200, 62w Imperial Airways *Frobisher* class liner boxed — £180

Set No. 60 containing 60a, b, c, d, e, f. boxed £1700, 998 Bristol Britannia *Canadian Pacific* boxed £240 at Phillips Sale on 11.6.86.

Auction price results

Christies, 85 Old Brompton Road, London SW7 3LD

Sale dated 28.1.88:

62k Kings aeroplane — £110

Sale dated 8.10.87:

Set 60 — £1900

Model No. 63 'Mayo Composite' — £700

(Both prices believed to be world record auction prices for the models concerned)

Set 66 (medium bomber) missing — £550

Red 'Spitfire Fund' brooch — £350

60c & 60k (as one lot) — £420

All models in fine condition and boxed.

Dinky Buses, Taxis & Trams

Ref. No.		Model Type	Model Features and Size	Rarity and Price Grading	

Note: For a description and diagrams of the different types of Buses see page 60.

Ref. No.		Model Type	Model Features and Size	Rarity and Price Grading	
27	1934-38	'OVALTINE' Tram	Red/White, Blue/White or Or/White, WW *Drink Delicious Ovaltine Every Day.* 77 mm.	£250	GP ☐
27	1934-38	'LIPTON'S TEA' Tram	Red and White body. 77 mm.	£250	GP ☐
29	1934	'Q' type Double Decker Motor Bus	Blue, Green or Yel body, Wh roof, MW *Marmite Definitely Does You Good.* 69 mm.	£200	GP ☐
29b	1935-40	Streamline Bus	TT Green or Blue body open RWD. 88 mm.	£100	GP ☐
29b	1948-50	Streamline Bus	Cream and Red body, No rear window. 88 mm.	£60	NC ☐
29c	1938-40	Double Decker Bus 'DUNLOP TYRES'	Blue and Cream body, 1st type (A.E.C.) with stairs. 100 mm.	£200	GP ☐
29c	1947-48	Double Decker Bus	Green or Red body, Cream or Grey top, no stairs 1st type (AEC) No adverts. 100 mm.	£85	NC ☐
29c (290)	1948-54	Double Decker Bus 'DUNLOP TYRES'	Red/Cream or Green/Cream, 2nd type LV *Dunlop The Worlds Master Tyre.* 100 mm.	£60	NC ☐
29e	1948-52	Single Deck Bus	Cream/Blue, TT Blue or TT Green body. 113 mm.	£45	NC ☐
29f (280)	1950-54	Observation Coach	Grey or Cream with Red flashes. 112 mm.	£55	NC ☐
		Colour change	Grey/Green with Red flashes.	£80	GP ☐
29g (281)	1953-54	Luxury Coach	Blue body, Cream flash.	£100	GP ☐
			Cream or Fawn body, Orange flash.	£60	NC ☐
			Cream body, Red flash.	£75	NC ☐
			Maroon body, Cream flash.	£50	NC ☐
29h (282)	1952-54	Duple Roadmaster Coach	Red or Blue body, Silver flashes.	£50	NC ☐
36g	1938-41	'TAXI' with Driver	Blue/Black, Green/Black or Yellow and Black body, with rear window *Taxi* cast on roof, Black/Silver HCLP. 72 mm.	£75	GP ☐
36g	1946-49	'TAXI' with Driver	Maroon/Black or Green/Black body, no rear window. 72 mm.	£65	NC ☐
40h (254)	1951-54	'TAXI'	Blue or Yellow body, *Taxi* CI roof. 94 mm.	£55	NC ☐
241	1977	'SILVER JUBILEE TAXI'	Silver body, 1977 IS/ODB. 112 mm.	£20	NC ☐
254 (40h)	1954-56	London 'TAXI'	Dark Blue or Yellow body. 94 mm.	£65	NC ☐
254	1956-62	London 'TAXI'	Green and Yellow body. 94 mm.	£55	NC ☐
265	1960-64	Plymouth U.S.A. Taxi	Yellow/Red *25c First ¹/s Mile 5c Additional* LHD/IS/WDS/A. 108 mm.	£45	NC ☐
266	1960-66	Canadian Plymouth Taxi	Yellow/Red *Taxi* and *450 Metro Cab.* 108 mm.	£45	NC ☐
268	1962-67	Renault Dauphine Mini Cab	Red body *Meccano, Kenwood* VADS. 90 mm.	£95	GP ☐
278	1978-79	Plymouth Yellow Cab	Yellow body, *Yellow Cab Co* PCH/PW/A. 134 mm.	£15	NC ☐
280	1954-60	Observation Coach	See details given for 29f.		
281	1954-60	Luxury Coach	See details given for 29g.		
282	1954-60	Duple Roadmaster Coach	Blue or Red body, Silver flashes.	£50	NC ☐
			Yellow body, Red flashes.	£110	GP ☐
			Light Blue or Green and Cream body.	£150	GP ☐
282	1967-68	Austin 1800 Taxi	Blue body, SL/FS/SS/ODB. 101 mm.	£75	GP ☐
283	1956-63	B.O.A.C. Coach	Blue body, White roof, *British Overseas Airways Corporation* and *B.O.A.C.* 120 mm.	£55	NC ☐
283	1971-77	'RED ARROW' Single Decker Bus	Red body, White band. ODB/Bell. 167 mm.	£30	NC ☐
			With Metallic paint finish.	£36	NC ☐
284	1972-79	London 'TAXI'	Black body, D/PW/SWS *Taxi.* 112 mm.	£15	NC ☐
289	1964-79	London Routemaster Bus	Several issues. 121 mm.	—	☐
	1964-65	'TERN SHIRTS FOR CRISPNESS'	Red body, *London Transport*	£75	NC ☐
	1965-69	'SSSCHWEPPES'	Red body *London Transport*	£65	NC ☐
	1970?	'FESTIVAL OF LONDON STORES'	Rare Promotional	£175	GP ☐
	1970-77	'ESSO'	Red body, RT or PW, RT price only	£20	NC ☐
	1977	'WOOLWORTHS'	Silver body, Jubilee Model	£20	NC ☐
	1979	'THOLLEN BECKS'	Gold body, '1929-1979'	£40	GP ☐
	1977-78	'MADAME TUSSAUDS'	Red body, *London Transport* White labels	£85	GP ☐
		Label change	With Blue labels	£65	GP ☐
290 (29c)	1954-63	Double Decker Bus 'Dunlop'	Red/Cream or Green/Cream, 2nd type AEC	£95	NC ☐
			With 3rd type Leyland radiator	£65	NC ☐
291	1959-63	Double Decker Bus 'EXIDE BATTERIES'	Red, Yellow/Black decals, *73 DBD* 3rd Type Radiator front. 103 mm.	£85	NC ☐
291	1974-77	Atlantean City Bus 'KENNING'	Orange body, White REC, *Kenning Car Van and Truck Hire* D/WDS. Leyland. 123 mm.	£20	NC ☐
		Colour change	Orange body, Blue rear engine cover	£20	NC ☐
		Colour change	Red, Blue, Silver or White body.	£25	GP ☐
292	1962-68	Atlantean Bus 'REGENT'	Red/White body, D/WDS *Regent for Peak Pulling Power* and *Corporation Transport.* Leyland. 121 mm.	£70	NC ☐
292	1962-66	Atlantean Bus 'RIBBLE'	Same model as 292 with *Ribble* replacing *Corporation Transport* D/WDS. Leyland. 121 mm.	£90	NC ☐
293	1963-68	Atlantean Bus 'BP'	Green/White body *BP is the Key to Better Motoring* and *Corporation Transport* D/WDS. With smooth roof	£55	NC ☐
		Casting change	With ribbed roof	£95	GP ☐
293	1973-78	Swiss Postal Bus	Yellow/Cream body, *P.T.T.* crest BUP. 119 mm.	£24	NC ☐
295	1960-64	Atlas Kenebrake Bus	Light Blue/Grey body, SS/WDS. 86 mm.	£30	NC ☐
		Colour change	With all Blue body.	£60	GP ☐
295	1973-74	Atlantean Bus 'YELLOW PAGES'	Yellow body, *Let Your Fingers Do the Walking,* YPRHBD. Leyland. 123 mm.	£45	NC ☐
295	1974-76	Atlantean 'YELLOW PAGES'	Deep Yellow type, YPCHBD. Leyland. 123 mm.	£35	NC ☐
			Pale Yellow type, YPCHBD. 123 mm.	£30	NC ☐
296	1972-75	Duple Viceroy 37 Luxury	Metallic Blue body.	£12	NC ☐

Dinky Buses, continued

Ref. No.		Model Type	Model Features and Size	Market Price Range		
		Coach	Yellow and Cream body.	£18	NC	☐
297	1977	Silver Jubilee Bus .	Silver/Black body Leyland Atlantean	£16	NC	☐
297	1977	Woolworths Silver Jubilee Bus	Silver body Leyland Atlantean	£20	NC	☐
306	1973-75	Luxury Viceroy Coach	Metallic Red body	£25	NC	☐
949	1961-64	Wayne 'SCHOOL BUS'	Yellow/Red body, ST/WDS. 195 mm. with Red lining on sides	£135	GP	☐
			With Black lining on sides	£155	GP	☐
952	1964-71	Vega Major Luxury Coach	Light Grey with Cerise or Maroon flash, with flashing indicators, ST/SS/ODB. 242 mm.	£65	NC	☐
		Colour change	White body with Cerise or Maroon flash	£55	NC	☐
953	1963-65	Continental Touring Coach	Blue/White body *Dinky Continental Tours* ST/WDS. 195 mm.	£250	GP	☐
954	1972-77	Vega Major Luxury Coach	As 952 without flashing indicators	£50	MPR	☐
961	1973-77	Vega Major Coach PTT	Yellow/Cream body, *P.T.T.* plus emblem. 242 mm.	£100	NC	☐
			Rare Swiss box — red/white/yellow *Autocar Postal — Postauto* etc. plus 20%			

Gift Set

Ref. No.		Model Type	Model Features and Size	Market Price Range		
300	1978-80	London Scene Set	Contains 289 Esso PW and 284 taxi	£30	NC	☐

Auction Price Results 30.4.86
Phillips, 7 Blenheim Street, New Bond Street, London
Pre-war No. 27 Tramcar 'DRINK OVALTINE' — £280, 29b Streamline Bus TT Blue, no fatigue — £100

Dinky Road Making Equipment

Ref. No.		Model Type	Model Features and Size	Rarity and Price Grading		
25p (251)	1948-54	Aveling Barford Diesel Roller	Green/Red body, driver and hook. 110 mm.	£30	NC	☐
279	1967-79	Aveling Barford DRL	Orange/Green or Orange/Yellow body. 116 mm.	£15	NC	☐
430	1977-80	Johnson 2 ton Dumper	Orange/Yellow body, Blue driver. 166 mm.	£15	NC	☐
436	1963-69	'ATLAS COPCO' Lorry	Yellow MB, compressor, FS/OEC. 89 mm.	£35	NC	☐
437	1962-80	Muir Hill 2WL Loader	Yellow body, hook, BUP. 105 mm.	£22	NC	☐
561 (961)	1949-55	Blaw Knox Bulldozer	Red body, rubber tracks, driver, ST. 138 mm.	£40	NC	☐
562 (962)	1948-65	Muir Hill Dumper	Yellow body, rubber tyres. 105 mm.	£10-£15	MPR	☐
563	1948-64	Blaw Knox Heavy Tractor	Red body, rubber tracks, hook, ST. 116 mm.	£40	NC	☐
924	1972-76	Aveling Barford 'CENTAUR'	Red/Yellow body, dump truck. 180 mm.	£25	NC	☐
959	1961-68	Foden DTR & Bulldozer	Red/Orange body, MN badge/ST/D/WDS. 165 mm.	£55	NC	☐
960	1960-68	Albion Lorry CMX	Orange/Yellow/Blue body, SPW/ST. 128 mm.	£35	NC	☐
961 (561)	1955-64	Blaw Knox Bulldozer	Red body, rubber tracks, driver, ST. 143 mm. AVI Yellow body.	£40	NC	☐
962 (562)	1955-66	Muir Hill	Yellow body, hook, ST. 108 mm.	£15	NC	☐
963	1955-59	Blaw Knox Heavy Tractor	Red body, rubber tracks, hook, ST. 116 mm.	£40	NC	☐
963	1973-75	Road Grader	Yellow/Red/Silver body, BUP. 238 mm.	£20	NC	☐
965	1955-69	'EUCLID' Dump Truck	Yellow body, *Stone Ore Earth*, CEM. 142 mm.	£50	NC	☐
965	1969-70	'TEREX' Rear Dump Truck	Yellow body. 142 mm.	£85	GP	☐
966	1960-64	Marrel Multi Bucket Unit	Yellow body, Grey buckets, ST. 115 mm. (Leyland)	£55	NC	☐
967	1973-78	Muir Hill Loader/Trencher	Yellow/Red or Orange/Black body. 163 mm. RT/MT.	£15	NC	☐
973	1971-75	Eaton 'YALE' Tractor Shovel	Red/Silver/Yellow body, BUP. 178 mm.	£15	NC	☐
975	1963-67	Ruston Bucyrus Excavator	Yellow/Red/Grey body, rubber tracks. 190 mm. CO.	£175	GP	☐
976	1968-76	'MICHIGAN' Tractor Dozer	Yellow/Red body, BUP, D/EC/DDC. 147 mm.	£20	NC	☐
977	1973-78	Shovel Dozer	Yellow/Red/Silver, BUP. 151 mm.	£15	NC	☐
984	1974-79	Atlas Digger	Red/Yellow, plastic tracks. 247 mm.	£35	NC	☐

Gift Set

Ref. No.		Model Type	Model Features and Size	Rarity and Price Grading		
900	1964-65	Building Site Set	Contains 437, 960, 961, 962, 965	£350	NPE	☐

Dinky Ships

Ref. No.		Model Type	Model Features and Size	Rarity and Price Grading		
50a	1934-40	Battle Cruiser 'Hood'	Battleship Grey UB	£35	GP	☐
50b	1934-40	Battleship 'Nelson'	Battleship Grey UB	£35	GP	☐
50c	1934-40	Cruiser 'Effingham'	Battleship Grey UB	£35	GP	☐
50d	1934-40	Cruiser 'York'	Battleship Grey UB	£35	GP	☐
50e	1934-40	Cruiser 'Delhi'	Battleship Grey UB	£35	GP	☐
50f	1934-40	Destroyer 'Broke' Class	Battleship Grey UB	£35	GP	☐
50g	1935-40	Submarine 'K' Class	Battleship Grey UB	£35	GP	☐
50h	1935-40	Destroyer 'X' Class	Battleship Grey UB	£35	GP	☐
51a	1936-38	'United States of America'	Black/White hull, Red/Black FN/BX	£35	GP	☐
51b	1934-40	'Europa'	Black/White hull, Brown FN	£35	GP	☐
51c	1934-40	'Rex'	Black/White hull, Red/Green F/UB	£35	GP	☐
51d	1934-40	'Empress of Britain'	White hull, Cream FN	£65	GP	☐
51e	1935-40	'Strathaird'	White hull, Brown FN/UB	£35	MPR	☐
51f	1934-40	'Queen of Bermuda'	Grey/White hull, Red/Black FN	£35	MPR	☐
51g	1934-40	'Britannia'	Black/White/Brown hull Black F	£35	MPR	☐
52	1934-35	Cunard-White Star Liner 'Queen Mary' '534'	Boxed without rollers Black/White hull Red Black FN	£75	GP	☐
52a/b	1935-40	'Queen Mary'	Same model boxed WW runers	£50	GP	☐
52m	1936-40	'Queen Mary'	Same model boxed without runners	£40	GP	☐
52a	1947-49	'Queen Mary'	Unboxed with brass runners	£30	NC	☐
52c	1935-40	'Normandie'	Black/White/Blue hull, Red/Black FN/BX	£30	GP	☐
53az	1938-39	Battleship 'Dunkerque'	Battleship Grey, Black on funnel FI/B	£30	GP	☐
281	1973-76	Military Hovercraft	Green/Black 'Army' UJ/gunner/A	£10-£15	MPR	☐
290	1970-76	SRN6 Hovercraft	Red/White/Yellow ODB/radar	£10-£15	MPR	☐
671	1976-78	Mk I Corvette	Grey/Brown/Black, fires rockets	£10-£15	MPR	☐
672	1976-77	OSA 2 Missile Boat	Grey, fires missiles	£10-£15	MPR	☐
673	1977-78	Submarine chaser	Grey, fires depth charges	£10-£15	MPR	☐
674	1977-78	Coastguard Missile Launch	Grey, fires missiles *Coastguard*	£5-£10	MPR	☐
675	1973-77	Motor Patrol Boat	Grey hull	£5-£10	MPR	☐
678	1974-77	Air Sea Rescue Launch	Grey, Orange dinghy, pilot/launch	£10-£15	MPR	☐
796	1960-62	Healey Sports Boat	Cream/Green 2 figures	£25	NC	☐

Gift Set, Ships

Ref. No.		Model Type	Model Features and Size	Rarity and Price Grading		
50	1935-40	Warship Gift Set	Contains 50a, b×2, c, d, e, f×3, k	£200	GP	☐
51	1935-40	Great Liners Set	Contains 51b, c, d, e, f, g	£200	GP	☐

Auction Price Results

Christies, 85 Old Brompton Road, London SW7 3LD
Sale dated 28.5.87:
Warships Gift Set No. 50 — £150

Lacey Scotts, Bury St Edmunds
Sale dated 13.8.88
Set No. 51 — £200

Dinky Trains and Trams
Single and Gift Sets

Ref. No.		Model Type	Model Features and Size	Rarity and Price Grading		
16	1935-40	Silver Jubilee Set	Loco 2 coaches in Silver	£225	GP	☐
16	1946-50	L.N.E.R. Set	*L.N.E.R.* livery	£75	GP	☐
16	1954-56	British Rail Set	*B.R.* livery	£75	GP	☐
17	1935-40	Passenger Train Set	Loco, tender coach guards van	£225	GP	☐
18	1935-40	Goods Train Set	Tank loco, 3 wagons	£225	GP	☐
19	1935-40	Mixed Goods Set	Loco, tanker, 2 wagons	£225	GP	☐
20	1935-40	Passenger Train Set	Loco, 2 coaches guards van	£225	GP	☐
21	1935-40	Modelled Miniatures Set	Goods train	£225	GP	☐
26	1934-48	G.W.R. Rail Car	Red/Cream runs on bobbins. 106 mm.	£100	GP	☐
26z	1937-40	Diesel Rail Car	Cream/Orange runs on bobbins FI. 99 mm.	£125	NPE	☐
784	1972-75	Goods Train Set	Various colours	£30	NC	☐
798	1954-59	Express Passenger Set	Various colours	£75	GP	☐

Auction Price Results
Lacy Scotts, Bury St. Edmunds Sale 13.6.87
Set 20 — £240, Set 19 — £220, Set 16 — £240
Phillips Son & Neale, 7 Blenheim Street, New Bond Street, London Sale 30.4.86
Model 26 realised £120.

Novelty, Space and Film/TV Link Up Models

Ref. No.		Model Type	Model Features and Size	Rarity and Price Grading	
100	1967-75	Lady Penelope FAB 1	Pink, SS/SL/D/PS/fires rockets. 107 mm.	£50	NC ☐
101	1967-73	Thunderbird 2 and 4	Green with yellow Thunderbird 4. 143 mm.	£30	NC ☐
102	1969-74	Joe's Car	Green body/battery powered/D. 139 mm.	£35	NC ☐
103	1968-74	Spectrum Patrol Car	Met Red body, *Spectrum* badge A/SS. 121 mm.	£30	NC ☐
104	1968-74	Spectrum Pursuit	Met Blue body, *SPV* decal/badge/2A. 160 mm.	£45	NC ☐
105	1968-70	Maximum Security	White/Red body, Isotope crate SS/A. 137 mm.	£35	NC ☐
106	1967-70	'Prisoner' Mini Moke	White body, Red/White canopy. 73 mm.	£100	GP ☐
106	1974-79	Thunderbird 2 and 4	Blue body, Reissue of 101. on black base.	£22	NC ☐
107	1967-69	Stripey the Magic Mini	White body, Yellow Red/Blue stripes. 75 mm.	£75	GV ☐
108	1969-71	Sam's Car	Red or Grey body, *Win* badge, keyless motor. 111 mm.	£25	NC ☐
109	1969-71	Gabriel Model T Ford	Yellow/Black body, *Gabriel* D/SW/SPW. 79 mm.	£25	NC ☐
111	1976-78	Cinderella's Coach	White/Gold/Pink body, D/PS/4 horses. 242 mm.	£5-£10	MPR ☐
112	1978-80	Purdey's TR7	Yellow body, Silver decal *P* PW/PCH. 98 mm.	£10-£15	MPR ☐
115	1977	United Biscuits UB TAXI	Blue/Black/Yellow (promotional). 86 mm.	£15	NC ☐
120	1976-78	Happy Cab	White/Blue/Yellow plus flowers. 86 mm.	£5-£10	MPR ☐
267	1978-79	Paramedic Truck	Red with Yellow cylinders. 119 mm.	£5-£10	MPR ☐
281	1968-70	'PATHE NEWS' Camera Car	Black body, camera and operator, OD.	£55	GP ☐
350	1970-71	Tiny's Mini Moke	Red body, White/Yellow canopy. 73 mm.	£30	NC ☐
351	1971-78	U.F.O. Interceptor	Met Green body *Shado* decal. 194 mm.	£22	NC ☐
352	1971-75	Ed Straker's Car	Red body, keyless motor, WDS. 124 mm.	£28	NC ☐
353	1971-79	*Shado* 2 Mobile	Met Green body, *Shado 2* decal. 145 mm.	£20	NC ☐
		Colour change	With Blue body.	£30	NC ☐
354	1972-79	Pink Panther	Pink body and panther. 175 mm. 1st issue	£20	NC ☐
			2nd issue (no motor).	£15	NC ☐
355	1972-75	Lunar Roving Vehicle	Met Blue, White PS, pivoting W. 114 mm.	£15	NC ☐
357	1977-79	Klinger Battle Cruiser	Met Blue/White, fires pellets. 220 mm.	£5-£10	MPR ☐
358	1976-80	'U.S.S. Enterprise'	White body, *NCC 1701* (from Star Trek). 234 mm.	£20	NC ☐
359	1975-79	Eagle Transporter	White, Metallic Green logo. 222 mm.	£15	NC ☐
360	1975-79	Eagle Freighter	White/Blue, Yellow drums cargo. 222 mm.	£10-£15	MPR ☐
361	1978-79	Galactic War Chariot	Metallic Green, White PS, rockets. 126 mm.	£5-£10	MPR ☐
362	1978-79	Trident Star Fighter	Black/Orange, fires rockets. 170 mm.	£5-£10	MPR ☐
363	1979	Zygon Patroller	Metallic Silver/Blue, 2 pilots. 210 mm.	£20	NC ☐
364	1979	Space Shuttle	White body, *United States* 5 U.S. flags. 186 mm.	£50	GP ☐
367	1979	Space Battle Cruiser	White/Red body, pilot, P. weapons. 187 mm.	£30	GP ☐
368	1979	Zygon Marauder	Red/White 4PS/Z decals	£15	NC ☐
368	1979	Cosmic Cruiser	Blue body, (Marks and Spencer issue)	£40	NPE ☐
370	1969-76	The Dragster	Yellow/Silver/Pink/White, large Wheel	£15	NC ☐
371	1979	U.S.S. Enterprise	White body, small scale, BUP	£35	GP ☐
372	1979	Klingon Cruiser	Blue body, small scale, BUP	£35	GP ☐
475	1964-66	Model T Ford	Blue/Black/Gold body, D/PS (female). 79 mm.	£40	GP ☐
476	1967-69	Morris Oxford (Bullnose)	Yellow body, Blue CH, Fawn head, D. 92 mm.	£40	GP ☐
477	1970-72	Parsley's Car	Green body, animal figure. 92 mm.	£35	GP ☐
485	1964-67	Santa Special Model T Ford	Red/White body, Santa Claus, Xmas decals, Xmas tree and toys. 79 mm.	£65	GP ☐
486	1965-69	Dinky Beats Morris Oxford (Bullnose)	White/Green/Gold body, *Dagear* etc 3 figures playing music. 92 mm.	£65	GP ☐
602	1976-79	Armoured Command Car	MG, D/WS/sparks gun. 160 mm.	£15	NC ☐
803	1978-79	U.S.S. Enterprise	White body, *NCC-1701* BUP/MV	£50	GP ☐
804	1978-79	Klingon	Blue, Bubble pack, MV	£50	NPE ☐

Gift Sets

Ref. No.		Model Type	Model Features and Size	Rarity and Price Grading	
309	1978-80	Star Trek Gift Set	Contains 357 and 358	£35	NC ☐

Miscellaneous

Dinky Dublo

Ref. No.		Model Type	Model Features and Size	Rarity and Price Grading	
061	1958-59	Ford Prefect	Fawn body. 58 mm.	£25	NC ☐
062	1958-60	Singer Roadster	Orange body, Red seats, OC. 50 mm.	£30	NC ☐
063	1958-60	Commer Van	Blue body. 53 mm.	£25	NC ☐
064	1957-62	Austin Lorry	Green body. 64 mm.	£20	NC ☐
065	1957-60	Morris Pick-up	Red body. 55 mm.	£25	NC ☐
066	1959-69	Bedford Flat Truck	Grey body. 116 mm.	£25	NC ☐
067	1959-64	Austin Taxi	Blue and Cream body. 59 mm.	£35	NC ☐
068	1959-64	Royal Mail Van	Red body *Royal Mail, EIIR*, WDS. 47 mm.	£40	NC ☐
069	1959-64	Massey Harris Tractor	Blue body, hole for driver. 36 mm.	£15	NC ☐
070	1959-64	A.E.C. Mercury Tanker	Green cab, Red tank, WDS *Shell Petroleum Products BP*. 91 mm.	£55	GP ☐
071	1960-64	Volkswagen Delivery Van	Yellow body, Red *Hornby Dublo* decal, WDS. 54 mm.	£45	NC ☐
072	1959-64	Bedford Articulated Truck	Yellow cab, Red trailer, WDS. 116 mm.	£35	NC ☐
073	1960-64	Landrover/Trailer/Horse	Green/Orange, with White horse, WDS. 103 mm.	£35	NC ☐
076	1960-64	Lansing Bagnall Tractor & Trailer	Maroon/Blue, D/H/TB. 75 mm.	£30	NC ☐
078	1960-64	Lansing Bagnall Trailer	Maroon body, H/towbar. 49 mm.	£10	NC ☐

Motor Cycles

Ref. No.		Model Type	Model Features and Size	Rarity and Price Grading	
37a	1938-40	Civilian Model	Black MC, Green or Brown rider, fine detail to paintwork, SWRW. 46 mm.	£45	GP ☐
37a	1946-48	Civilian Model	Black MC, Green or Brown rider, crude paintwork detail, SBRW. 45 mm.	£35	NC ☐
37b	1938-40	Police Motor Cyclist	Black MC, Blue rider, SWRW. 46 mm.	£45	GP ☐
37b	1946-48	Police Motor Cyclist	Black MC, Blue rider, SBRW. 45 mm.	£35	NC ☐
37c	1938-41	Signals Despatch Rider	Green MC, Khaki rider, SWRW or SBRW. 46 mm.	£45	GP ☐
42b	1935-40	Police MC Patrol	Blue MC, Green SC, Blue RDR/PS, SWRW. 47 mm.	£45	GP ☐
42b	1948-55	Police MC Patrol	Blue MC, Green SC, Blue RDR/PS, SBRW. 47 mm.	£35	NC ☐
43b	1936-40	R.A.C. MC Patrol	Black MC, Blue/Wh RDR, Red sash, SWRW. 46 mm.	£45	GP ☐
43b	1946-50	R.A.C. MC Patrol	Black MC, Blue rider, OC/SBRW. 45 mm.	£35	NC ☐
44b	1935-40	'AA' Motor Cycle Patrol	Black MC, Yel SC, Blue sash, SWRW. 46 mm.	£45	GP ☐
44b	1946-50	'AA' Motor Cycle Patrol	Black MC, Yellow SC, SBRW. 45 mm.	£35	NC ☐
270 (44b)	1959-62	'AA' Motor Cycle Patrol	Black MC, Yellow S with AA. 46 mm.	£35	NC ☐
271	1959-62	TS MC Patrol	Yellow MC, Swiss 'AA' version	£55	GP ☐

Gift Set

		Model Type	Model Features and Size		
	1938-40	Motor Cycles Set	Contains 37a, b, c.		NGPP ☐
	1978-80	Dinky Way Set	Contains 207, 256, 412, 382 with Roadway and Signs	£35	NC ☐

Caravans

Ref. No.		Model Type	Model Features and Size	Rarity and Price Grading	
30g	1936-40	Caravan	Two Tone Green, 2W/H. 81 mm.	£55	GP ☐
30g	1948-50	Caravan	Orange/Cream *Caravan Club*, TB/H. 81 mm.	£45	GP ☐
117	1963-65	Four Berth Caravan	Blue/Cream, clear roof, SS/H/DI. 118 mm.	£25	NC ☐
188	1961-63	Four Berth Caravan	Green/Cream or Blue/Cream, OC/WDS/OD/DI/SS/H. 132 mm.	£25	NC ☐
190	1956-60	Caravan	Orange/Cream OC tow bar. 118 mm.	£25	NC ☐

Large Scale Models

Ref. No.		Model Type	Model Features and Size	Rarity and Price Grading	
2162	1974-76	Ford Capri	Met Blue, Black roof, SS/WDS/CP/NP. 175 mm.	£30	NC ☐
2214	1974-76	Ford Capri Rally Car	Red/Black, *Shell*, SS/WDS/CP/WM/NP. 175 mm.	£30	NC ☐
2253	1974-76	Ford Capri Police Car	White/Orange body, SL/SS/WDS/CP/WM/NP. 175 mm.	£30	NC ☐

Convoy Series

Ref. No.		Model Type	Model Features and Size	Rarity and Price Grading	
380	1977-78	Skip Wagon	Green cab, Orange skip. 112 mm. OC.	£8-£13	MPR ☐
381	1977-79	Farm Wagon	Blue cab, Yellow cattle carrier. 110 mm. OC.	£8-£13	MPR ☐
382	1978-79	Dumper Truck	Yellow cab, Orange tipper. 118 mm. OC.	£8-£13	MPR ☐
383	1978-79	Truck	Yellow *National Carriers*. 110 mm. OC.	£8-£13	MPR ☐
384	1977-79	Fire Rescue Truck	Red/White *Rescue*. 126 mm.	£8-£13	MPR ☐
385	1977-79	Royal Mail Truck	Red *Royal Mail*. 112 mm.	£8-£13	MPR ☐
399	1977-79	Convoy Gift Set	Contains 380, 381, 382	£18-£25	☐
687	1978-79	Army Truck	Military Green *Army*. 110 mm.	£8-£13	MPR ☐

Dinky Action Kits — All issued mid seventies

Ref. No.	Model Type	Model Features and Size	Rarity and Price Grading	
No model number on Base Plates etc.				
1001	RR Phantom V	Various colours	£10-£15	MPR ☐
1002	Volvo 1800 S Coupe	Yellow or Green	£10-£15	MPR ☐
1003	VW 1300	Red and White	£10-£15	MPR ☐
1004	Ford Escort Police Car	Blue and White	£10-£15	MPR ☐
1006	Ford Escort Mexico	Red	£10-£15	MPR ☐
1007	Jensen F.F.	Various colours	£10-£15	MPR ☐
1008	Mercedes Benz 600	Yellow or Green	£10-£15	MPR ☐
1009	Lotus F.1.	Red and Gold, OC	£10-£15	MPR ☐
1012	Ferrari 213-B2	Red	£10-£15	MPR ☐
1014	Beach Buggy	Blue	£10-£15	MPR ☐
1017	Routemaster Bus	Red *Esso* adverts	£15	NC ☐
1018	Leyland Atlantean Bus	Various colours and adverts	£35	GP ☐
1023	A.E.C. Single Decker Bus	Green *Greenline Bus*	£30	NC ☐
1025	Ford Transit Van	Red *Avis Truck Rental*	£10-£15	MPR ☐
1027	Lunar Rover Kit	Blue/White	£10-£15	MPR ☐
1029	Ford D800 Tipper Truck	Yellow, OC.	£10-£15	MPR ☐
1030	Land Rover Breakdown Truck	Red/White body	£10-£15	MPR ☐
1032	Army Land Rover	M.G. plus transfers	£10-£15	MPR ☐
1033	U.S.A. Army Jeep	M.G.	£10-£15	MPR ☐
1034	Mobile Gun	M.G.	£10-£15	MPR ☐
1035	Striker Anti-Tank Vehicle	M.G. plus transfer	£10-£15	MPR ☐
1036	Leopard Tank	M.G. plus transfers	£10-£15	MPR ☐
1037	Chieftain Tank	M.G. plus transfers	£10-£15	MPR ☐
1038	Scorpion Tank	M.G. plus transfers	£10-£15	MPR ☐
1039	Leopard Recovery Tank	M.G. plus transfers	£10-£15	MPR ☐
1040	Seaking Helicopter	Blue/White plus transfers	£10-£15	MPR ☐
1041	Hawker Hurricane	Camouflage RAF roundels	£10-£15	MPR ☐
1042	Spitfire Mk II	Camouflage RAF roundels	£10-£15	MPR ☐
1043	S.E.P.E.C.A.T. Plane	Blue/Green	£10-£15	MPR ☐
1044	Messerschmitt BF109E	Brown, Luftwaffe transfers	£10-£15	MPR ☐
1045	Multi-Role Combat Aircraft	Camouflage plus transfers	£10-£15	MPR ☐
1050	Motor Patrol Boat	Black/Blue/White	£10-£15	MPR ☐

Mini-Dinky Models

These were issued in 1968 and were made in Hong Kong and Holland.
The compiler has no value information and the list of models shown is almost certainly incomplete. It is also doubtful whether many of the models were actually issued. The compiler would welcome any further details concerning these models.

10	Ford Corsair	£25 GP	23	Rover 2000	£25 GP
11	Jaguar 'E' Type	£25 GP	24	Ferrari Superfast	£25 GP
12	Corvette Stingray	£25 GP	25	Ford Zephyr 6	£25 GP
13	Ferrari 250 LM	£25 GP	26	Mercedes 250 SE	£25 GP
14	Chevrolet Chevy II	£25 GP	27	Buick Riviera	£25 GP
15	Rolls Royce Silver Shadow	£25 GP	28	Ferrari F.I.	£25 GP
16	Ford Mustang	£25 GP	29	Ford F.I.	£25 GP
17	Aston Martin DB6	£25 GP	30	Volvo P. 1800	£25 GP
18	Mercedes Benz 230 SL	£25 GP	31	V.W. 1600 TL Fast Back	£25 GP
19	MGB	£25 GP	32	Vauxhall Cresta	£25 GP
20	Cadillac Coup de Ville	£25 GP	33	Jaguar Mk X	£25 GP
21	Fiat 2300 Station Wagon	£25 GP			
22	Oldsmobile Tornado	£25 GP			

Dinky Cars made in Hong Kong

Models manufactured 1965-67

Ref. No.	Model Type	Model Features and Size	Rarity and Price Grading		
001	Buick Riviera	Blue body, White roof	£70	GP	☐
002	Chevrolet Corvair Monza	Red body, Black roof	£70	GP	☐
003	Chevrolet Impala	Yellow body, White roof	£70	GP	☐
		All Yellow body	£70	GP	☐
004	Dodge Polara Cabriolet	White body, Blue roof	£70	GP	☐
005	Ford Thunderbird Coupé	Blue body, White roof	£70	GP	☐
006	Rambler Classic	Green body, Silver end to roof	£70	GP	☐

Model manufactured in 1978

Ref. No.	Model Type	Model Features and Size	Rarity and Price Grading		
008	Rover 3500 Saloon	White body	£10-15	MPR	☐

Airfix Products Ltd Dinky Production

Ref. No.	Model Type	Model Features and Size	Rarity and Price Grading		
Made in France 1/43 scale - 500 Series Circa 1980					
500	Citroen 2CV	Red/Orange body, Duck Motive, open roof.	£5-£10	MPR	☐
500	Citroen 2CV	Red/Orange body, Duck Motive, closed roof	£5-£10	MPR	☐
500	Citroen 2CV	Green body, Duck Motive, open roof	£5-£10	MPR	☐
500	Citroen 2CV	Green body, Duck Motive, closed roof	£5-£10	MPR	☐
501	Fiat Strada	Blue, no decals	£5-£10	MPR	☐
501	Fiat Strada	Metallic Bronze, no decals	£5-£10	MPR	☐
502	BMW 530	Purple. Flame decal on doors	£5-£10	MPR	☐
502	BMW 530	Metallic Green (decal?)	£5-£10	MPR	☐
503	Alfetta GVT	Red, Green Shamrock on bonnet	£5-£10	MPR	☐
503	Alfetta GVT	Yellow, Green Shamrock on bonnet	£5-£10	MPR	☐
504	Citroen Visa	Red. No decals.	£5-£10	MPR	☐
505	Peugeot 504	Blue, Flame decal on doors	£5-£10	MPR	☐
505	Peugeot 504	Greeny Gold Black Panther decal on door	£5-£10	MPR	☐
506	Alfa-Sud	Not Seen			
507	Renault 14	Not Seen			
508	Ford Fiesta	Not Seen			
Airfix — Match box size miniatures made in Hong Kong 1980					
101	56 Corvette	White/Red flash, BUP. 68 mm.	£5-£10	MPR	☐
103	Chevette Hatchback	Yellow body, *Turbo* decal, BUP. 68 mm.	£5-£10	MPR	☐
104	Honda Accord	Lilac Orange flash, BUP. 68 mm.	£5-£10	MPR	☐
105	Toyota Celica	Red body, BUP. 68 mm.	£5-£10	MPR	☐
106	Datsun 2802	Brown body, BUP. 68 mm.	£5-£10	MPR	☐
107	BMW Turbo	Orange body, Black and Yellow flash, BUP. 68 mm.	£5-£10	MPR	☐
108	Alfa Romeo	Purple body, Yellow flash, BUP. 68 mm.	£5-£10	MPR	☐
110	Stepride Pick up	Blue/Brown body, BUP. 68 mm.	£5-£10	MPR	☐
111	Camper	Yellow/two tone Brown body. 68 mm.	£5-£10	MPR	☐
113	Pick up	Red/Black body, *4×4* decal. 68 mm.	£5-£10	MPR	☐
114	Firebird	Black body. 68 mm.	£5-£10	MPR	☐
115	Camaro	Red RN 'Z28'. 68 mm.	£5-£10	MPR	☐
116	63 Corvette	Metallic Blue body. 68 mm.	£5-£10	MPR	☐
117	71 Corvette	Yellow body, *Vette* decal. 68 mm.	£5-£10	MPR	☐
119	Ford Van	Blue body, Orange flash. 68 mm.	£5-£10	MPR	☐
120	Renegade Jeep	Yellow body, Green flash	£5-£10	MPR	☐
121	Chevy Blazer	Red body. 68 mm.	£5-£10	MPR	☐
122	Sun Van	Orange body, *Sun Van* decal. 68 mm.	£5-£10	MPR	☐
123	Yamaha 250 MX	Blue body, *Yamaha* decal. 82 mm.	£5-£10	MPR	☐
124	Honda MT 250	Orange body, *Honda* decal. 82 mm.	£5-£10	MPR	☐
125	Kawasaki F11250	Red body, *Kawasaki* decal. 82 mm.	£5-£10	MPR	☐
126	Suzuki TM400	Yellow/Black body *CCI, Suzuki* decals. 82 mm.	£5-£10	MPR	☐
129	T Bird Convertible	Red/White body. 68 mm.	£5-£10	MPR	☐
130	Chevy Convertible	Met Blue/White body	£5-£10	MPR	☐

Extremely doubtful whether all the models listed were in fact issued.

MATCHBOX — DINKY TOYS

Matchbox toys bought the Dinky trademark in early 1987. Prior to the launch of the new Dinky products in 1988 the following *Matchbox* miniatures were released packaged in blister cards featuring the *Dinky Toys* trademark:-
MB17 VW Golf; MB44 Citroen CV15; MB51 Firebird SE; MB60 Toyota Supra; MB69 1984 Corvette; MB74 Fiat Abarth.
The models have *Matchbox* on their bases.

Dinky Accessories — Pre-War

Ref. No.		Model Type	Model Features and Size	Rarity and Price Grading		
1	1934-40	Station Staff (6)	Station Master, Guard, Ticket collector, Driver, Porter with bags, Porter, BX	£75	GP	☐
2	1934-40	Farmyard Animals (6)	2 horses 2 cows pig sheep, BX	£35	GP	☐
3	1934-40	Passengers (6)	Woman and child, business man, male hiker, female hiker, newsboy, woman, BX	£45	GP	☐
4	1934-40	Engineering Staff (5)	2 Blue figures, 3 Brown figures, BX	£75	GP	☐
5	1934-40	Train & Hotel Staff (6)	A conductor, 2 waiters, 2 porters, BX	£75	GP	☐
6	1934-40	Shepherd Set (6)	Shepherd, sheepdog, 4 sheep, BX	£45	GP	☐
12a	1935-40	G.P.O. Pillar Box 'G.R.'	Red, with or without *Post Office* notice on top in Yel/Red, White panel. 50 mm.	£20	GP	☐
12b	1935-40	Air Mail Pillar Box	Blue body *Air Mail*, White panel. 50 mm.	£20	GP	☐
12c	1936-40	Telephone Box	Cream/Silver body. 62 mm.	£15	GP	☐
12d	1938-40	Telegraph Messenger	Blue body, Brown pouch. 35 mm.	£15	GP	☐
12e	1938-40	Postman	Blue body, Brown post bag and badge. 35 mm.	£15	GP	☐
13	1934-40	'HALLS DISTEMPER'	Various colours, two men plus advert	£100	NPE	☐
13a	1938-40	Cook's Man	Blue Coat on standing man	£10	NC	☐
15		Railway Signals Set		£15	GP	☐
42a	1936-40	Police Box	Blue body *Police* in Silver	£10	GP	☐
42c	1936-40	Point duty policeman	White coat. 42 mm.	£10	GP	☐
42d	1936-40	Point duty policeman	Blue *R.A.C.* badge. 40 mm.	£10	GP	☐
43a	1935-40	'R.A.C.' box	Blue with *R.A.C.* emblem. 81 mm.	£75	GP	☐
43b	1935-40	'R.A.C.'	See Section on Motor Cycles			
43c	1935-40	'R.A.C.' Guide	Blue with Red sash. 37 mm.	£10	GP	☐
43d	1935-40	'R.A.C.' guide saluting	Blue with Red sash. 36 mm.	£10	GP	☐
44a	1935-40	'A.A. box'	Yellow *A.A.* badge and 3 signs. 81 mm.	£75	GP	☐
44b	1935-40	'A.A.' Motor Cycle Patrol	See Section on Motor Cycles			
44c	1935-40	'A.A.' Guide	Yellow body, Blue sash. 3 mm.	£10	GP	☐
44d	1935-40	'A.A.' Guide Saluting	Yellow body, Blue sash. 36 mm.	£10	GP	☐
45	1935-40	Garage	Tinplate, opening doors	£100	GP	☐
46	1937-40	Pavement Set	Grey cardboard box	£10	GP	☐
47		12 Road Signs	Black, Red and White, BX	£150	GP	☐
47a	1935-40	4 Face Traffic Lights	Black and White, Yellow beacon, White base	£5	GP	☐
47b	1935-40	3 Face Traffic Lights	Black and White, White base	£5	GP	☐
47c	1935-40	2 Face Traffic Lights	Black and White (back/back) White base	£5	GP	☐
47c	1935-40	2 Face Traffic Lights	Black/White (right angles) White base	£5	GP	☐
47d	1935-40	Belisha Beacon	Black/White/Orange, White base	£5	GP	☐
48	1935-40	Filling Station/Garage	*Filling and Service Station*, MLCD body, many ADS, TP	£100	GP	☐
49a	1935-40	Bowser Petrol Pump	Green body, White rubber pipe. 46 mm.	£15	GP	☐
49b	1935-40	Wayne Petrol Pump	Blue body, White rubber pipe. 39 mm.	£15	GP	☐
49c	1935-40	Theo Petrol Pump	Brown body, White rubber pipe. 58 mm.	£15	GP	☐
49d	1935-40	'SHELL' Petrol Pump	Red body, White rubber pipe. 53 mm.	£15	GP	☐
49e	1935-40	'Pratts' Oil Bin	Yellow body, *Pratts Motor Oil*. 32 mm.	£15	GP	☐
		Dolly Varden	Dining Room Set	£150	GP	☐
		"Furniture"	Kitchen Set	£150	GP	☐
		Dolly Varden Doll's House		£500	NPE	☐

Gift Sets — Accessories

	1938-40	12 Series Set	Contains 12a, b, c, d, e, 34b	£125	NPE	☐
	1934-40	Railway Signals Set	Contains 15a, b, c, d, e, f	£50	NPE	☐
	1936-40	42 Series Set	Contains 42a, b, c, d	£50	NPE	☐
	1935-40	43 Series Set	Contains 43a, b, c, d	£250	GP	☐
	1935-40	44 Series Set	Contains 44a, b, c, d	£250	GP	☐
	1935-40	49 Series Set	Contains 49a, b, c, d, e	£100	NPE	☐

Auction Prices Results
Model No. 1 Station Staff realised £140 at Lacy Scotts, Bury St. Edmunds Sale 13.6.87
Model 45 realised £100 at Phillips auction on 2.9.87.

Dinky Accessories — Post-War

Ref. No.		Model Type	Model Features and Size	Rarity and Price Grading		
001	1960-	Station Staff	Blue, 5 figures. 35 mm.	£45	GP	☐
002	1960-	Farmyard Animals	Set of six various colours	£35	GP	☐
003	1960-	Passengers	Set of six, various colours. 35 mm.	£35	GP	☐
004	1960-	Engineering Staff	2 Blue, 3 Brown. 35 mm.	£35	GP	☐
005	1960-	Train and Hotel Staff	Set of 5, various colours. 35 mm.	£35	GP	☐
006	1960-	Shepherd Set	Set of 6, shepherd, dog, 4 sheep	£45	GP	☐
007	1960-68	Petrol Pump Attendants	White coats 1 male 1 female. 35 mm.	£15	GP	☐
008	1961-68	Fire Station Personnel Set	Blue uniforms, 6 plus hose. 35 mm.	£30	GP	☐
009	1962-68	Service Station Personnel Set	Various colours/stances 8 in set. 35 mm.	£30	GP	☐
010	1962-68	Road Maintenance Personnel Set	6 workmen using pick, barrow, shovels, drill etc, hut, brazier, barrier, 4 lamps. 35 mm.	£30	GP	☐
011	1952-	Telegraph Messenger	Blue body. 35 mm.	£10	GP	☐
012	1952-	Postman	Blue body. 35 mm.	£10	GP	☐
013	1952	Cook's Man	Blue Coat, Box of six (50174)	£35	NC	☐
051	1960-	Station Staff	Set of six. 35 mm.	£35	GP	☐
053	1960-	Passengers	Set of six 3 male 3 female. 35 mm.	£35	GP	☐
12c	1946-48	Telephone Box	Red/Silver body. 62 mm.	£10	NC	☐
502	1961-63	Garage	Blue/Grey body, OD/FI/P. 272 mm.	£65	GP	☐
750	1960-74	Telephone Call Box	Red body. 58 mm.	£10	NC	☐
751 (42a)	1954-60	Police Box	Blue. 66 mm.	£10	NC	☐
752	1953-54	Goods yard crane	Blue/Yellow body. 100 mm. 195 mm.	£35	NC	☐
753		Police Crossing	Grey/Black/White body plus PM. 151 mm.	£35	NC	☐
754	1958-62	Pavement Set		£15	NC	☐
755	1960-64	Lamp Standard (Single)	Grey/Fawn/Orange body. 145 mm.	£10	NC	☐
756	1960-64	Lamp Standard (Double)	Grey/Fawn/Orange body. 145 mm.	£10	NC	☐
760	1954-60	Pillar Box	Red/Black, *EIIR* decals. 42 mm.	£10	NC	☐
763	1959-64	Posters for Hoarding	Red/Black *EIIR* decals, different colours etc. 42 mm.	£10	GP	☐
764	1959-63	Posters for Hoarding	Different colours on six posters	£10	GP	☐
765	1959-64	Road Hoardings (6 Posters)	Green, *David Allen and Sons Ltd.*	£10	GP	☐
766	1959-64	British Road Signs Country Set	Signs of the times (6). 55 mm.	£75	NC	☐
767	1959-64	British Road Signs Country Set	Signs of the times (6)	£75	NC	☐
768	1959-64	British Road Signs Town Set	Signs of the times (6). 55 mm.	£75	NC	☐
769	1959-64	British Road Signs Town Set	Signs of the times (6). 55 mm.	£75	NC	☐
771	1953-65	International Road Signs	Various colours, 12 signs	£45	NC	☐
772	1959-65	British Road Signs	Various colours, 24 signs	£100	NC	☐
773	1959-63	Four Face Traffic Lights	Black/White, Black base. 62 mm.	£5	NC	☐
777	1959-63	Belisha Beacon	Black/White/Orange, Black base. 51 mm.	£5	NC	☐
778	1962-65	Road Repair Boards	Green and Red, 6 different. 30-40 mm.	£10	NC	☐
781	1955-62	'ESSO' Pump Station	*Esso* sign, kiosk, 2 pumps. 114 mm.	£35	NC	☐
782	1960-68	'SHELL' Pump Station	*Shell* sign, kiosk, 4 pumps. 203 mm.	£35	NC	☐
783	1960-63	'BP' Pump Station	*BP* sign, kiosk, 4 pumps. 203 mm.	£35	NC	☐
785	1960-66	'SERVICE STATION'	*BP* sign	£35	NC	☐
786	1960-66	Tyre rack with tyres	21 assorted tyres *Dunlop*	£15	NC	☐
787	1960-66	Lighting Kit	Bulb and wire	£10	NC	☐
788	1960	Spare bucket for 966	Grey	£5	NC	☐
790	1960	Granite Chippings	Plastic bag 50790	£5	NC	☐
791	1960	Imitation Coal	Plastic bag	£5	NC	☐
		1 Dozen Tyres	Yellow box 50091/No 14095	£10	NC	☐
792	1960-64	Packing Cases (3)	White/Cream P. *Hornby Dublo*	£5	NC	☐
793	1960-64	Pallets	Orange for use in 930 van	£5	NC	☐
846	1961-	Oil Drums	French issue 6 drums	£5	NC	☐
847	1961-	Barrels	French issue 6 barrels	£5	NC	☐
849	1961-	Packing Cases	French issue 6 cases	£5	NC	☐
850	1961-	Crates of bottles	French issue 6 crates	£5	NC	☐
851	1961-	Sets of 846/7/9/50	Two of each	£10	NC	☐
994		Loading Ramp	Blue body	£10	NC	☐

SPOT ON MODELS

INTRODUCTION

Spot On collectors will be pleased to learn that the 3rd Edition listings contain more than seventy new model colour variations plus much more detail e.g. registration numbers. The source of this information was probably the finest Spot On collection in Britain which is housed in the Cowes I.O.W. Toy and Model Museum. The Catalogue compiler would like to express his thanks to Roger Magillus for his kind permission in allowing his collections to be used. Collectors will find a 'Red Funnel' day trip to the museum to be most rewarding for there are also fine displays of Dinky and Corgi toys, plus much more.

Spot On Models were first introduced in 1959 as an offshoot of Triang Toys.

They were determined to compete successfully against Dinky Toys and the newly established Corgi Toys so all of the models contained many features and were extraordinarily detailed for toys.

They were built in a large modern factory in Belfast, Northern Ireland, to the slightly larger scale of 1/42.

Each item in the range was 'SPOT-ON' to scale with all the other items and was issued to the correct colour specifications of their real life counterparts.

In addition all the early models also included in the box a coloured picture of the real model.

The commercial vehicles are extremely sought after today and command high prices. They are particularly noted for their attractive real life liveries and detailed chassis.

Probably the most sought after in this range is the 'SHELL-BP' Tanker which was produced in the perfect livery of its period and is today extremely hard to find.

One of the rarest of all the Spot On commercials was introduced in 1963 and was Model No 145 the 'Ovaltine' A.E.C. Routemaster Bus which is now among the rarest of all the Post War Buses sought by collectors.

Another rarity is the Gift Set number 806 'Royal Occasion'. This featured H.M. the Queen and H.R.H. Prince Philip seated in the rear of the Royal Rolls-Royce Phantom V Limousine. Again the model detail is exceptional for a toy.

The A.E.C. Routemaster and the Royal Rolls Royce have been featured on the cover.

Spot-on models were issued for about eight years and during this period produced over one hundred different designs.

SPOT ON MARKET SURVEY

The market survey indicated an across the board increase in prices with specific areas being particularly sought after as follows:

i) The models in pristine condition were in short supply and consequently they commanded much higher prices than the excellent to good graded models.

ii) Similarly the gap between most colours and the normal issue models widened considerably.

iii) Prices for the big saloons and commercial vehicles have hardened considerably.

PRICE AND RARITY CHANGES AT A GLANCE

			1981-83 Survey		1985 Survey		1988 Survey	
SALOONS	102	Bentley 4 door Sports	£45	NC	£95	GV	£135-£180	MPR
	103	Rolls Royce Silver Wraith	£50	GV	£100	GV	£135-£180	MPR
SPORTS CARS	191	Sunbeam Alpine Hardtop	£21-£26	MPR	£50	NC	£60-£80	MPR
	279	M.G. Midget	£20-£25		£35	NC	£35-£40	MPR
COMMERCIALS	109/2	E.R.F. with Flat Float	£55	NC	£135	GV	£150-£170	MPR
	106A/1C	Austin Prime Mover	£55	NC	£165	NVE	£190-£220	MPR
	111A/1	Ford Thames	£75	NC	£150	GV	£150-£180	MPR
VANS	122	'UNITED DAIRIES' Milk Float	£35	GV	£65	GV	£65-£75	MPR
	265	'TONIBELL ICE CREAM'	£45	GV	£65	GV	£75-£85	MPR
	315	'GLASS & HOLMES'	£35	NC	£65	NC	£60-£70	MPR
BUS	145	1st type Routemaster	£150	GV	£375	GV	£475-£525	MPR
POLICE	309	'Z CARS' Zephyr	£35	NC	£45	NC	£50-£60	MPR
GIFT SET	801	HOME WITH TOMMY SPOT	£45	GV	£95	GV	£130-£160	MPR

SPOT ON
IDENTIFICATION

COMMON FEATURES

a Manufacturers Name and Trade Mark
All models have clearly stamped on their chassis 'SPOT-ON' and 'MODELS by Tri-ang'.

b Model Types
All models indicate on their chassis their type:—
eg 'A.E.C. MAJOR 8'.

c Model Numbers
These are always shown on the boxes but are not always on the models eg. 215 Daimler SP250 Dart.

d Model Scale
All models have 1/42 scale stamped on the chassis.

e Wheel Hubs for Cars
All the wheels are assumed to have spun metal appearance with a raised hub cap in the centre unless otherwise described eg Cast In Spoked Wheels or Plastic Spoked Wheels.

f Wheel Hubs for Heavy Commercial Vehicles
All the heavy commercial vehicles are assumed to have the following sets of wheels.

At the Front — Four single wheels with a bulbous pattern showing six cast-in broad spokes.

At the Rear — Four double wheels with special double tyres. The wheels hubs are different from the front having a hollowed out appearance showing six cast in broad spokes.

In addition a single spare wheel (SPW) is suspended beneath the rear end of the chassis.

The exceptions to the foregoing such as the Model 158, Bedford 'S' Type Tanker and others have individual descriptions.

g Number Plates
Assumed that all the standard issues of production models have number plates front and rear.

The only exceptions to this being the later issues which had plastic chassis such as Model 266 Bull Nose Morris (1923) and Model 279 MG PB Midget (1935).

h Windscreens and Windows
All models have either plastic windows or windscreen.

i Tyres
All models assumed to have treaded rubber tyres.

j Seats, Suspension, Steering Wheels and Windows
All car models are fitted with these.

k Model Colours
Models were issued in a wide variety of colours and new combinations are still being discovered.

ABBREVIATIONS — EXAMPLE OF USE

110/3   A.E.C. Mammoth Major 8
         British Road Services. 210 mm.

Red body, Blk cab roof, Sil CH and trim, 4 DW/4 SGW/ SPW/DDTB/DPBA/FFS/CEMS

Red body, Black cab roof, Silver chassis and trim, 4 double wheels, 4 single wheels, spare wheel, drop down tailboard, detailed propshaft and back axle, flat float with sides, company emblems.

SPOT ON PRICES AND MODEL GRADING SYSTEM

It is important to understand that the high top of the market price range prices shown refer to mint models and boxes in pristine condition. These models are rare and hence their high market prices. The normal run of models encountered are usually of only average condition and consequently command considerably lower prices. Similarly the high top of the market price range prices shown for some cars refers only to the rare colours issued with the common colours again commanding a considerably smaller price.

N.B. As the Market Price Range Grading System is ideally suited for Spot On all the models have been put into this grade. The only exceptions being those models not possible to grade at present (NGPP) and those not issued (NPP) no prices possible.

Saloons Estates and Sports Cars

Ref. No.		Model Type	Model Features and Size	Market Price Range	
100	1959	Ford Zodiac without lights	Red/Cream, Blue/Cream or Green body or All Red or All Cream body. 107mm.	£45-£60	☐
100SL	1959	Ford Zodiac with lights	Yellow/White body, BOWL/PP. or Grey/Blue, TT Blue or TQ/Grey body. 107 mm.	£55-£75	☐
101	1959	Armstrong Siddeley '236' Sapphire Saloon	Blue and Grey, Yellow and Black or Blue and Black body or all Mauve body, Red seats, or Lilac/White body. 108mm.	£135-£180	☐
102	1959	Bentley 4 Door Sports Saloon	Met Green and Silver, Maroon and Silver or Grey and Silver body or Blue/Silver body or Met Grey/Met Dark Blue with Cream seats or two tone Grey body and Red seats. 127 mm.	£135-£180	☐
103	1959	Rolls Royce Silver Wraith	Met Silver and Maroon body, White seats, or Met Silver and Met Light Blue, Cream seats, or Met Silver and Met Green body. All with ORG. 131 mm.	£135-£180	☐
104	1959	M.G.A. Sports Car	Red, Blue or White body, DI/ORG. 95 mm.	£130-£150	☐
105	1959	Austin Healey 100-SIX	Blue or Green, OC/DD/WS/SW/S/ORG or Grey body, Red seats. 89 mm.	£130-£150	☐
107	1960	Jaguar XKSS	Red or Green, WS/SW/S/NP/FHD/ORG or Met Blue body, Cream seats. 91 mm.	£120-£160	☐
108	1960	Triumph TR '3'	Green or Blue body, WS/SW/S/NP/ORG. 88 mm.	£125-£150	☐
112	1960	Jensen 541	Green, Red or Yel/Black body, OC/ORG or Lemon/Grey body. 106 mm.	£85-£110	☐
113	1960	Aston Martin DB3	Met Green, Blue or Yel body, OC/ORG. 104 mm.	£90-£125	☐
114	1960	Jaguar 3.4 Litre Mk1	All Maroon body or All Blue body with Cream seats or all Cream or all Metallic Light Blue with Red seats	£75-£100	☐
115	1960	Bristol 406	Met Green, Blue or Red body, OC/ORG. 116 mm.	£90-£125	☐
118	1960	BMW Isetta Bubble Car	Yellow, Green or Blue body, OC. 57 mm.	£50-£60	☐
119	1960	Meadows Frisky Sport	Orange body, Grey hood, Dark Red or Turquoise body with black hood or Red body with White hood.	£45-£55	☐
120	1960	Fiat Multipla	Green or Red body, Silver trim, OC or Blue body, Cream seals or Mauve body, Red seats and shiny wheels. 85 mm.	£38-£48	☐
131	1960	Goggomobile 'Super'	Green or Red body, OC/ORG or Grey/Black or Yellow Black body. 70 mm.	£50-£60	☐
135	1960	14 ft G.P. Sailing Dinghy and Trailer	No details	£25-£35	☐
154	1960	Austin A40	Red/Black, Blue or Green body, OC/ORG or TQ body, Black roof, Cream seats or Beige body, Cream seats. 88 mm.	£50-£75	☐
157		Rover 3 Litre without lights	Grey or Blue body, OC/ORG/PP/SW. 107 mm.	£60-£80	☐
157SL		Rover 3 Litre with lights	Same as previous with BOWL or all Beige body, with no seats or all Grey body, Cream seats. 107 mm.	£80-£110	☐
		with Dinghy	Version with White/Blue dinghy, Turquoise trailer, Yellow hatch, Blue mast NB. Model issued at same time as real car released.	£120-£140	☐
165	1961	Vauxhall Cresta PA	Maroon, Blue or Green body, OC/ORG or Dark Blue body, White roof, Red seats or all Beige body, White seats. 108 mm.	£80-£110	☐
166	1960	Renault Floride Convertible	Red or Yellow body, OC/BB/WS/SW or Dark Grey body, Red seats or White body, Red seats. 101 mm.	£60-£80	☐
183	1963	Humber Super Snipe Estate Car	Green/White, Blue/Black or Green/White body with wing mirrors. Or Metallic Bronze without mirrors. See also Model No. 306.	£60-£80 £70-£85	☐ ☐
184	1963	Austin A60 with skis	Green, Red or Blue body, OC/RR/PP/ORG or White body and seats, Brown skis on roof rack. 106 mm.	£60-£80	☐
185	1963	Fiat 500	Red or Blue body, WM/PP/ORG. 73 mm.	£50-£70	☐
191	1963	Sunbeam Alpine Convertible	Green or Blue body, OC/WS/ORG/PP. 95 mm.	£60-£80	☐
191	1963	Sunbeam Alpine Hardtop	Blue/White or Red/White body, OC/ORG/PP. 95 mm.	£60-£80	☐
193	1963	N.S.U. Prinz	Blue or Cream body, OC/ORG/PP or all Grey body. 84 mm.	£60-£80	☐
195	1963	Volkswagen Rally Car	Red or Blue body, OC, 2 flags, SL/RN/SPW. 110 mm.	£140-£160	☐
210	1960	Morris Mini Minor	Only seen in Catalogue — not issued	NGPP	☐
211	1963	Austin Baby Seven	Blue, Red or Yellow, OC/ORG/PP. 73 mm.	£80-£110	☐
212	1963	Car, Dinghy and Trailer Set (Sunbeam Alpine Convertible)	Blue body, Blue/White boat. 222 mm.	£115-£130	☐
213	1963	Ford Anglia Saloon	Grey, Red or Blue body, OC/ORG/PP or all White or all Beige body. 95 mm.	£60-£70	☐
215	1962	Daimler SP250 Dart	Blue, Red or Yellow, OC/PP/ORG/WS/SW/S or Brown body, Dark Cream seats. 97 mm.	£90-£115	☐
216	1963	Volvo 122S	Blue, Grey or Red body, with sliding roof or all Yellow body, cream seats and all Green body, White seats.	£60-£80	☐
217	1962	'E' Type Jaguar	Red, Blue or Green body, OC/OBN/ORG or all Cream body, White seats and Yellow body, Black roof, Cream seats. 106 mm.	£130-£160	☐
218	1963	Mk 10 Jaguar	Light Blue or Dark Green body, or all Metallic Brown body, Red seats, Grey driver, or all Green body. 122 mm.	£60-£80	☐
219	1962	Austin Healey Sprite	Red body, White seats, Brown driver, Blue body, Red seats, Grey driver.	£45-£55	☐
259	1963	Ford Consul Classic	Red or Blue body, OC/PP/ORF/ORG/SW or White body, Blue seats, or all Beige body, White seats. 105 mm.	£60-£70	☐
260	1963	Royal Rolls Royce Phantom V	Maroon body, Blue int, 2 flags on roof, DI/PP/ORG/S/SW/RB/NP. 143 mm. Queen & Prince Philip sitting in rear seats	£250-£300	☐
261	1963	Volvo P1800	1st type with opening bonnet and boot. Blue or Red body. 2nd type with just opening bonnet. Light Blue or Met Bronze body.	£55-£70 £70-£95	☐ ☐
262	1965	Morris 1100 Saloon	Blue or Red body, OBN/PP/ORG/DE or Dark Blue body, Grey seats or all Green body, Red seats or all Beige body, Red seats. 89 mm.	£35-£55	☐
263	1964	Vintage 4½ Litre Bentley (Supercharged)	Green body, Grey TN, RN '27', '11' or '15', Silver trim, D/FWS/FHD/UJ/SDB/ORG/PCH/PMG/SL/DEX/PC/SPW. 108 mm.	£40-£45	☐

Ref. No.		Model Type	Spot-On Cars continued	Market Price Range	
266	1965	Bull Nose Morris (1923) ¹/₄₈ Scale)	Red/Black body, OC/DPHD/PCH/ODS/D/SPW/PP/ORG/ DCH/NP/SDL/WS or Yellow body, Black roof and seats, Brown driver.	£35-£40	☐
267	1961	M.G. 1100 Saloon	Red/White or Blue/White, OBN/DE/ORG or White/Dark Green body, Red seats or all Red body, Cream seats. 88 mm.	£50-£60	☐
269	1965	Ford Zephyr Six and Caravan	Red body, D/ORG/PP/SW/H/OD, Blue/White/Red CRV, Red VB, TB. 262 mm.	£125-£150	☐
270	1965	Ford Zephyr Six	Blue or Red body, FDR/OD/PP/ORG/dog, or all Cream body, Red seats, or all Green body, Red seats, or all Red body, Grey seats. 110 mm.	£40-£55	☐
274	1965	Morris 1100 and Canoe	Blue or Red body, Brown/Bl boat, OC/DRG. 88 mm.	£65-£85	☐
276	1964	Jaguar 'S' Type	Met Gold or Met Blue MB, D/PS/PP/ORG. 114 mm.	£50-£65	☐
278	1965	Mercedes Benz 230SL	Metallic Red, OC/FDR/PS/PP/ORG. 103 mm.	£50-£60	☐
279	1965	MG PB Midget (1935)	Red/Blk, DD/PCH/WS/PP/CISPKW/ORG or Blue body, Black seats. 79 mm.	£35-£40	☐
280	1965	Vauxhall Cresta PB	Red/Fawn or Blue/White body.	£35-£40	☐
281	1966	MG Midget Mk II Based on 219	Red body, chrome radiator with MG badge. Driver. Dark green version (New Zealand)	£45-£50 NGPP	☐ ☐
286	1965	Austin 1800	All Blue, or all Cream, all Green or all Beige body with Red seats or all Red body with Grey seats.	£35-£50	☐
287	1965	Hillman Minx	Pale Green body, Red seats. 84 mm or all Cream body, Red seats. Model with roof rack and 2 brown suitcases	£35-£40 £50-£60	☐ ☐
289	1963	Morris Minor 1000	All Metallic Blue body, Red seats. 87 mm. or all Red body or all Metallic Green body	£90-£110 £150-£200	☐ ☐
306	1963	Humber Super Snipe Estate	Brown, Green or Blue, OC/RR/PP/ORG/LG. 113 mm.	£60-£80	☐
307	1965	Volkswagen Beetle 1200	Met Blue body, Blue interior, ORG. 89 mm.	£140-£160	☐
308	1965	Land Rover and Trailer	Green body, Brown roof and trailer. 170 mm.	£50-£70	☐
401	1966	Volkswagen Variant with Skis	Dark Blue body, roof rack, opening rear door, original radiator grille.	£1000	☐
405	1966	B.E.A. Vauxhall Cresta	Dark Green, Red *BEA* fig/PP/ORG. 110 mm.	£45-£50	☐
406	1966	Hillman Minx and Dinghy	Models fitted Brown roof rack with 2 suitcases. Pale Green or Cream body. Red body or Metallic paint finishes NB. Trailer is turquoise with Blue/White dinghy with Yellow hatch, White mast, no sail. Other dinghy colours known.	£40-£70 £70-£90	☐ ☐
407	1966	Mercedes 230SL	Brown body, Red interior, LG/PP/ORG. 103 mm.	£40-£50	☐
408	1966	Renault Caravelle	Only seen in catalogue with Red body	NGPP	☐
410	1966	Austin 1800 and Rowboat	Olive Green car, Red boat, OBN/DE/ORG/PP. 100 mm. Beige car, Orange boat	£70-£85	☐

Vans

Ref. No.		Model Type	Model Features and Size	Market Price Range	
122	1961	'UNITED DAIRIES' Milk Float Van	Red/White body and crest, chains, *Lada the New Yoghourt*, CEMS. 98 mm.	£65-£75	☐
210	1961	Morris Mini Minor Van	Bright Yellow, S/SW/NP/SS. 79 mm.	£70-£80	☐
210/1	1962	Morris Mini Minor Van 'ROYAL MAIL'	Red body, Post Office crest, S/SW/NP/SS *EIIR*. 79 mm.	£70-£80	☐
265	1964	'TONIBELL DAIRY ICE CREAM' Van	Blue body, Red flash, OWD, attendant *Soft Ice Cream*. 107 mm.	£75-£85	☐
271	1965	'EXPRESS DAIRIES' Milk Float Van	Blue/White body, RC/RCH/3W/D *Drink Express Milk*, CEMS. 98 mm.	£70-£80	☐
273	1965	'SECURITY EXPRESS LTD' Commer Van	Green/Gold, CEMS/OD/PP/NP/SS/ORG driver and seated guard. Money Box roof. 126 mm.	£60-£70	☐
315	1965	'GLASS & HOLMES' Commer Van	Blue/Yellow, OD/LD/2 figs/ORG/PP *Window Cleaning Company Est 1891*. 126 mm.	£60-£70	☐
404	1966	Morris Mini Minor Van 'SHELL'	Yellow body with Silver trim, CEM/SS/S/SW/LD/fig. 79 mm.	£550	☐
404	1966	Morris Mini Van	Same as previous model with no decals	£400	☐
404	1966	Version	Only seen in catalogue in Yellow	NGPP	☐

Spot On Commercial and Utility Vehicles.
Lorries, Tankers, Mobile Cranes and Land Rovers

Ref. No.		Model Type	Model Features and Size	Market Price Range	
106A/1	1959	Austin Prime Mover with Flat Float with Sides	Red cab and float sides, Silver float bed, cab CH and trim, BRT/4DW/2SGW/AV. 234 mm. Also Orange body and float	£170-£200	☐
106A/1C	1960	Austin Prime Mover with Flat Float with Sides and Crate Load	Blue cab sides, Silver float bed, cab CH and trim, BRT/4DW/2SGW/AV. 234 mm.	£190-£220	☐
106A/0C	1960	Austin Prime Mover with MGA Sports Car in Crate	Red cab and FFWS, Sil trim and chassis, Cream crate, *British Motor Corporation Ltd*, on trailer and crate, BRT/4DW/2SGW/AV. 234 mm.	£275-£350	☐
109/2	1960	E.R.F. with Flat Float	Turquoise body, Black cab roof, OC/DPBA/RB/4DW and 4SGW/SPW/SW/S. 210 mm.	£150-£170	☐
109/2P	1960	E.R.F. 68G with Flat Float without Sides with Planks	Turquoise body, Black cab roof, OC/DPBA/RB/4DW and 4SGW/SPW/SW/S. 210 mm.	£180-£220	☐
109/3	1960	E.R.F. 68G with Flat Float with Sides	Dark Blue cab, Pale Blue float, OC/DPBA/RB/4DW and 4SGW/SPW/SW/S. 210 mm. Also all Turquoise body. Also Yellow body, Black cab roof	£150-£180	☐
109/3B	1960	E.R.F. 68 with Sides and Barrel Load	Turquoise cab and float, Sil float bed, OC/RB/DPBA/4DW and 4SGW/SPW/SW/S. 210 mm.	£350-£400	☐
110/2	1960	A.E.C. Mammoth Major 8 Flat Float without Sides	Red body, Silver chassis, DPBA/4DW/4SGW/SPW/SW/S/ORG. 210 mm.	£170-£200	☐
110/2B	1960	A.E.C. Mammoth Major 8 'LONDON BRICK COMPANY LTD'	Red body, Black cab roof, Brown load, CEM/SW/S/ORG/DPBA/4DW/4SGW/SPW. 210 mm.	£170-£200	☐
110/3	1960	A.E.C. Mammoth Major 8 'BRITISH ROAD SERVICES'	Red body, Black roof, Sil chassis and trim, 4DW/4SGW/SPW/DDTB/DPBA/FFA/CEMS. 210 mm.	£160-£180	☐
110/3D	1962	A.E.C. Mammoth Major 8 Oil Drums Load	Red body, Black roof, Sil chassis and trim, FFS/DPBA/DDTB/SW/S/4DW/4SGW/SPW. 210 mm.	£500-£600	☐
110/4	1961	A.E.C. Mammoth Major 8 'SHELL-BP' Tanker	Green cab, Red tank, Black chassis and catwalk, Silver trim, DPBA/4DW/4SGW/SPW/CEMS. 210 mm.	£400-£450	☐
110/4	1963	A.E.C. Mammoth Major 8 'SHELL-BP' Tanker	Yellow cab, White/Yel tank, Silver chassis and catwalk, DPBA/4DW/4SGW/SPW/CEMS. 210 mm.	£1250-£1500	☐
111A/1	1959	Ford Thames Trader 'BRITISH RAILWAYS'	Mrn and White body, AV/4DW/2SGW/SPW/FFS, *4884 BG M* and *M1741GT6* on cab/TRL. 219 mm.	£150-£180	☐
111A/1	1960	Ford Thames Trader 'R. HALL & SON LTD. FULHAM, LONDON'	Green cab and float, logo on car door and float. (Model may not have been issued)	NGPP	☐
111A/1S	1960	Ford Thames Trader with Sack Load	Dark Blue cab, Pale Blue float, Blk chassis, OC/FFS/SW/S/ORG/AV/4DW/2SGW/SPW. 219 mm.	£500-£600	☐
111A/30T	1961	Ford Thames Trader with Log Load	TT Blue cab and float, Silver chassis, OC/FF/SW/S/ORG/AV/4DW/2SGW/SPW. 219 mm.	£300-£350	☐
111A/30G	1962	Ford Thames Trader with Garage Kit	Orange cab and float, Silver chassis and trim, FFS/S/SW/ORG/AV/4DW/4SGW/SPW/CPL. 219 mm.	£300-£350	☐
117	1963	'JONES' Mobile Crane	Red/White body, Black lower body.	£160-£200	☐
			Red/White body, Grey lower body	£180-£220	☐
158A/2	1961	Bedford 'S' Type 2000 Gal 'SHELL-BP' Tanker	Green cab, Red tank, Black chassis, Sil trim, AV/4DW/2SGW/ORG/CEMS, *P33A37*. 199 mm.	£450-£500	☐
158A/2	1962	Bedford 'S' Type 2000 Gal 'SHELL-BP' Tanker	Yellow cab, White tank, Silver trim, AV/4DW/2SGW/ORG/CEMS, *P33A37*. 202 mm.	£1000-£1250	☐
158A/3C	1961	Bedford Low Loader with Cable Drum	Red cab and loader, Blue wheels, AV Silver trim. In cat but not seen. 270 mm.		☐
161	1961	Land Rover with L.W.B.	Grey body, White roof, SPW. 108 mm.	£40-£50	☐
258	1963	'R.A.C.' Land Rover	Blue *Radio Rescue* SPW/ORG/A. 108 mm.	£60-£75	☐
308	1965	Land Rover and Trailer	Green body, Beige HD, Brown TRL. 170 mm.	£45-£55	☐
402	1966	Crash Service Land Rover	Orange body, WCJ/H *Motorways Crash Service* in Blue. 125 mm.	£60-£70	☐

Bus, Coach and Taxi Cab

Ref. No.		Model Type	Model Features and Size	Market Price Range	
145	1963	Routemaster Bus 'LONDON TRANSPORT'	Red/Black body, DI/2DW/2SGW/ORG *Ovaltine the Worlds Best Nightcap*. 198 mm. 1st Type with diecast radiator	£475-£525	☐
			2nd type with cased radiator	£375-£425	☐
155	1961	Austin F×4 Taxicab	Black body, Red seats *Taxi*, ORG. 117 mm.	£40-£55	☐
156	1961	Mulliner Luxury Coach (Guy Warrior)	Pale Blue/Grey body, Red flash, OC *Triang Tours*. 213 mm. NB: Shades of the Blue exist	£250-£300	☐
		Colour change	Yellow/White body, Brown flash White	£650-£800	☐

Spot-On

Military and R.A.F. Models

Ref. No.		Model Type	Model Features and Size	Market Price Range	
415	1965	R.A.F. Land Rover	Blue/Grey, R.A.F. EM, hose/FP/AM. 111 mm.	£50-£60	☐
416	1965	'LEYLAND' Military 'AMBULANCE'	Olive Green body, RCS/SQM/SS/PP/3SLDS. 114 mm.	NPP	☐
417	1965	Military 'FIELD KITCHEN'	MG, Olive Green body, SQM/OW/SS/3SLDS/MNP. 108 mm.	£60-£75	☐
418	1965	'LEYLAND' Military Bus	MG, Olive Green body, *Army Personnel*, SQM/MNP/3SLDS. 114 mm.	NPP	☐
419	1965	Land Rover with Missile Carrier	MG, Olive Green body with 3 white Missiles	£175-£230	☐

Roadmaking Equipment and Tractors

Ref. No.		Model Type	Model Features and Size	Market Price Range	
116	1959	Caterpillar Tractor D9	Brown/Silver body, White RTR. 153 mm.	£450-£500	☐
123	1959	Bamford Excavator	Red/Yellow body, J.C.B. 272 mm.	NPP	☐
137	1962	'MASSEY HARRIS' Tractor	Red/Silver/Blue body, driver/SW. 79 mm.	£500-£750	☐

Emergency Services
Fire, Police and Ambulances (Civilian)

Ref. No.		Model Type	Model Features and Size	Market Price Range	
207	1964	Wadham 'AMBULANCE'	Cream body without Red crosses	£350-£500	☐
			White body with Red crosses	£450-£550	☐
256	1966	3.4 Jaguar 'POLICE' Car	White or Black body — few exist with undamaged aerial or roof sign	£250-£300	☐
309	1965	BBC 'Z' Car (Zephyr)	1st type with aerial and 'POLICE'	£50-£60	☐
			Sign on mast with White body	£55-£65	☐
			2nd type with no aerial or police sign. Black body version	£600-£700	☐
			White body version	£500-£600	☐
316	1966	'FIRE DEPT' Land Rover	Red body, Brown HD, RC/SS/S/2FM. 112 mm.	£50-£60	☐
402	1966	Land Rover 'MOTORWAYS'	Orange/Blue body, JIS/H. Blue 'CRASH SERVICE' logo	£55-£65	☐
409	1966	'LEYLAND' Black Maria	Blue body, *Police*, ORD/SS/SL/PM/robber. 114 mm.	NPP	☐

Caravans and Boats

Ref. No.		Model Type	Model Features and Size	Market Price Range	
135	1964	14ft GP Sailing Dinghy	Brown or Yellow boat on BR TRL. 128 mm.	£30-£35	☐
139	1960	Eccles E. 16 Caravan	Blue body, White roof, TB. 146 mm.	NPP	☐
264	1962	Tourist Caravan	Blue body, White roof, TB. 152 mm.	£40-£45	☐

Motor Scooter

Ref. No.		Model Type	Model Features and Size	Market Price Range	
229	1966	Lambretta	Blue body, Red or White rear casing	£200-£250	☐

Spot-On

Presentation and Gift Sets

Ref. No.	Model Type	Model Features and Size	Market Price Range	
1960	No 0 Presentation Set	Contains 106A/1, 100, 103, 104 and 113	£500-£600	☐
1960	No 1 Presentation Set	Contains 100, 101, 103 and 104	£600-£700	☐
1960	No 2 Presentation Set	Contains 109/3, 101, 102 and 105	£600-£700	☐
1960	No 3 Presentation Set	Contains 111A/1, 101, 104, 108, 112, 113, 114	NGPP	☐
1960	No 4 Presentation Set	Contains 106A/1, 109/3, 100, 107, 112	NGPP	☐
1963	No 4 Presentation Set	Contains 104, 105, 107 and 108	NGPP	☐
	No 5 Presentation Set	Contains 118, 119 and 131	NGPP	☐
	No 6 Presentation Set	Contains 131, 185, 193 and 211	NGPP	☐
	No 7 Presentation Set	Contains 166, 191, 211, 213, 215, 217	NGPP	☐
	No 8 Presentation Set	Contains 157, 191, 213, 216, 258	NGPP	☐
	No 9 Presentation Set	Contains 122, 145, 193, 207, 211, 256	NGPP	☐
	No 10 Presentation Set	Contains 122, 145, 157, 158A/2, 165, 166, 185, 211, 215 and 262	NGPP	☐
	Gift Set 702	Contains Zephyr Six, 274 Morris 1100 and canoe, 286 Austin 1800, and 135	£150-£225	☐

These sets were originally large and expensive so not many were sold. Hence their extreme rarity nowadays and reason for the lack of price information. Collectors may get an idea of the set prices by relating the models in the sets to the individual prices shown. This of course ignores any additional value caused by rarity.

Tommy Spot Gift Set Series

Ref. No.	Model Type	Model Features and Size	Market Price Range	
801	Home with Tommy Spot	Hillman Minx with Mr Spot, Ford Zephyr Six with driver, BK/TSP	£130-£160	☐
802	Cops 'n Robbers with Tommy Spot	BBC 'Z' car with driver and robber, Jaguar 'S' with driver, BK/TSP	£150-£170	☐
803	Superville Garage Service with Tommy Spot	Austin 1800 with Driver, Austin Healey Sprite with Driver, 2 garage workers, BK/TSP	£150-£170	☐
804	Sailing with Tommy Spot	Vauxhall Cresta and sailing dinghy with Mr Spot, BK/TSP	£130-£160	☐
805	Fire with Tommy Spot	Land Rover and trailer (both Red) two firemen, BK/TSP	£140-£160	☐
806	Royal occasion with Tommy Spot	Royal Rolls Royce with D/PS/BOL 6 guardsmen, BK/TSP	£500-£600	☐
807	Pit stop with Tommy Spot	Mercedes 230 SL and Jaguar 'S', 2RD/BK/TSP	£250-£325	☐
808	Motorway Rescue with Tommy Spot	Crash service Land Rover and mechanic, A.A. van/A.A. man, BK/TSP	£400-£500	☐

Auction Price Results
Phillips, New Bond Street, London Sale 24.10.87
Gift Set 702 realised £130; 802 — £160; 269 — £80; Presentation Pack O — £380; 265 — £85; 106 A/OC without MGA — £220;
110/4 Tanker — £410 (mint boxed); 110/2B — £180 (mint boxed); 109/2P pale green (mint boxed) — £150; 109/2 turquoise (mint boxed) — £150;
106A/1C turquoise (excellent boxed) — £250
Lacy Scotts Auction 27.2.88
110/2 realised £200, 111A/1 realised £210, 216 — £48, 215 — £48, 115 — £65, 100 — £50, 191 — £55, 157 — £50, 154 — £65, 229 — £55

Christies, 85 Old Brompton Road, London SW7 3LD
Sale dated 28.1.88:
Model No. 116, Caterpillar D9 — £350

Christies, 85 Old Brompton Road, London SW7 3LD
Sale dated 28.1.88:
Model No. 260 Royal Rolls Royce — £190

MATCHBOX TOYS

INTRODUCTION

Since the first edition was published Lesney & Co. the founders of Matchbox Toys have been taken over by the mighty Universal International Co. of Hong Kong and now trade as the Matchbox Group of Companies. Being a large company Universal International have secured the long term production of Matchbox Toys which is excellent news for the toy collector.

Compared to the first edition many improvements and new models have been included in the second edition as follows:—

i) 'Matchbox Miniatures' Many more variations have been included.

ii) 'Models of Yesteryear' To ensure accuracy the listings have been linked to the Matchbox Toys publication 'THE COLLECTION'. Details of the 'Giftware' models have also been included.

iii) Matchbox 'King Size' Models — included for the first time

iv) 'Twin Packs' TP Series — included for the first time.

v) The Early Lesney Toys — included for the first time.

Much of the additional information has resulted from visiting the home of the 'Matchbox International Collectors Association (MICA) at the Chester Toy Museum which houses the finest Matchbox collection in the world. The Catalogue compiler would like to express his personal thanks to Kevin McGimpsey and Stewart Orr for their co-operation in allowing the compiler open access to their unique collection. If you are a diecast collector a visit to the Chester Toy Museum is a must for apart from the superb Matchbox collection there is also a good display of Dinky Toys and much more besides.

Since the first edition was published the 'Matchbox International Collectors Association' (MICA) has been formed as the official Matchbox Toys Collectors Club and has already become well established with many members the world over.

MATCHBOX MINIATURES
Incorporating the 1-75 Series

The first 1-75 Series toys were produced by Lesney Products Ltd. in 1953.

They were packaged and marketed by the Moko Company who specialized in the distribution of toy manufacturers products. Consequently the early boxes reflected this arrangement by displaying the name 'MOKO LESNEY'. This partnership lasted until the late fifties, when Lesney began distributing their products themselves and issued the first catalogue which depicted just 42 models.

Lesney Products had in fact been formed just after the war, when the unrelated Leslie and Rodney Smith set up their factory and linked their names to form 'Lesney' Products Ltd. They were soon joined by Jack O'dell who was a recognised die-casting expert.

Various Products were made prior to the launch of the 1-75 Series, probably the most well known of which was the 1953 Coronation Coach and horses.

Since those early days the number of models issued in the 1-75 Series has topped well over five hundred. This large range therefore provides collectors with many opportunities for collecting specific types of models whether they be buses or racing cars. With new low cost models continually being issued each year, this is an ideal collecting area for the younger generation.

For the specialist collector the early models are greatly sought after and most importantly the price levels are still within the reach of most people. Furthermore reasonable quantities are available for building up a collection.

Matchbox have been known to produce the staggering figure of 100 million models a year to satisfy the demands made by collectors in 140 different countries, particularly in the USA. Many of todays adult collectors were probably unwittingly hooked at an early age by the little models they could buy at the corner shop for just a few coppers of their pocket money. Today no doubt many of them collect 'The Models of Yesteryear' Series but that's another story!

It is to be hoped that the Matchbox Toys 1-75 Series models continues to bring joy to many more generations of school children.

In 1982 Lesney Products were purchased by UNIVERSAL INTERNATIONAL of HONG KONG since which time production of 1-75's has continued to flourish to the satisfaction of collectors the world over. .

PRICE AND RARITY CHANGES 1981-1988

			1981-83 Survey		1985 Survey		1988 Survey	
CARS	19a	M.G. Sports Car	£14	NC	£25	NC	£35	NC
	32a	Jaguar Fixed Head Coupe XK140	£9	NC	£20	NC	£20	NC
	75a	Ford Thunderbird	£4-£5	MPR	£12	NC	£20	NC
COMMERCIALS	11a	Yellow Tanker	£10	NC	£25	GP	£45	GP
	20b	ERF Heavy Lorry 'EVER READY'	£8	NC	£16	NC	£20	NC
	37a	Karrier Bantam 'COCA COLA'	£9	NC	£25	GP	£50	GP
VANS	25a	Bedford 'DUNLOP'	£8-£10	MPR	£20	NC	£24	NC
	42a	Bedford 'EVENING NEWS'	£8-£9	MPR	£20	NC	£25	NC
	59a	Ford 'SINGER'	£10	NC	£24	NC	£24	NC
BUSES	21a	Long Distance Coach	£15	NC	£25	NC	£30	NC
	56a	'PEARDRAX' Trolley Bus	£15	NC	£20	NC	£25	NC
FIRE	59b	'FIRE CHIEF' Car	£5-£6	NPR	£12	NC	£14	NC
POLICE	55b	'POLICE CAR' Car	£3-£4	MPR	£12	NC	£12	NC
AMBULANCE	14a	Daimler	£9		£18	NC	£18	NC
ROADMAKING	18a	Caterpillar Bulldozer	£9		£15	NC	£20	NC
MILITARY	62a	General Service Lorry	£4-£5	MPR	£12	NC	£12	NC
MISCELLANEOUS	7a	Horse Drawn Milk Float	£25	GP	£30	GP	£45	GP
FARM	72a	Fordson Tractor	£4-£5	MPR	£12	NC	£15	NC
GIFT SET	G1	1960 Commercial Set			£250	GV	£350	GP

MATCHBOX MINIATURES
which includes the 1-75 Series Models

MODEL IDENTIFICATION

Many models have common identifying features and these are shown below to avoid unnecessary repetition.

Model Number

With the exception of the very first models which did not have model numbers all the remainder have the number of the model either cast on the model itself or on the base plate or chassis.

The only exceptions to this rule are models from the TP Series where no model numbers are shown.

'Lesney'

It has been assumed that all models issued between 1953 and 1982 had the word 'LESNEY' either cast on the model itself or on the base plate or chassis.

Model Name

It has been assumed that all models issued after 1957 had the model name stamped on the base plate or chassis. The only exceptions to this rule being those models issued without a base plate e.g. No 24 Hydraulic Excavator.

'Matchbox' or 'Matchbox Series'

Assumed that all models after 1965 had 'MATCHBOX' stamped onto the baseplate or chassis.

Suspension & Windows

Assumed that all Saloon Cars issued after 1961 were fitted with windows and with suspension after 1965.

Windscreeens, Seats, Steering Wheels

All assumed to be Plastic.

Lengths of Models

The figures given have either been taken from original Matchbox catalogues, or from the models themselves. Fortunately the measurements were shown in both mm and inches in the first Lesney issued catalogue in 1958. Models 1-42 were included in this issue.

Boxes

In the 'Packaging' section which follows pictures are shown of all the main types of boxes. Collectors should appreciate that the same models were issued in different box styles.

Base plates

Assumed that all Base plates were of metal construction until the late seventies when plastic became increasingly used. Models issued 1983 onwards are stamped 'Made in Macau'. As from 1986 models appeared with 'Made in China' on the base plate.

Wheels

All the early models had metal wheels which were gradually changed to a Grey Silver or Black Plastic construction before Superfast wheels were introduced in the late sixties. Models issued in 1968/9 often had both regular wheel and Superfast versions.

Model Names

The catalogue has tried to give the original catalogue description in respect of each of the model names listed.

However the manufacturers catalogue listings are known to be inaccurate concerning the colour range depicted. This is because the model photos shown are taken from mock-ups produced many months before production commences.

Rolamatics

Some models issued in the seventies had built in working parts which operated when the model was pushed. They have been indicated in the model listings by the abbreviation RLM.

Normal Retail Price (NRP)

Where this grading has been shown in the Price and Rarity grading column expect the price not to exceed £3 and refers to models which have yet to attain real collectable value.

MATCHBOX MINIATURES

1-75 SERIES PACKAGING

1953-54 (Approx)

1954-55 (Approx)

1955-56 (Approx)

1956-57 (Approx)

1957-58 (Approx)

1958-59 (Approx)

MATCHBOX MINIATURES
1-75 SERIES PACKAGING

1959-63 (Approx)

1962-64 (Approx)

1971 (Approx)

1973 (Approx)

1981 The Bubble Pack

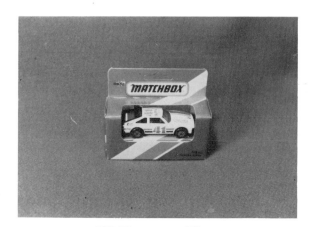

1983 The new type Window Box

Other Box designs will also be found

MATCHBOX MINIATURES
1-75 SERIES SPECIALISED PACKAGING

A special box for James Bond

Collection Card Issues circa 1987

American Edition Issues circa 1986

Matchbox Miniatures

Ref. No.		Model Type	Model Features and Size	Price and Rarity Grading	

NB. All model numbers are prefixed with the letters 'MB'.

Ref. No.		Model Type	Model Features and Size	Price	Rarity
1a	1953	Diesel Road Roller (Aveling Barford)	Light Green body, Red MRW, Gold trim, Tan D, No number, crimped axles, tow hook. 49 mm.	£50	GP
		Casting change	With curved lower canopy ends	£50	GP
		Colour change	With Dark Green body	£25	NC
1b	1955	Diesel Road Roller (Aveling Barford)	Pale Green body, Red MRW, Lt or Dk Tan D, high peaked canopy, CA/NN/H. 55 mm.	£30	NC
1c	1958	Diesel Road Roller (Aveling Barford)	Lt or Dk Green body and driver, Red MRW number cast in, CRA/HPC/H. 64 mm.	£30	NC
1d	1962	Diesel Road Roller (Aveling Barford)	Green body and driver, Red PRW, MIECI. 67 mm.	£14	NC
1e	1968	Mercedes Truck	Green or Gold body, Orange or Yellow CNP. 76 mm.	£3-5	MPR
		Colour change	Military Green, 'USA 48350'	£20	GP
		Design change	Red body, 'Transcontinental', Yellow canopy	£3-£5	MPR
		Design change	Blue body. 'IMS' Logo	£3-£5	MPR
1f	1972	Mod Rod	Yellow body, Silver ERE, cat LB, TW/SF. 73 mm.	£1-£3	MPR
		Colour change	SAPM with flower label	£10	NC
		Colour change	SAPM with Red int. or wheels	£5-£7	MPR
			NB. Many other variations exist		
1g		Silver Streak	U.S. issued model	£5-£8	MPR
1h	1976	Dodge Challenger	Red body, White roof, Silver int., CW/SF. 74 mm.	£5-£7	MPR
		Colour change	Blue body, red interior	£5-£7	MPR
		Colour change	Dark Blue body, Red interior	£3-£5	MPR
	1982	Dodge Challenger	Blue or Orange body, *Revin Rebel*, CW/SF. 74 mm.	£2-£4	MPR
	1983	Dodge Challenger	Yellow body, Black roof, *Toyman*, CW/SF	£2-£4	MPR
1i	1988	Jaguar XJ6	Red body, silver trim. ARDT	NRP	
	1988	'WHYTE & MACKAY'	Promotional — Black body, Gold bonnet design	NRP	
2a	1953	Dumper Truck	Dark Green body, Red DMP. 42 mm.	£30	NC
		Colour change	SAPM with unpainted metal wheels	£25	NC
2b	1957	Dumper Truck	Colours SAPM, Tan D, CA/NCI/MW. 46 mm.	£15	NC
		Wheel change	SAPM with Grey plastic wheels	£10	NC
2c	1962	(Muir Hill) Dumper Truck	Red body, Green DMP, *Laing*, BPW. 54 mm.	£10	NC
2d	1968	Mercedes Trailer	Green body, Yellow canopy, BPW/SF/H. 90 mm.	£3-£5	MPR
			Military Green 'USA 48350'	£20	NC
		Colour change	Red Transcontinental, Yellow canopy	£3-£5	MPR
		Colour change	Blue 'IMS' logo	£3-£5	MPR
	1970	Colour change	Gold body, Orange canopy	£3-£5	MPR
2e	1972	Jeep Hot Rod	Pink with Green base, Cream seats, SF.	£3-£5	MPR
		Variants	Pink with White base	£20	NC
			Red with Green base	£20	NC
			Red with White Base	£3-£5	MPR
			Military Green body 'Jeep' on base	£15	NC
			NB Many other variations exist		
2f	1977	Rescue Hovercraft	Green/Fawn body, *Rescue* SF. 77 mm.	£2-£4	MPR
		Colour change	Met Green/Tan body, Chrome/Red top *Rescue* SF. 77 mm.	£5-£7	MPR
		Colour change	Pale Green/Black body, Chrome/Red top *2000*	£5-£7	MPR
			NB Many other variations exist		
2g	1980	Mazda RX7	Yellow or Green body, JIM	£6	NC
2h	1981	S-2 Jet	Black/Yellow body, four wheels, FWT/TCC. 76 mm.	£1-£3	MPR
	1982	Colour change	Blue/White body, Red flash, *Viper*	£1-£3	MPR
2i	1985	Pontiac Firebird	Black body, *Halleys Comet'* (USIM)	£3-£5	MPR
2j	1985	Pontiac Fiero	White/Blue/Orange body. RN85	NRP	
	1986	Colour change	Blue body, Yellow/Red panels	NRP	
	1987	Colour change	White/Red body	NRP	
2k	1988	Rover Sterling	Red body, Black chassis, OSR	NRP	
3a	1953	Cement Mixer	Blue body, Orange MW or GPW, NN/CA. 45 mm.	£20	NC
3b	1961	Bedford Tipper Truck	Grey cab, Bright Red or Maroon tipper, opening tailboard, GPW/BPW. 64 mm.	£8-£12	MPR
3c	1968	MBENZ BINZ Ambulance	White body, Red + decals, STR/BPW/SF/OTG. 73 mm.	£5-£8	MPR
		Colour change	Military Green, Chrome hubs	£10	NC
3d	1973-	Monteverdi Hai	Red body, Blue TW, Sil trim, RN '3', OD/SF. 74 mm.	£1-£3	MPR
		Label change	Red body, RN '16'	£10	NC
3e	1979	Porsche Turbo	Brown or Silver body, OD/SF. 74 mm.	£2-£4	MPR
	1981	Colour change	Green body, Yellow interior, OD/SF	£2-£4	MPR
		Colour change	With Red interior	£5-£7	MPR
	1982	Colour change	Red body, White RN '90' and *Porsche*, OD/SF	£2-£4	MPR
	1985	Colour change	Black body, Red *Turbo* RN '90'	NRP	
	1987	Colour change	White body	NRP	
			NB. Many other variations exist		

Ref. No.		Model Type	Matchbox Miniatures continued	Price and Rarity Grading	
4a	1954-	Massey Harris Tractor	Red body, Tan D, CTR, FMW, SRMW/NN. 40 mm.	£30	NC ☐
4b	1957-	Massey Harris Tractor	SAPM with solid FMW/hollow RMW/NCI. 45 mm.	£25	NC ☐
		Wheel change	SAPM with Grey plastic wheels	£15	NC ☐
4c	1960-	Triumph MC & SC	Steel Blue body, Silver SPKW, BPT. 57 mm.	£25	NC ☐
		Colour change	With a Copper main body, BPT.		NGPP ☐
4d	1967	(Dodge) Stake Truck	Yellow cab and CH, Blue SB, BPW/SF/H. 73 mm.	£50	GP ☐
		Colour change	Yellow Cab/CH, Green Stake body	£4-£6	MPR ☐
4e	1972	Gruesome Twosome	Gold body, Pink TW/RF, Silver EE, SF. 73 mm.	£2-£4	MPR ☐
4f	1976-	Pontiac Firebird	Met Blue body, Silver trim, Orange TW, SF. 73 mm.	£2-£4	MPR ☐
4g	1981-	'57' Chevy	Met Mauve body, Silver trim and E, OD, SF. 75 mm.	£2-£4	MPR ☐
	1982	Colour change	All Red body, *Cherry Bomb*, labels, SF. 75 mm.	£2-£4	MPR ☐
	1983	Colour change	Black/Red/Yellow, 'on fire effect', SF. 75 mm.	£2-£4	MPR ☐
4h	1985	Chrysler Daytona	White body, (VSIM)	£3-£5	MPR ☐
4i	1988	F X 4R Taxi	All Black body, Silver trim		NRP ☐

No. 5 London Bus

Ref. No.		Model Type	Matchbox Miniatures continued	Price and Rarity Grading	
5a	1954	'BUY MATCHBOX SERIES'	Red body, Gold RG, No '5' CI, Yellow/Green paper label, MW/CA/DD. 50 mm.	£30	NC ☐
5b	1957	'BUY MATCHBOX SERIES'	Red body, Gold RG, Yellow decal, MW or GPW. 57 mm.	£30	NC ☐
		'PLAYERS PLEASE'	SAPM Silver grille, GPW	£75	GP ☐
		'BP VISCOSTATIC'	SAPM Silver grille, GPW	£30	NC ☐
5c	1961	'PLAYERS PLEASE'	Red body, No. 5 on Baseplate GPW. 66 mm.	£60	GP ☐
		'PEARDRAX'	SAPM — GPW or BPW	£20	NC ☐
		'VISCOSTATIC'	SAPM — GPW or BPW	£20	NC ☐
5d	1965	'LONGLIFE'	Red body, BPW 70 mm.	£10-£15	MPR ☐
		'BP VISCOSTATIC'		£10-£15	MPR ☐

NB. Promotionals issued 1961-66 — 'The Baron of Beef' (beware fakes) 'Mecca Ltd, 'Pegram'.

Ref. No.		Model Type	Matchbox Miniatures continued	Price and Rarity Grading	
				£25	GP ☐
5e	1969	Lotus Europa	Met Blue, Silver trim, OD/SF/H. 71 mm.	£4-£6	MPR ☐
		Variants	Pink body with '20' labels	£10	NC ☐
			Met Green body, Bulgarian issue	£20	NC ☐
			Met Blue body, Bulgarian issue	£20	NC ☐
			Green body, Bulgarian issue	£20	NC ☐
			NB. Many other variations exist		
5f	1976	Seafire Motor Boat	Blue/White body, Yellow D, *Seafire*. 75 mm.	£2-£4	MPR ☐
		Variants	Red/Blue body	£45	GP ☐
			White/Brown body	£20	NC ☐
5g		Nissan Fair Lady 2802X	Red or Met Red body JIM	£6	NC ☐
			Police Car variant White/Black	£5	NC ☐
5g	1980	U.S. Mail Truck	Blue body, White roof, *U.S. Mail*, SF. 59 mm.	£2-£4	MPR ☐
		Variants	Pale blue US issue 'No. 38 Jeep'	£7	NC ☐
			Yellow body, 'GLIDING CLUB' Logo	£7	NC ☐
5h	1982-	4 × 4 Jeep	Bronze body, large wheels, black ARBB. 50 mm.	£2-£4	MPR ☐
5i	1984	Peterbilt Tanker, 'SHELL'	White/Grey body, Yellow Red design	£2-£4	MPR ☐
		'AMOCO'	Black body, Black SMS etc.	£2-£4	MPR ☐
	1985	'AMOCO'	Black body, Chrome SMS etc.	£12	NC ☐
		'AMPOL'	Australian issued model	£8	NC ☐
		'SUPERGAS'	Black/Yellow (USIM 56)	£3-£5	MPR ☐
		'GETTY'	Red/Chrome (USIM 56)	£3-£5	MPR ☐
	1988	'SHELL'	White/Chrome body, Yellow/Red design		NRP ☐

Ref. No.		Model Type	Matchbox Miniatures continued	Price and Rarity Grading	
6a	1954	Quarry Truck	Orange body, Grey tipper with 6 ribs, MW. 55 mm.	£18	NC ☐
		Wheel change	With Grey plastic wheels	£15	NC ☐
6b	1958	Quarry Truck (Euclid)	Yellow body, 4 ribs, 6GBPW/DCS. 63 mm.	£12	NC ☐
		Wheel change	With Black plastic wheels	£9	NC ☐
6c	1963	Quarry Truck (Euclid)	Yellow body, A or B, CI/6BPW/CRA. 67 mm.	£6-£8	MPR ☐
6d	1969	Ford Pick Up	Red body, White DCV, ASM/BPW/SF. 75 mm.	£6-£8	MPR ☐
6e	1974-	Mercedes 350SL	Orange body, Black CV top, Yel int, SF. 75 mm.	£3-£5	MPR ☐
	1978	Colour change	Yellow body	£2-£4	MPR ☐
	1980	G15 Gift Set Model	Met Silver body, Black hood, White seats, *Rennservice*.	£15	NC ☐
	1981	Colour change	Red body, White CV top, SF. 75 mm.	£1-£2	MPR ☐
		Colour change	Met Red body, White top	£5-£7	MPR ☐
6f	1982	Mercedes 350 Convertible	Blue body, White seats, Silver trim, SF. 75 mm.	£2-£4	MPR ☐
	1986	F1 Racer	Red body, RN '3', FIAT		NRP ☐
6g	1988	F1 Racer	Yellow body, Red D & design		NRP ☐

Ref. No.		Model Type	Matchbox Miniatures continued	Price and Rarity Grading	
7a	1954	Horse Drawn Milk Float 'PASTEURISED MILK'	Orange body, Brown horse, Orange driver, MSPKW, Gold trim, CRA. 55 mm.	£35	NC ☐
		Wheel change	With Grey plastic wheels	£50	GP ☐
		Colour	With Chocolate horse, White driver	£35	NC ☐
		Colour change	With Pale Orange body, White logo or hat	£35	GP ☐
7b	1961	Ford Anglia	Lt Blue body, Green TW, GPW, 67 mm.	£12	NC ☐
		Wheel change	With Silver plastic wheels	£35	GP ☐
		Wheel change	With Black plastic wheels	£12	NC ☐

Ref. No.		Model Type	Matchbox Miniatures continued	Price and Rarity Grading	
7c	1968	Ford Refuse Truck	Orange or Red MB, Silver DMP, TW/BPT/SF. 76 mm.	£5-£7	MPR
7d	1973	Hairy Hustler	Met Orange body, RN '5', CLW, Purple or Yellow windows	£3-£5	MPR
		Colour change	White body, Amber windows, streaker design	£3-£5	MPR
		Colour change	Yellow body, Flame design	£3-£5	MPR
			NB. Many other variations exist.		
7e	1977-	Volkswagen Golf	Green body, Yellow TW, 2 Black SB, SF/H. 72 mm.	£2-£4	MPR
	1981	Colour change	Yellow body, Red seats, BB/SF/H	£2-£4	MPR
	1982	Colour change	Silver body, Green flash *Golf,* SF, Red interior	£2-£4	MPR
		Colour change	With Tan interior	£20	NC
		Export issues	'ADAC' GIM & JIM	£12	NC
7f	1983	IMSA Mazda	Blue body, orange/white flash, *Mazda.* 76 mm.	£2-£4	MPR
7g	1986	'Porsche' 959	Silver body, *Porsche*		NRP
	1988	Colour change	Met Dark Grey body, Red interior		NRP
7h		Rompin Rabbit	US issue model	£4-£6	MPR
7i		Ruff Rabbit	Yellow/Black body, 'VW' rabbits TPD, USIM	£4-£6	MPR
7j		London Bus	'Nice to Meet You' JIM	£4-£6	MPR
		Logo change	1984 'Yokohama' PRM, JIM	£35	GP
8a	1955	Caterpillar Tractor	Yellow body, Gold trim, MRW/RTR/CA/NN. 40 mm.	£18	NC
		Colour change	Orange body	£35	GP
8b	1959	Caterpillar Tractor	Yellow body and D, NCI (8), MRW/RT/CA. 43 mm.	£30	NC
8c	1961	Caterpillar Tractor	Yellow body and D, PRW or MRW, RT with NCI (8) or (18).		
		Casing change	48 mm.	£10	NC
		Wheel change	SAPM with silver plastic roller wheels	£40	GP
8d	1964	Caterpillar Tractor	Yellow body, No D BPRW, Green RT, NCI (8). 51 mm.	£9	NC
8e	1966	Ford Mustang Fastback	White body, Red seats, BPT or SF, CW/H. 74 mm.	£5-£7	MPR
	1970	Colour change	Red body, Yellow seats, SF. 74 mm.	£3-£5	MPR
8f	1970	Wildcat Dragster	Orange body, Black Wild Cat decal, SF/TW. 74 mm.	£3-£5	MPR
8g	1975	De Tomaso Pantera	White or Blue body, Red seats, RN '8' and *Panther.*	£3-£5	MPR
		Colour change	SAPM with Red interior	£5-£7	MPR
		Label change	SAPM with 'SUN' label	£5-£7	MPR
8h	1981	Rover 3500	Red body, Cream seats SF, Black base. 73 mm.	£2-£4	MPR
8i	1983-	Rover 3500 'POLICE' Car	White body, Yel/Black decal, 2 Blue, FL. 73 mm.	£2-£4	MPR
	1984	Rover 3500 'POLICE' Car	SAPM plus roof light bar		NRP
		Rover 3500 'POLICE' Car	SAPM only Red/Black stripes		NRP
8j	1986	Greased Lightnin'	Red body, RN31, USIM	£4-£6	MPR
8k	1986	1962 Corvette	Orange body	£3-£5	MPR
	1988	Colour change	Met Green body	£3-£5	MPR
8l	1988	Astra Police	White body, Red flash, FLLB		NRP
9a	1955	Fire Escape (Dennis)	Red body, WW Gold trim, NFB/CA/NN/MW. 55 mm.	£25	NC
9b	1958	Fire Escape (Dennis)	Red body, Gold trim, CA/NCI/MW/FB. 59 mm.	£30	GP
		Wheel change	SAPM with Grey plastic wheels	£100	NC
9c	1959	Fire Engine (Merryweather Marquis)	Red body with Tan ladder, GPW. 67 mm.	£15	NC
		Ladder change	With Gold ladder GPW	£25	NC
		Wheel change	With Gold ladder BPW	£15	NC
		Ladder change	With Silver ladder BPW	£50	NPE
9d	1966	Boat and Trailer	Blue deck, White hull, Blue TRL, BPW. 89 mm.	£6-£8	MPR
	1970	Colour change	White deck, Blue hull and TRL. 89 mm.	£4-£6	MPR
9e	1972	AMX Javelin	Met Lime Green, Yel seats, TW, SF, OD. 77 mm.	£2-£4	MPR
			With Chrome scoop	£5-£7	MPR
			With Cream or Orange interior	£5-£7	MPR
			With Red body, 'DR PEPPER', RN4		NRP
	1983	Colour change	Met Silver, Red/Black labels, RN '9'. 77 mm.	£2-£4	MPR
9f	1978	Ford Escort	White body, *Shell* and *Ford* decals, SF. 74 mm.	£2-£4	MPR
	1981	Colour change	Met Green, White grille, *Seagull,* SF. 74 mm.	£2-£4	MPR
			With Red interior	£75	GP
9g		Cam Cracker	Blue body, VSIM	£4-£6	MPR
9h		Caterpillar	Dark Red body, 'DR PEPPER' design		NRP
		Bulldozer	Yellow body, Black cab roof		NRP
10a	1955	Scammell Mech' Horse	Red cab, Grey SMB, TRL, 56 mm. 5MW/NN/CA.	£25	NC
10b	1957	Scammell Mech' Horse	Red Cab, Brown TRL, 75 mm. 5MW/NN/CA	£25	NC
10c	1961	'TATE & LYLE' Truck	Blue body, Yel decal with crown, GBPW. 67 mm.	£25	GP
	1962	Decal changed	Crown removed from decal	£20	NC
10d	1966	Pipe Truck	Red body, Silver base, Grey pipes, 73 mm.	£5-£8	MPR
		Colour change	With White base, 6 or 7 pipes	£4-£6	MPR
10e	1973	Piston Popper	Met Blue, Silver EE, SF/RLM/OC. 75 mm.	£2-£4	MPR
		Colour change	White body	£50	GP
		Hot Popper	(USIM) No details known	£4-£6	MPR
10f	1979-	Plymouth Gran Fury	White/Black body, 2FL/SF *Police* decals. 75 mm.	£2-£4	MPR
	1985	Design change	White/Blue, 'POLICE', shield design		NRP
	1986	Colour change	Dark Blue body, 'STAR' design		NRP
10g	1988	Buick Le Sabre	Black body, RN'4', '355 CID'		NRP

Ref. No.		Model Type	Matchbox Miniatures continued	Price	Rarity
11a	1955	'ESSO' Road Tanker (E.R.F.)	Green body, Gold trim, ERF cast in, LSM decal, NN/MW/CA. 50 mm.	£200	GP ☐
		Colour change	Yellow body, ERF CI, Silver trim, MW/CA/NN	£35	GP ☐
		Colour change	Red body, large or small decal	£25	NC ☐
11b	1958	'ESSO' Petrol Tanker (E.R.F.)	Red body, Silver trim, ERF CI, MGSBPW/NCI. 64 mm.	£20	NC ☐
11c	1965	Jumbo Crane	Yellow body, Red HL, Red or Yel box, BPW. 76 mm.	£5-£7	MPR ☐
11d	1969	Scaffolding Truck	Silver body, Yellow SCF, *Builders Direct Supply.*	£5-£7	MPR ☐
11e	1973	Flying Bug	Red/Yellow body, Silver DH, SF. 73 mm.	£2-£4	MPR ☐
11f	1978	Car Transporter	Orange/Cream body, Black grille, 3 cars, SF. 75 mm.	£2-£4	MPR ☐
	1983	Colour change	Orange/White body, Silver grille	£2-£4	MPR ☐
11g		Cobra Mustang	Orange body, USIM	£2-£4	MPR ☐
11h		Imsa Mustang	Green/White USIM	£2-£4	MPR ☐
11i		Ferrari 308 GTB	Yellow body, USIM	£2-£4	MPR ☐
11j	1985	Lamborghini Countach	Red body, Yellow seats		NRP ☐
	1986	Colour change	Black Orange body, Red RN '5'		NRP ☐
	1988	Colour change	Yellow body, 'COUNTACH' in Black		NRP ☐
12a	1955	Land Rover	Green body, WW Sil trim, Tan D, CA/NN/MW. 42 mm.	£18	NC ☐
12b	1959	Land Rover	Dark Green body, No D, BB/BPW/CRA.	£8-£11	MPR ☐
		Wheel change	With Grey plastic wheels	£15	NC ☐
12c	1966-	Safari Land Rover	Green or Blue body, Tan LG/CW/BPW/H. 72 mm.	£7-£9	MPR ☐
	1970	Colour change	Metallic Gold, BPW/SF. 72 mm.	£5-£7	MPR ☐
12d	1970	Setra Coach	Gold, Yellow or Magenta MB, White roof, Red lights, CW/SF. 76 mm.	£6-£9	MPR ☐
12e	1975	Big Bull	Orange body, Green DB, Red wheels, SF. 63 mm.	£2-£4	MPR ☐
			With Black wheels	£30	GP ☐
12f	1980-	Citroen CX	Met Blue body, Yel S, Sil base, OTG/SF/H. 77 mm.	£2-£4	MPR ☐
			With Red interior	£50	GP ☐
	1982	Colour change	Yellow body, *Matchbox* decal	£2-£4	MPR ☐
			Yellow body with Blue windows	£10	MPR ☐
	1983	'AMBULANCE'	White body, Red DCS, Blk/Wh cross, SF		NRP ☐
12g	1986	Pontiac Firebird Racer	Yellow body, Blue chassis RN '56'		NRP ☐
	1987	Colour change	White/Blue body		NRP ☐
12h	1986	Chevy Prostocker	White body (USIM)	£3-£5	MRP ☐
12i	1988	Modified Racer	Orange body, Red RN '12'		NRP ☐
13a	1955	Wreck Truck (Bedford)	Tan body, Red crane and hook, MW/CA. 50 mm.	£18	NC ☐
13b	1958	Wreck Truck (Bedford)	Tan body, Red CEQ, 13 CI, MW/GPW/CRA. 55 mm.	£40	GP ☐
13c	1960	Thames Trader Wreck Truck	Red body, Silver trim, Red or Silver hook, Yellow decal, MLCD letters, GPW/WWCLW. 64 mm.	£35	GP ☐
		Wheel change	With Black plastic wheels	£25	NC ☐
13d	1965	(Dodge) Wreck Truck	Green/Yellow body, *BP*, Red P hook, BPT. 76 mm.	£4-£6	MPR ☐
13e	1972	Baja Buggy	Green, Black/Red trim, Silver E, SF. 66 mm.	£2-£4	MPR ☐
			With Police shield label	£10	NC ☐
13f	1977	Snorkel Fire Engine	Red body, Yellow hoist and FM, Sil trim, SF. 78 mm.	£2-£4	MPR ☐
	1983	Colour change	Red body, White hoist and FM, 'METRO FIRE DEPT.'	£2-£4	MPR ☐
		Colour change	SAPM with White jibs, UNP/Silver base	£20	GP ☐
13h	1985	Volvo Container	Blue body, White CNT 'COLDFRESH'		NRP ☐
14a	1956	Ambulance (Daimler)	Cream body, Silver trim, WW RCS, CRA, *Ambulance* cast onto sides, MGPW/NN. 50 mm.	£30	NC ☐
14b	1958	Daimler Ambulance	Cream body, BB, SAPM, 59 mm.	£20	NC ☐
		Colour change	Offwhite body, MGPW	£20	NC ☐
		Wheel change	SAMPM with Silver plastic wheels	£35	GP ☐
14c	1962	Bedford Lomas Amb.	White body, 'LCC Ambulance' in Blue BGSPW.	£18	NC ☐
		Colour change	Off White body, SPW, GPW, BPN	£12	NC ☐
		Colour change	SAPM with logo in Black lettering	£12	NC ☐
14d	1968	Iso Grifo	Blue body, BPT/SF/H/CW. 76 mm.	£2-£4	MPR ☐
14e	1977	Mini-Ha-Ha	Red body, Blue seats, Silver trim, driver. 60 mm.	£2-£4	MPR ☐
14f		Rallye Royale	Silver or White body (USIM)	£3-£5	MPR ☐
14g	1982	(Leyland) Petrol Tanker	Red body, White tank, *Elf*, PLP, SF. 77 mm.	£2-£4	MPR ☐
14h	1985	Jeep Laredo	Black body, White roof (USIM 20)		NRP ☐
	1986	Colour change	Red body, White roof Grey S/BN		NRP ☐
14i	1986	BMW Cabriolet	White body (USIM)	£3-£5	MPR ☐
14j	1988	Grand Prix R.C.	Blue/White body, Red driver		NRP ☐
15a	1956	Prime Mover	Yellow body, 6 MW, 55 mm. NN/H/SPWBC.	£18	NC ☐
		Colour change	Orange body, MW or GPW	£12	NC ☐
15b	1959	Atlantic Tractor	Orange body, Silver trim, H/GBPW. 67 mm.	£10	NC ☐
15c	1963	Refuse Truck	Blue body, Grey DMP with OD, PFTT	£8-£11	MPR ☐
		Tyre change	With knobby tread tyres	£20	NC ☐
15d	1968	Volkswagen 1500 Saloon	Off white body, Silver trim, CW/BPT/SF/H. 72 mm.	£6-£9	MPR ☐
	1970	Colour change	Red body. 72 mm.	£5-£7	MPR ☐
15e	1973	Fork Lift Truck	Red body, Yel forks, *Lansing Bagnall*. 70 mm.	£2-£4	MPR ☐
	1982	Colour change	Red body, White forks. 70 mm. 'H Lift'	£2-£4	MPR ☐
15f		'Hi-ho Silver'	(USIM) no details known.	£3-£5	MPR ☐
15f	1985	Peugeot 205 Turbo 16	White body, RCN '205'		NRP ☐
	1986	Design change	Blue/Red TPD, 'SHELL' AD on LRS		NRP ☐

Ref. No.		Model Type	Matchbox Miniatures continued	Price and Rarity Grading	
16a	1956	Transporter Trailer	Tan body, 6MW. 77 mm.	£12	NC ☐
16b	1960	Atlantic Trailer	Tan body, GPW, towbar. 79 mm.	£10	NC ☐
		Colour change	With Orange body, BGPW	£25	NC ☐
16c	1963	Scammell Snowplough	Grey cab & CH, Orange TPR, Red/WH DBL. 76 mm.		
16d	1969	Case Bull-Dozer TRT	Red/Yellow body, Black PR, DCNP/H. 64 mm.	£4-£6	MPR ☐
16e	1974	Badger Truck	Bright Red, White Radar, 6 BPW/RLM/TW. 68 mm.	£2-£4	MPR ☐
			Military Green issue	£15	NC ☐
16f	1981	Pontiac	Gold body, Red seats, eagle decal, SF. 77 mm.	£2-£4	MPR ☐
	1982	Colour change	White body, Blue flash, *Firebird*	£2-£4	MPR ☐
	1983	Colour change	Black body, Red seats, *Turbo*	£2-£4	MPR ☐
	1986	Colour change	Silver body, Red flash, Yel/Red design		NPR ☐
16g	1988	Land Rover Ninety	Blue body, White roof, Orange flash		NRP ☐
17a	1956	Bedford Removals Van	Light Blue body, Silver trim MW/NN, 'MATCHBOX REMOVALS SERVICE' in White. 55 mm.	£35	NC ☐
		Colour change	Maroon body, Silver or Gold trims	£35	NC ☐
		Colour change	Green body, open or closed cab window	£25	NC ☐
17b	1958	Casting and decal change	Green body, with slight roof curve, with or without number '17' cast into cab roof and with or without a black outline around 'REMOVALS' MW or GPW	£25	NC ☐
	1959	Colour change	Dark Green body, Silver trim, GPW	£50	GP ☐
17c	1960	Austin Taxi	Maroon or Red body, Silver trim, GPW. 61 mm.	£20	NC ☐
		Wheel change	SAPM with Silver plastic wheels	£40	GP ☐
17d	1964	Foden Tipper	Red cab and CH, Orange tipper, 8 BPW. 76 mm.	£7-£10	MPR ☐
17e	1969	Horse Box	Red or Orange cab, Cream or Green box, 2 White horses, BPW or SF, H. 74 mm.	£6-£9	MPR ☐
17f	1972	Londoner Bus Issues 1st Type 'ATLANTEAN'	Unless otherwise shown each has a Red body, White seats, Black metal or PBP. One door opening, two open rear windows, DD/SF. 78 mm. 5 spoke wheels		
	i)	'SWINGING LONDON'	Red body MLCD Label 'CARNABY ST'	£5-£8	MPR ☐
	ii)	'THE BARON OF BEEF'	Red body, White logo.	£25	GP ☐
	iii)	'PRESTON M.G.'	Red body, green label, 'MERCHANT GUILD'	£25	GP ☐
	iv)	'BUSCH GARDENS C'	Red/White body, 'BRITISH AIRWAYS'	£25	GP ☐
	v)	'SELLOTAPE'	Red body, 2 different labels	£25	GP ☐
	vi)	SELLOTAPE (GIM)	Red body, 'SELBESTKLEBEBANDER'	£25	GP ☐
	vii)	'TYPHOO'	White and Black decals. Metal BP. VJ EM	£35	GP ☐
	viii)	'CHAMBOURCEY'	Multicoloured decal with countryside scene	£35	GP ☐
	ix)	'IMPEL 73'	Red/White body, Red/Black logo	£25	GP ☐
	x)	'IMPEL 76'	Off White body, Brown VPD, White label	£25	GP ☐
	xi)	'ESSO EXTRA'	Red, White and Blue decals. Metal BP.	£25	GP ☐
	xii)	'AIM BUILDING'	Black and White decal. Metal BP.	£30	GP ☐
	xiii)	'JACOBS BISCUITS'	Orange or Red body, Black/White decals.	£20	GP ☐
		'SILVER JUBILEE'	Silver or Red body.	£5-£7	MPR ☐
	xiv)	'MATCHBOX' '1953-78'	Red/Yellow/Orange/Black decals, Metal BP Red, Blue, Brown versions	£5-£7	MPR ☐
	xv)	'KENSINGTON HILTON'	Red body, Black logo	£25	GP ☐
	xvi)	'LONDON HILTON'	Red body, Black logo	£25	GP ☐
	xvii)	'BISTO'	Red body, 'BISTO KIDS' on Yellow labels	£7-£10	MPR ☐
	xviii)	'AVIEMORE CENTRE'	Red body, Blue logo/EM	£12	NC ☐
	xix)	'SELFRIDGES'	Red body, White label, Black logo	£10	NC ☐
	xx)	'BARCLAYS BANK'	Red body, Blue/White label.	£10	NC ☐
	xxi)	'ILFORD HPS'	Red body, Black/White label	£10	NC ☐
	xxii)	'AMCEL'	Red body, White label, Orange logo	£10	NC ☐
	xxiii)	'LONDON MUSEUM'	Red body, Black/White label 'NEW' logo	£30	NC ☐
	xxiv)	BERGER PAINTS'	a) Red body, Purple/Orange/Gold LWB	£3-£5	MPR ☐
			b) Silver body	£20	NC ☐
			c) Gold body	£20	NC ☐
			d) Coffee/Cream body	£15	NC ☐
			e) Red/Yellow body (Made in Brazil)	£30	NC ☐
			f) Red/White body (Made in Brazil	£30	NC ☐
			g) Blue/White body (Made in Brazil)	£30	NC ☐
			NB. Paint brushes may be either end of label.		
	xxv)	'KEDDIES' 'No. 1 in ESSEX'	Blue body, White interior, White paper round end labels — sold in blue box (900)	£35	GP ☐
			NB. Beware fakes with square cut label ends sold in white boxes.		
	From 1982 onwards	New casting 2nd type	London Bus — Leyland Titan Double Decker. The model is Red with two door opening and three open rear windows unless differently described.		
	i)	LAKER SKY TRAIN'	Red, White and Blue label	£2-£4	MPR ☐
	ii)	'CHESTERFIELD'	Green body, Green and White label	£2-£4	MPR ☐
	iii)	'YORK FESTIVAL'	Red body, Purple LWB 'MYSTERY PLAYS'	£1-£3	MPR ☐
	iv)	'RAPPORT'	Maroon body, Yellow LWB 'SALES FROM WALES'	£1-£3	MPR ☐
	v)	'JAPAN 84'	Red body, 'NICE TO MEET YOU', JIM	£3-£5	MPR ☐
	vi)	'NESTLES'	Red body, 'MILKY BAR' label.	£2-£4	MPR ☐
		Colour change	With Blue body	£10	NC ☐
	vii)	'ROWNTREES'	Red body, 'FRUIT GUMS' label	£2-£4	MPR ☐
		Colour change	With Cream body	£10	NC ☐
	viii)	'KEDDIES'	Blue body, White label, Red logo No. 1 in ESSEX	£35	GP ☐
	ix)	'MB' London BUS	Red body, Red/Yel/Wh/Blue label		NRP ☐
	x)	'YOU'LL LOVE NEW YORK'	Red body, White label, 'USA & TWA'	£2-£4	MPR ☐

Ref. No.		Model Type	Matchbox Miniatures continued	Price and Rarity Grading		
	xi)	'MATCHBOX No. 1'	Blue/White body, White label	£10	NC	☐
		Colour change	With Red body	£10	GP	☐
	xii)	'YOKOHAMA FAIR'	Red body, Yellow label, JIM	£15	NC	☐
	xiii)	'STAFFS POLICE'	White/Blue body, 'CHARITY APPEAL' logo	£15	NC	☐
	xiv)	'CITYRAMA'	All Blue body, MLCD label of flags		NRP	☐
	xvi)	'MIDLAND MUSEUM'	Brown/White body, 'Bus & Transport — Wythall'		NRP	☐
	xvi)	'TRAMWAY' MUSEUM	All Blue body, Red logo, 'THE NATIONAL CRICH'		NRP	☐
	xvii)	'BAND AID'	Red body, White label 'Playbus'		NRP	☐
	xviii)	W.H. SMITH & SONS	Orange/White body	£10	NC	☐
	xix)	'WEST MIDLANDS TRAVEL'	Blue/Cream body, White label, Blue logo		NRP	☐
	xx)	'AROUND LONDON'	Red body, 'TOUR BUS' label		NRP	☐
	xxi)	'MICA Commemorative Bus'	All White body, SBX/PRM, Red/White/Blue/Yellow label	£75	GP	☐
	xxii)	'DENNY'	White body, Red/Blue labels, Blue TPD		NRP	☐
18a	1956	Caterpillar Bulldozer	Yellow body, Red DBL, Green RT, 45 mm. NN.	£20	NC	☐
18b	1958	Larger casting	Yellow body, & DBL, Green RT, '8' or '18' CI. 50 mm.	£30	NC	☐
18c	1960	Larger casting	Yellow body, DBL, Green RT. 58 mm.	£7-£10	MPR	☐
18d	1964	No driver casting	Yellow body, Green RT, SPR or BPR. 62 mm.	£4-£6	MPR	☐
18e	1969	Field Car	Yellow body, Tan roof, ASM/H/BP.	£4-£6	MPR	☐
		Colour change	With Green wheel hubs	£150	GP	☐
		Colour change	Military Green issue, WW star	£12	NC	☐
18f	1975	Hondarora	Red body, Black seat, Sil Trim, *Honda,* SPKW. 63 mm.	£2-£4	MPR	☐
		Colour change	With White seat	£45	GP	☐
		Colour change	Dark Military Green	£14	NC	☐
18g	1981	Colour change	Red body, Black seat and front forks	£2-£4	MPR	☐
	1982	Colour change	Yellow body, Black seat and front forks	£2-£4	MPR	☐
	1984	Fire Engine	Red body, White ladder, FLLB		NRP	☐
	1987	Design change	'FIRE DEPT' Living		NRP	☐
19a	1956	MG Midget MD	Cream or White body, Red S, Tan D, SPW/NN. 50 mm.	£40	GP	☐
19b	1958	MG A Sports Car	Cream body, Tan D, Red & Gold trim, MW. 55 mm.	£40	GP	☐
		Colour change	Cream body, Red & Silver trim, with Grey plastic wheels	£60	GP	☐
		Wheel change	With Silver plastic wheels	£80	GP	☐
19c	1961	Aston Martin Racing Car	Met Green body, Grey or White RCD, various RN '3' '5', '4' or '52', WRW. 63 mm.	£20	NC	☐
19d	1965	Lotus Racing Car	Dark Green body, White D, Yel hubs, BPT, RN '3'.	£6-£9	MPR	☐
		Colour change	Orange body, Yellow hubs	£18	NC	☐
	1970	Colour change	Purple body	£5-£7	MPR	☐
19e	1971	Road Dragster	Red body, Silver EE, CW/SF. 76 mm.	£2-£4	MPR	☐
		Design change	With Scorpion labels	£10	NC	☐
		Design change	Pink with 'WYNNS' labels	£30	GP	☐
19f	1976	Cement Truck	Red body, Yellow barrel with Red stripes. 75 mm.	£2-£4	MPR	☐
		Colour change	Grey barrel with Black stripes	£2-£4	MPR	☐
19g	1982	Peterbilt Cement Truck	Met Green/Orange/Blue, 'BIG PETE', Green DDS		NRP	☐
	1984	Colour change	SAPM with Yellow door design		NRP	☐
	1985	'CEMENT COMPANY'	Blue body, Yellow mixer drum		NRP	☐
20a	1956	Heavy Lorry (E.R.F.)	Light Green body, Silver trim, MW, 57 mm.	£100	NPE	☐
		Colour change	Maroon body, Gold or Silver trim, MW/GPW	£20	NC	☐
		Colour change	Dark Red body, Silver trim, MW/GPW	£20	NC	☐
20c	1965	CHEV Impala Taxi	Orange/Yellow body, *Taxi* GPW, Red Int. 76 mm.	£30	GP	☐
		Wheel change	With Black plastic wheels	£7-£10	MPR	☐
		Colour change	Yellow body, Red int. BPW	£7-£10	MPR	☐
20d	1969	Lamborghini Marzal	Met Dark Red, White seats, Sil TR, SF. 70 mm.	£2-£4	MPR	☐
		Colour change	Pink body	£4-£6	MPR	☐
		Colour change	Yellow body	£14	NC	☐
20e	1975	Police Range Rover	White body, Orange flash *Police,* FL. 82 mm.	£2-£4	MPR	☐
	1981	Colour change	White body, Red/Yel/Blk flash	£2-£4	MPR	☐
	1983	Colour change	Gold, *Securite Rallye Paris Dakar 83*	£6-£8	MPR	☐
	1984		SAPM but no design on BN, UNP/CH	£4-£6	MPR	☐
		Colour change	Military Green body, 'AMBULANCE' RCS	£20	NC	☐
		Colour change	Military Green body, 'POLICE'	£20	NC	☐
		Colour change	(USIM) White with SHERIFF	£2-£4	MPR	☐
		Colour change	Orange body, 'SITE ENGINEER'	£5-£8	MPR	☐
			NB. There are many other variations			
20f		'Desert Dawg'	White body, Red roof. 'JEEP' logo	£3-£5	MPR	☐
20g		Volvo container	Truck			
	1985	'COLD FRESH'	Blue body, White box		NRP	☐
	1986	'FEDERAL EXPRESS'	(USIM) no detail available	£3-£5	MPR	☐
	1987	MATCHBOX 'MB 75'	Blue body, Red/Yellow design. 'No. 1 Selling Toy 86-5-4-3'	£30	GP	☐
	1987	'SCOTCH CORNER'	No details available		NRP	☐
	1987	'CROOKEY'	Dark Blue body, Red/White design		NRP	☐
20h	1988	VW Transporter	White body, Orange stripe and cross		NRP	☐

Ref. No.		Model Type	Matchbox Miniatures continued	Price and Rarity Grading	
21a	1956	Long Distance Coach 'LONDON-GLASGOW'	Green body, Sil trim, Red/Yel decal, NN/BB, metal wheels. 55 mm. (Bedford Duple)	£30	NC ☐
21b	1958	Long Distance Coach 'LONDON-GLASGOW'	Green body, Silver trim, Red/Yel decal, number, metal wheels. 69 mm. (Bedford Duple) MW or GPW	£25	NC ☐
		Colour change	Dark Green body, GPW	£30	GP ☐
21c	1961	Milk Delivery Truck 'DRINK MORE MILK'	Pale Green body, Cream load, CTW, Red cow or bottle decal on doors. Black plastic wheels. 57 mm.	£14-£18	MPR ☐
21d	1968	Foden Concrete Truck	Orange/Yellow body, Orange RVD, BPW or SF. 76 mm.	£9-£12	MPR ☐
21e	1973	Road Roller	Yellow body, Red seats, Black PRL. 70 mm.	£2-£4	MPR ☐
21f	1978	Renault 5TL	Blue body, Silver trim, Tan seats, SF. 65 mm.	£2-£4	MPR ☐
		Colour change	With Red int. and Silver or Black base	£14	NC ☐
	1980	Colour change	Yellow body, Le Car decals, opening tailgate	£2-£4	MPR ☐
	1981	Colour change	Silver body, Orange flash Le Car, opening tailgate	£2-£4	MPR ☐
	1982	Colour change	White body, Green labels, Michelin decals etc	£2-£4	MPR ☐
	1983	Colour change	White body, 'RADIO MONTE CARLO' design	£2-£4	MPR ☐
	1984	Colour change	Black body, Red/Yellow design 'ROLOIL'		NRP ☐
21g	1986	Breakdown Van	Red body, White hoist '24HR SERVICE'		NRP ☐
21h		Corvette Pace Car	US issued Model	£3-£5	MPR ☐
22a	1956	Vauxhall Cresta	Maroon body, Cream roof, CA/MW/NN. 64 mm.	£18	NC ☐
22b	1958	Vauxhall Cresta	Pink body, No. WDS, GPW, Red RL.	£75	GP ☐
		Component change	SAPM with Green windows, GPW	£75	GP ☐
		Colour change	Cream body, GPW, WW-WDS, GPW	£25	NC ☐
		Colour change	Pink body, Green side panels, GPW, WDS.	£75	GP ☐
		Colour change	Met Brown body, Green side panels, GPW, WDS.	£75	GP ☐
		Colour change	Grey body, Mauve sides, WDS, GSPW.	£75	GP ☐
		Colour change	Met Gold or Copper, Green WDS, GSBPW	£35	NC ☐
22c	1964	Pontiac Grand Prix	Orange or Purple body, BPW/SF/OD/BB. 76 mm.	£6-£8	MPR ☐
			Red body — extremely rare		NGPP ☐
			With no patent number on base	£25	GP ☐
22d	1971	Freeman Inter City	Mauve body, White seats, Arrow Motif, SF. 76 mm.	£2-£4	MPR ☐
22e	1976	Blaze Buster	Red body, Fire on rear, Yellow LD, SF. 77 mm.	£2-£4	MPR ☐
		Ladder change	With Black ladder	£7-£9	MPR ☐
22f		'BIG FOOT'	Grey body, White roof '26', USIM	£4-£6	MPR ☐
22g	1984	Jaguar XK120	Green body, Red seats, WS	£1-£2	MPR ☐
	1986	Colour change	White body, RN '414', Red seats		NRP ☐
22h	1988	Saab 9000 Turbo	All Red body, opening doors		NRP ☐
23a	1956	(Berkeley Cavalier) Caravan	Pale Blue body, On Tow MB23, TB/MW/CA. Slight body outlines. 64 mm.	£25	GP ☐
23b	1951	Casting change	SAPM with strong body outlines	£14	NC ☐
		Colour change	Lime Green body, MW or GPW	£50	GP ☐
		Colour change	Met Lime Green body, GPW	£50	GP ☐
23c	1961	Bluebird Dauphine Caravan	Metallic Lime Green body, GPW. 64 mm.	£250	GP ☐
	1962	Colour change	Met Mauve body, GPW or BPW	£7-£10	MPR ☐
		Wheel change	With Silver plastic wheels	£11-£15	MPR ☐
23d	1965	Trailer Caravan	Yel/White or Pink/White body, DRF/PW. 76 mm.	£5-£8	MPR ☐
23e	1970	Volkswagen Camper	Blue or Orange body, Orange or White Int, OC/EM/NP/SF. 67 mm.	£4-£6	MPR ☐
23f		Pizza Van	US issued model	£4-£6	MPR ☐
23g	1976	Atlas Truck	Metallic Blue Cab and CH, Orange, DMP/SF. 71 mm.	£2-£4	MPR ☐
	1981	Colour change	Red cab and chassis, Silver dumper, SF	£2-£4	MPR ☐
23h	1983	Tipper Truck	Yellow body, Grey DMP, Sil trim, Dirty, SF. 76 mm.	£2-£4	MPR ☐
	1985	Design change	SAPM plus Blue/White 'PACE' design		NRP ☐
23i	1986	GT350	US issued model	£3-£5	MPR ☐
23j	1987	Honda ATC 250R	US issued model	£3-£5	MPR ☐
24a	1956	'Hydraulic' Excavator	Orange/Yel body, MW, 'WEATHERILL'. 58 mm.	£15	NC ☐
		Colour change	With Yellow body, 'WEATHERILL' MW	£15	NC ☐
24b	1959	'Hydraulic' Excavator	Yellow body, Lesney cast in, GPW. 67 mm.	£10	NC ☐
24c	1967	Rolls Royce Silver Shadow	Met Red or Gold body, Ivory Int, Silver hubs BPT, Black, Green, Pink or Grey base plate.	£5-£8	MPR ☐
24d	1973	Team 'MATCHBOX'	Metallic Red body, RN '8' in Blk, D/SF.	£2-£4	MPR ☐
		Colour change	Yellow body, RN '8' label	£100	GP ☐
		Colour change	Met Green body, RN '8' label	£20	GP ☐
		Colour change	Orange body, with Tan or Yellow driver	£25	GP ☐
24e	1979	Diesel Shunter	Green or Yellow body, Railfreight or D1496RF.	£2-£4	MPR ☐
24f	1983	Datsun 280 ZX	Black body, Gold flashes, OD/SF/CW. 74 mm.	£2-£4	MPR ☐
	1984	TPD change	SAPM plus Gold on BN 'TURBO 2X'		NRP ☐
	1986	Nissan 3002X	Silver body, Black/Yellow stripes		NRP ☐
	1987	Design change	'FUJI FILM', design		NRP ☐

112

Ref. No.		Model Type	Matchbox Miniatures continued	Price and Rarity Grading	
25a	1956	Bedford 12 cwt Van	Dark Blue body, 'DUNLOP', MW/GPN/BPW. 53 mm.	£24	NC ☐
25b	1960	Volkswagen Sedan	Silver Blue body, OREC/EE, TW/GSPW. 60 mm.	£15	NC ☐
25c	1964	Bedford 'BP' Tanker	Yel cab, Grn CH, Wh tank, BP crest, BPW/SF. 76 mm.	£10	NC ☐
25cc	1964	German Issue	Blue cab and chassis, 'ARAL' logo	£35	GP ☐
25d	1968	Ford Cortina G.T.	Brown body, White int, OD/BPW/SF. 67 mm.	£6-£9	MPR ☐
		Colour change	Metallic Blue body.	£6-£9	MPR ☐
		Colour change	Metallic Brown body	£20	GP ☐
		Colour change	Gold or Green body (Bulgarian)	£20	GP ☐
25e	1972	Mod Tractor	Purple or Red body, Silver engine, SF. 57 mm.	£2-£4	MPR ☐
		Casting change	Headlamps on mudguards	£10	NC ☐
25f	1979	Flat Car and Container	Black CH, Red/Beige CNT, NYK and USL. 72.5 mm.	£2-£4	MPR ☐
25g		Toyota Celica	US issued model	£3-£5	MPR ☐
25h		Yellow Fever	US issued model	£3-£5	MPR ☐
25i	1982	'AUDI SPORT'	White body, Brown/Red panels, RN. 76 mm.		NRP ☐
	1985	Colour change	Black body, Gold 'TURBO' design		NRP ☐
	1986	Colour change	Maroon body, White 'QUATTRO' design		NRP ☐
25j	1987	Ambulance	'Paramedics' — US issued model	£2-£4	MPR ☐
26a		'E.R.F.' Cement Mixer	Orange body, Gold trim, MW. 45 mm.	£18	NC ☐
		Trim/wheel change	SAPM with silver trim, MW, GPW or SPW	£16	NC ☐
26b		'E.R.F.' Cement Mixer	Orange body, Dark Grey barrel, GPW. 66 mm.	£100	GP ☐
		Colour change	SAPM with Light Grey barrel, GPW. 66 mm.	£100	GP ☐
		Colour change	Orange body and barrel, Silver plastic wheels	£35	GP ☐
		Wheel change	SAPM with GPW or BPW	£12	NC ☐
26c	1968	G.M.C. Tipper Truck	Red cab, Green CH, TW/OTE/BPT/SF. 66 mm.	£4-£6	MPR ☐
26d	1972	'BIG BANGER'	Red body, Silver EE and trim, SF. 76 mm.	£2-£4	MPR ☐
26e		Brown Sugar	US issued model	£4-£6	MPR ☐
26e	1976	Site Dumper	Yellow body, Black base, SF. 64 mm.	£2-£4	MPR ☐
	1981	Colour change	Red body, Silver dumper, SF. 64 mm. MOV	£2-£4	MPR ☐
26f	1982	Cable Truck	Yellow body, Blk/Grey cable drums, TW/SF. 77 mm.		NRP ☐
	1984	Colour change	Yellow/Red body		NRP ☐
26g		'Cosmic Blues'	White body, Blue stars design, USIM	£3-£5	MPR ☐
26h	1985	Volvo Tilt Truck 'FRESH FRUIT'	Blue body, Yellow tilt		NRP ☐
	1986	'FERRYMASTERS'	Yellow body, white cab & side panel, CCC		NRP ☐
	1986	'HI BRAIN'	White/Green body, Red design		NRP ☐
	1986	TT86 'ISLE OF MAN'	Two tone Blue body with Red roof		NRP ☐
27a	1956	Bedford Low Loader	Light Blue cab, Dark Blue trailer, 6MW. 78 mm.	£20	NC ☐
		Colour change	Light Green cab, Light Brown trailer	£20	NC ☐
27b	1959	Bedford Low Loader	Light Green cab, Light Tan trailer. 95 mm.	£25	NC ☐
		Colour change	Dark Green cab version, GPW	£35	NC ☐
27c	1960	Cadillac Sedan	Light Metallic Green body, White roof, SPW.	£50	GP ☐
		Colour change	Silver Grey body, off White roof, SPW.	£35	GP ☐
		Colour change	Metallic Lilac body, Pink roof, SPW or GPW	£20	NC ☐
27d	1966	Mercedes 230SL	White body, Red seats, Silver TR, OD/BPT/SF. 71 mm.	£4-£6	MPR ☐
	1970	Colour change	Yellow body, Red or Black seats, BPW/SF	£2-£4	MPR ☐
27e	1973	Lamborghini Countach	Yellow or Orange/Red MB, RN '3', TW/SF. 74 mm.	£2-£4	MPR ☐
27f	1981	Swing Wing 'JET'	Red/White MB, TW/BPW, RTT wings. 76 mm.		NRP ☐
	1986	Jeep Cherokee	White body, MLCD/SPN, CCC		NRP ☐
	1988	Colour change	Yellow/Green body, 'FOREST RANGER'		NRP ☐
28a	1956	Bedford Compressor	Orange/Yellow body, Silver trim, CA/MW. 45 mm.	£18	NC ☐
		Colour change	Yellow body, Silver trim, MW.	£15	NC ☐
28b	1959	Ford Thames Compressor	Yellow body, Silver trim, BPW/CRA. 60 mm.	£16	NC ☐
28c	1964	Mark Ten Jaguar	Metallic Brown body, White seats, GBPW. 70 mm.	£5-£8	MPR ☐
28d	1969	Mack Dump Truck	Orange or Light Green body, BPW. 67 mm.	£2-£4	MPR ☐
		Colour change	Military Green issue	£14	NC ☐
28e	1974	Stoat	All Gold body, driver rotates, SF/RLM. 67 mm.	£2-£4	MPR ☐
		Colour change	Olive Green body, Chrome hubs	£10	NC ☐
		Colour change	Drab Military Green body	£45	GP ☐
			NB. Many other variations exist.		
28f	1979	Lincoln Continental	Red body, White roof, Tan seats SF. 72 mm.	£2-£4	MPR ☐
28g	1982	Formula Racing Car	Gold and Black, RN '8', White D, SF. 75 mm.	£2-£4	MPR ☐
	1983	Colour change	Met Green and Black body		NRP ☐
28h	1985	Dodge Daytona	Brown/Grey body, OBN		NRP ☐
	1986	Colour change	Silver/Red/Black body		NRP ☐
	1988	Colour change	Red body, Blue/Yellow design		NRP ☐
29a	1956	Bedford Milk Delivery Van	Light Brown body, White bottle load, MW. 55 mm.	£18	NC ☐
29b	1961	Austin Cambridge	Two tone Green body, Silver trim, GPW. (9×20) 57 mm.	£24	GP ☐
		Wheel change	Same with SPW or BPW	£14	NC ☐
29c	1966	Fire Pumper	Red body, White EQ, Denver BPW. 76 mm.	£4-£6	MPR ☐
29d	1971	Racing Mini	Met Bronze body, RN '29' on Yellow label. 57 mm.	£6-£9	MPR ☐
		Colour change	Deep Orange body, Cream int. RN '29' etc.	£5-£8	MPR ☐
		Colour change	Pale Orange body, RN '29' etc.	£5-£8	MPR ☐
		Label changed	Orange models issued with RN '29' on Yellow labels with Green border	£3-£5	MPR ☐
		Colour change	Red body, RN '29' etc.	£5-£8	MPR ☐
29e	1977	Shovel Nose Tractor	Yellow body, Red shovel, Black trim. 72 mm.	£2-£4	MPR ☐
	1981	Colour change	Orange body, Black shovel, Grey trim		NRP ☐
	1982	Colour change	Yellow body, Black shovel		NRP ☐
			NB. Many other variations exist.		

Ref. No.		Model Type	Matchbox Miniatures continued	Price and Rarity Grading		
	1956	Ford Prefect	Light Brown body, Red or Silver trim, MW or GPW, WWPTL/TB/CRA. 58 mm.	£14	NC	☐
		Colour change	Light Blue body, MW or GPW, WWPTL. 58 mm.	£14	NC	☐
30b	1961	6 Wheel Crane Lorry	Light Brown body, Red jib/H, GPW	£30	GP	☐
		Colour change	Same but with Orange jib and hook	£20	NC	☐
		Colour change	Silver body, Orange jib and hook, SPW.	£30	GP	☐
		Colour change	Same but with Silver hook, SBGPW	£20	NC	☐
30c	1965	8 Wheel Crane Lorry	Green body, Orange jib, Yellow or Red hook.	£12	NC	☐
		Colour change	With Turquoise body, Yellow hook	£35	GP	☐
30d	1970	Beach Buggy	Met Mauve or Yellow body, *Clover* motif SF. 65 mm.	£2-£4	MPR	☐
30e	1976	'SWAMP RAT'	Olive Green body, superfast. 77 mm.	£2-£4	MPR	☐
30f	1981	Articulated Truck	Blue cab, Sil TRL, *Leyland* on front SF. 77 mm.	£2-£4	MPR	☐
30g	1983	Colour change	Blue cab, Yel TRL, *International*	£2-£4	MPR	☐
	1984	Logo change	Blue body, White RG/FL, 'PAULS'	£25	NC	☐
30h	1985	MBenz 280GE	Red body, White RF, 3 FLL, 'RESERVE'	NRP		☐
	1988	POLIZEI'	Green/White body, 3 Blue FLL.	NRP		☐
31a	1957	Ford Station Wagon	Yellow body, WWPTL/BB/MW/GPW/H. 67 mm.	£18	NC	☐
31b	1960	Ford Station Wagon	Yellow body, GPW or SPW. 69 mm.	£12	NC	☐
		Colour change	Green body, Pink roof, SGBPW.	£10	NC	☐
31c	1964	Lincoln Continental	Blue, Green or Lime Grn MB, OBT/BPW/SF. 76 mm.	£4-£7	MPR	☐
31d	1972	Volks-dragon	Red body, Silver EE, eyes decal. 66 mm.	£2-£4	MPR	☐
31e	1977	Caravan	White, Orange door and WDS, OD. 70 mm.	£2-£4	MPR	☐
	1981	Colour change	White, Blue door, Orange TW	£2-£4	MPR	☐
31f	1983	'MAZDA RX7'	Met Gold and Black, Red seats, OD/SF. 76 mm.	NRP		☐
		Colour change	Black body, Gold shape (USIM)	£5-7	MPR	☐
31g		Lady Bug	US issued model	£3-£5	MPR	☐
31h		R.R. Silver Cloud	Cream body	NRP		☐
32a	1957	Jaguar XK140 FAC	Offwhite body, BB, MW or GPW. 60 mm.	£20	NC	☐
		Colour change	Red body, BB, GPW	£100	GP	☐
32b	1962	'E' Type Jaguar	Met Red body, Cream int, WRW-GPT/BPT. 66 mm.	£20	NC	☐
32c	1968	Leyland 'BP' Tanker	Dark Green body, White tank, Yellow logo, BPW/SF.	£6-£9	MPR	☐
		Colour change	With White grille and base	£15	NC	☐
		Leyland 'ARAL' Tanker	Blue body, White tank, Blue logo	£30	GP	☐
32d	1972	Maserati Bora	Met Pink body, Yel int, RN '8', OD/SF. 76 mm.	£2-£4	MPR	☐
		Design change	With a '3' Label	£10	NC	☐
32e	1977	Field Gun and Diorama	Military Green and Black, 2 figs, 4 shells. 77 mm.	£2-£4	MPR	☐
32f	1981	Excavator	Orange cab, Black base and grab, cab SMV. 80 mm.	£2-£4	MPR	☐
	1982	Colour change	Yellow cab, Black base and grab	NRP		☐
33a	1957	Ford Zodiac	Dark Green body, Black base, MW, no WDS. 68 mm.	£15	NC	☐
		Colour change	Blue body, MW, no windows	£12	NC	☐
		Colour change	Sea Green body, MW — GPW, no windows	£10	NC	☐
	1961	Colour change	Metallic Mauve body, Orange side panels, Green windows, GPW or SPW	£20	NC	☐
33b	1963	Ford Zephyr	Sea Green body, CW/H/GB PW. 64 mm.	£10	NC	☐
33c	1969	Lamborghini Miura	Yellow MB, Red seats, opening doors, SF. 77 mm.	£12	NC	☐
	1971	Colour change	Met Gold MB, Cream seats, SF, Red Int.	£10	NC	☐
33e	1973	Datsun 126X	Yellow body, Orange BP, Silver E, TW/OREC. 76 mm.	£2-£4	MPR	☐
33f	1977	POLICE Motor Cycle	All White body, Silver E, Blue rider. 74 mm.	£2-£4	MPR	☐
		U.S. Issue	U.S. issue with L.A.P.D. decal	£5-£7	MPR	☐
	1982	Colour change	White and Black body, Blue rider, white stripes	NRP		☐
	1984	Colour change	Black body, White PNS, Yellow stripes	NRP		☐
34a	1957	Volkswagen Microvan	Blue body, Metal or BGSPW, Yellow lettering. 55 mm.	£20	NC	☐
34b	1961	Volkswagen Camping Car	Light Green body, Dark Green int, OD/GBPW. 65 mm.	£8-£12	MPR	☐
34c	1967	Volkswagen Camper	Silver body, Orange int, TW/BPW. 65 mm.	£6-£8	MPR	☐
34d	1971	Formula 1 Racing Car	Met Pink, Orange, Blue or Yellow MB, RN '15' or '16'.	£2-£4	MPR	☐
34e	1976	Vantastic	Orange body, White BP and int, EE/TW/SF, RN '34'.	£2-£4	MPR	☐
34f	1981	Chevy Pro-Stocker	White and Blue body, RN '34', *Lightning*, SF. 76 mm.	£2-£4	MPR	☐
34g	1983	Chevy Stock Car	Yellow body, Orange/Blk ST, RN '4' *Chevy*. 76 mm.	£2-£4	MPR	☐
	1984	'PEPSI'	Red/White body, RN '14'	NRP		☐
	1986	'7 UP'	Green/White body	NRP		☐
34h	1988	Ford RS2000	White body, Blue design, RN '7'	NRP		☐
35a	1957	(E.R.F.) Horse Box	Red body, Brown box, DDR, MW/CA. 53 mm.	£18	NC	☐
		Wheel change	With Silver plastic wheels	£35	GP	☐
35b	1964	Snowtrac Tractor	Dark Red body, White RT, *Snow-Trac*.	£10	NC	☐
35c	1969	M.M. Fire Engine	Met Red body, *London Fire Service.*	£6-£9	MPR	☐
		Colour change	With Cream base	£10	NC	☐
	1981	US Issue	Los Angeles City Fire Department	£5-£8	MPR	☐
35d	1975	Fandango	White or Red body, RN '35', SF. 75 mm.	£2-£4	MPR	☐
			White body, RN '6'	£10	NC	☐
			Red body, purple WDS	£4-£6	MPR	☐

Ref. No.	Year	Model Type	Description	Price	Grade	
35e	1982	Zoo Truck	Red body, Blue cage, Yel lions, TW/SF. 77 mm.	£1-£3	MPR	☐
	1985	Pick Up Camper	Red/White body, 'Aspen Ski Holidays'		NRP	☐
	1988	'SLD Pumps'	Promotional — White body.		NRP	☐
35f	1986	Pontiac T.Roof	Black body — USIM	£3-£5	MPR	☐
35g	1988	Ford Bronco II	White/Orange body, big wheels		NRP	☐
36a	1987	Austin A50	Blue-Green body, MW, 60 mm.	£12	NC	☐
		Wheel change	With GPW	£18	NC	☐
		Colour change	Pale Blue body, GPW	£12	NC	☐
36b	1960	Lambretta SCT & SC	Pale Met Green MC and SC, BPW. 57 mm.	£25	NC	☐
36c	1966	Opel Diplomat	Met Gold body, White seats, OBN/SF. 70 mm.	£7-£10	MPR	☐
36d	1970	Hot Rod Draguar	Met Red or Pink body, Silver E, Draguar SF. 72 mm.	£2-£4	MPR	☐
36e	1976	Formula 5000	Orange body, Blue D, RN '3' Formula 5000 74 mm.	£3-£5	MPR	☐
		Colour change	Red body, 'Texaco' etc.	£2-£4	MPR	☐
36f	1980	Refuse Truck	Met Red and Yellow body, 'Collectomatic'.	£2-£4	MPR	☐
		Design change	SAPM without 'Collectomatic'.	£20	GP	☐
	1982	Colour change	Blue and Orange body		NRP	☐
	1983	Colour change	Blue and Cream body		NRP	☐
	1984	Colour change	Blue/Grey body with 'Collectomatic'.		NRP	☐
	1987	Colour change	Green/Yellow body		NRP	☐

NB. Collectors should appreciate that the price grading shown for 37a is high as it is virtually impossible to find a model in perfect mint condition — most having damage to the decals.

Ref. No.	Year	Model Type	Description	Price	Grade	
37a	1957	Karrier Bantam	Yellow body, UNEVEN crate load, MW. 57 mm.			☐
		2 ton Lorry	Large or small 'Coca-Cola' side decals	£90	GP	☐
		Colour change	Orange/Yellow body, MW, 'Coca-Cola' MW.	£50	GP	☐
37b	1958	Casting change	Yellow body, EVEN crate load, 57 mm. Large or small 'Coca-Cola' decals MW/GPW.	£25	NC	☐
		Colour change	Orange/Yellow body, MW, 'Coca-Cola' 57 mm.	£25	NC	☐
		Variant	SAPM with GPW and small side decals	£35	GP	☐
37c	1960	Casting change	Yellow body with EVEN load, 'COCA-COLA'. 61 mm.	£25	NC	☐
37d	1966	(Dodge) Cattle Truck	Yel/Grey body, BPW/SF/DDR/2AN/TW. 65 mm.	£3-£5	MPR	☐
		Colour change	Orange/Grey body	£6-£8	MPR	☐
		Colour change	Orange/Silver body	£65	GP	☐
37e	1973	Soopa Coopa	Met Blue or Purple, flower decal, SF. 74 mm.	£1-£3	MPR	☐
		Colour change	Orange body, 'Ja Ha Mobile'	£50	GP	☐
37f	1977	Skip Truck	Red Cab and CH, Yel skip, Silver trim. 69 mm. MOV	£2-£4	MPR	☐
	1981	Colour change	Blue cab and chassis	£2-£4	MPR	☐
37g	1982	Matra Rancho	Yel/Orange/Blk body, Black S, H/OTG/SF. 74 mm.	£2-£4	MPR	☐
	1985	Ford Escort Cabriolet	White body, Black seats, 'XR3i'		NRP	☐
	1986	Colour change	Blue body, Black tonneau, Red seats		NRP	☐
	1988	Colour change	Metallic Blue body, Black ARB.		NRP	☐
38a	1957	KB Refuse Wagon	Grey/Brown body, MW 53 mm.	£16	NC	☐
		Colour change	Grey body, MW or GPW	£16	NC	☐
		Colour change	Silver body version, SPW or GPW	£20	NC	☐
38b		Vauxhall Victor Estate	Yellow body, White seats, GSBPW/H. 64 mm.	£10	NC	☐
38c	1967	Honda MC & TRL	Met Green MC, Orange or Yellow TRL, Honda, BPW.	£6-£8	MPR	☐
	1971	Colour Change	Blue or Pink MC, Orange TRL. SF	£3-£5	MPR	☐
38d	1973	Stingeroo	Met Purple body, Cream HS, Sil TR, SF. 78 mm.		NRP	☐
38c	1976	Armoured Jeep	Green body, White star, Black gun. 61 mm.		NRP	☐
38f	1981	Camper	Red and Cream body, TW/SF. 76 mm.		NRP	☐
38g		Ford Model 'A' Van	A popular promotional (PRM) model			☐
	1982	'CHAMPION'	Blue body, White roof, Black chassis		NRP	☐
	1984	'US TOY FAIR'	Blue body, white roof (USIM)		NGPP	☐
	1984	'BEN FRANKLIN'	White body, Blue LWB, Red roof		NGPP	☐
	1984	'MATCHBOX USA'	White body (USIM)		NGPP	☐
	1985	'PEPSI COLA'	SAPM (USIM)		NRP	☐
	1986	'MATCHBOX SPEED SHOP'	Blue/Black body & roof, CCC		NRP	☐
	1986	'TT 86'	No details		NRP	☐
	1986	'BASS MUSEUM'	No details		NRP	☐
	1986	'ARNOTTS'	Australian issue	£7-£10	MPR	☐
	1986	'LARK LANE'	No details		NRP	☐
	1986	'TITTENSOR SCHOOL'	No details		NRP	☐
	1986	'PEPSI'	'COME ALIVE' no details		NRP	☐
	1986	'TOY COLLECTIONS'	No details		NRP	☐
	1986	'BRAINS FAGGOTTS'	No details	£15	NC	☐
	1986	'BBC 1925'	Green body, Black roof & LWB, White SPN		NRP	☐
	1987	'THE AUSTRALIAN'	'THE NATIONAL NEWSPAPER', AIM/PRM		NGPP	☐
	1987	'SMITHS POTATO CRISPS'	Blue body, Red LWB, AIM/PRM	£10	NC	☐
	1987	'I.O.M. TT 87'	Black body, Red roof & LWB, PRO	£3-£5	MPR	☐
	1987	'JUNIOR MATCHBOX'	Yellow body, Blue roof & LWB, PRM	£3-£5	MPR	☐
	1987	'MICA CONVENTION' 1987	All Black body, 5 Blue labels, PRM/SBX, 'MATCHBOX INTERNATIONAL COLLECTORS ASSOCIATION' '2'	£80	GP	☐
	1987	'SILVO' '1912-1987.'	Blue body, Black roof & LWB, PRM		NRP	☐
	1987	'ISLE OF MAN POST'	No details available PRM		NGPP	☐
	1987	'DEWHURST'	No details available PRM	£6-£8	MPR	☐
	1987	'WH SMITH'	Red body, Black roof & LWB	£25	GP	☐
	1987	'CHESTY BONDS'	White body, Black roof & LWB, AIM/PRM		NGPP	☐
	1987	'JOHN WEST'	Green body, Red roof & LWB, AIM, PRM		NGPP	☐
	1987	'MATCHBOX'	Blue body, Black LWB, Red roof. 'THIS VAN DELIVERS' logo,			☐

Ref. No.	Year	Model Type	Matchbox Miniatures continued	Price	Grading	
			PRM		NGPP	☐
	1987	'RICE KRISPIES'	Blue body, Black LWB, White RF, STR, PRM.	£2-£4	MPR	☐
	1988	'COBB'	Brown body, Black wings, White design, PRM.		NRP	☐
	1988	'ALEX MUNRO'	No details available — promotional		NRP	☐
	1988	'MICA NORTH'	No details of colours (5000) p.	£5-£7	MPR	☐
		American Convention				
	1988	'CHESTER TOY MUSEUM'	Pale Blue body, Black wings and roof, PRM/SBX		NRP	☐
	1988	'CHESTER HERALDRY CENTRE'	Pale Blue/Black body, Yellow shield design, PRM/SBX		NRP	☐
	1988	'POWER HOUSE'	Australian promotional no details available		NGPP	☐
	1988	'RAYNERS CRUSHA'	Red body, Black wings, Blue design. PRM		NRP	☐
	1988	'GUERNSEY POST OFFICE'	Blue body, Black wings, White design. PRM		NRP	☐
	1988	'ROWNTREES TABLE JELLY'	Green body, Black wings, jelly design. PRM		NRP	☐
	1988	'BARRATT SHERBET FOUNTAIN'	No details available. PRM		NRP	☐
38h	1986	Flareside Pick Up	Red body, White interior		NRP	☐
	1987	Colour change	Yellow body, Blue design		NRP	☐
39a	1957	Zodiac Convertible	Pale Peach body, Light Brown D, base, MW.	£15	NC	☐
		Colour change	SAPM with Green base, MW & GPW.	£15	NC	☐
		Wheel change	With Grey plastic wheels	£25	NC	☐
		Colour change	Dark Peach body, with Green base & INT, GPW.	£15	NC	☐
		Wheel change	SAPM with Silver plastic wheels	£25	NC	☐
39b	1962	Pontiac Convertible	Met Lilac body, Crimson base, SGPW, Red SW.	£20	NC	☐
		Colour change	Yellow body, Crimson base. SGPW.	£20	NC	☐
		Wheel change	Yellow body, Black plastic wheels	£9	NC	☐
39c	1967	Ford Tractor	Blue body, Yellow engine cover & wheels	£7-£10	MPR	☐
		Colour change	All Blue body, Yellow wheels	£20	NC	☐
		Colour change	Orange body, Yellow wheels	£25	GP	☐
39d	1973	Clipper	Met Pink, Yellow interior, OD/RLM. 77 mm.	£2-£4	MPR	☐
39e	1979	Rolls Royce Silver Shadow Mk II	Met Silver body, Red seats, OD/SF. 75 mm.	£2-£4	MPR	☐
	1981	Colour change	Metallic Red body, Cream seats	£2-£4	MPR	☐
	1982	Colour change	Metallic Gold body, White seats	£2-£4	MPR	☐
	1984	Colour change	Maroon body		NRP	☐
	1985	BMW 323i Cabriolet	Metallic Blue body		NRP	☐
	1986	Colour change	All Red body		NRP	☐
40a	1957	Bedford 7 Ton Tipper	Red body, Brown tipper, OTB, MGPW/WWPTL. 53 mm.	£17	NC	☐
40b	1961	Long Distance Bus	Met Grey body, Green WDS, GSBPW. 76 mm.	£6-£8	MPR	☐
40c	1968	Hay Trailer	Blue body, Yellow sides and wheels, OC. 86 mm.	£2-£4	MPR	☐
40d	1972	Vauxhall Guildsman	Pink body, Green WDS, Cream Int, H.	£3-£5	MPR	☐
		Colour change	Red body, Green windows, RN '40'	£3-£5	MPR	☐
		Colour change	Gold body (Bulgarian issue)	£20	GP	☐
			NB. Many other variations exist			
40e	1976	Horse Box	Orange and Cream body, Tan DDR, 2 WHS/SF. 72 mm.	£3-£5	MPR	☐
	1981	Colour change	Green and Cream body, Brown DDR	£2-£4	MPR	☐
	1983	Colour change	Orange and Brown body, White DDR, MOV.	£2-£4	MPR	☐
40f	1985	Rocket Transporter	White body, Red logo 'NASA'	NRP		☐
41a	1957	'D' Type Jaguar	Dark Green body, Tan D, RN '41' or '52'. 55 mm. MGPW/CA	£25	GP	☐
41b	1960	'D' Type Jaguar	Dark Green body, RN '41' or '5', GSBPW. 62 mm.	£20	NC	☐
		Colour change	With Red wheel hubs	£125	GP	☐
		Colour change	With White wheel hubs	£50	GP	☐
41c	1965	Ford GT	Yellow or White MB, Red S, Blue stripe, Yellow wheels, RN '6', BPW/SF/CW/H. 67 mm.	£5-£7	MPR	☐
			With Red wheel hubs	£50	GP	☐
	1970	Colour Change	Metallic Red body, Blue band, RN '6'.	£3-£5	MPR	☐
41d	1973	Siva Spyder	Met Red body and Silver band, OC and decals, SF.	£2-£4	MPR	☐
			Red body, Chrome rear panel	£8-£10	GP	☐
41e		Black Widow	Black windows, US issue	£7-£9	MPR	☐
41e	1979	'AMBULANCE'	White body, Red/Yel/Blk decal, RC/ORD/SF. 75 mm.	£2-£4	MPR	☐
	1981	Colour change	White body, Blue/Yellow decal	£2-£4	MPR	☐
		Colour change	Silver body, White doors	£25	NC	☐
		Colour change	Red 'NOTARTZ' German	£10	NC	☐
		Logo change	Small 'Ambulance' on labels	£8	NC	☐
41f	1983	Racing Porsche	TT Blue body, Team Porsche, Elf etc SF	£2-£4	MPR	☐
	1986	Racing Porsche	White body, Red RN '10' & 'PORSCHE', CCC		NRP	☐

Ref. No.		Model Type	Matchbox Miniatures continued	Price and Rarity Grading	
42a	1957	Bedford 'EVENING NEWS' Van	Yellow body, Red and White decals, news board, *First With The News* CRA/MW, GPW or BPW. 57 mm.	£25	NC ☐
42b	1965	Studebaker Station Wagon	Blue body, White int, ORF/PHD/CW/H/BPW. 76 mm.	£9	NC ☐
42c	1969	Iron Fairy Crane	Red body, Yellow or Green boom and H, OC/BPW/SF.	£6-£8	MPR ☐
	1971	Colour change	Orange body, Gold boom	£15	NC ☐
42d	1972	Tyre Fryer	Met Blue body, Yel int, Sil TR, BB/SF. 76 mm.	£2-£4	MPR ☐
		Colour change	Orange body, 'Jaffa Mobile'	£45	GP ☐
42e	1978	Mercedes Container Truck			
		'MATCHBOX'	Red body, Cream CNT.	£2-£4	MPR ☐
		'MAYFLOWER'	Met Dark Green body & CNT.	£2-£4	MPR ☐
		'SEALAND'	Red body, Cream CNT.	£2-£4	MPR ☐
		'KARSTADT'	Blue body, Blue CNT. (GIM)	£10	NC ☐
		'DEUTSCHE B'POST'	Yellow body & CNT. (GIM)	£10	NC ☐
		'CONFERN'	Red body, Cream/Red CNT. (GIM)	£10	NC ☐
		'NYK'	Red body, Cream CNT.	£2-£4	MPR ☐
		'OCC'	Red body, Cream CNT.	£2-£4	MPR ☐
42f	1983	57 'T' Bird	Red and White body, Red seats, Black US issue	£2-£4	MPR ☐
42g	1984	Mobile Crane	'REYNOLDS CRANE HIRE'		NRP ☐
43a	1958	Hillman Minx	Pale Green body, WWPTL, MW, H/CRA. 67 mm.	£20	NC ☐
		Colour change	Blue/Grey body, Pale Grey roof, MW or GPW	£20	NC ☐
		Colour change	Turquoise body, Cream roof	£14	NC ☐
43b	1962	Tractor Shovel	Yellow body, Yellow shovel, Red or Yel. D. 65 mm.	£20	NC ☐
		Colour change	With Red shovel, Yellow or Red D.	£5-£8	MPR ☐
43c	1968	Pony Trailer	Yellow MB, Grey DDR, BPW/SF/2WHS 67 mm.	£4-£6	MPR ☐
	1971	Colour change	Light Brown body, Dark Brown DDR	£2-£4	MPR ☐
43d	1973	'DRAGON WHEELS'	Green MB, Red decal, Sil E, LOB/SF/TW. 72 mm.	£2-£4	MPR ☐
43e	1979	Steam Locomotive	Red/Black body, Yel '4345', 0-4-0, H. 68 mm.		NRP ☐
43f	1984	M Benz 'AMG'	All White body		NRP ☐
	1985	Colour change	All Red body		NRP ☐
	1987	Colour change	Black body		NRP ☐
43g	1987	'Red Rider'	Red body, Chrome engine, USIM	£4-£6	☐
44a	1958	Rolls Royce Silver Cloud	Met Blue body, Red trim, MW, BB. 67 mm.	£20	NC ☐
	1960	Colour change	Light Metallic Blue body, MGSPW	£15	NC ☐
44b	1964	Rolls Royce Phantom V	Met Mauve body, Cream Int. SPW. 72 mm.	£15	NC ☐
		Wheel change	With Grey plastic wheels	£12	NC ☐
		Wheel change	With Black plastic wheels	£10	NC ☐
	1966	Colour change	Silver Grey body, SPW or BPW	£10	NC ☐
44c	1967	Refrigerator Truck	Red and Green body, Grey ORD, PW/SF. 77 mm.	£6-£8	MPR ☐
	1971	Colour change	Yellow and Red body	£4-£6	MPR ☐
44d	1972	Boss Mustang	Yellow body, Black OBN, EE, SF. 75 mm.	£2-£4	MPR ☐
44e	1979	Passenger Coach	Red/CR/Blk body, Green TW, *431-432*. 73 mm.	£2-£4	MPR ☐
44f	1983	Citroen 15	Black body, Tan seats, Silver trim, SF		NRP ☐
	1986	Colour change	Deep Blue body		NRP ☐
44g	1988	Skoda 130LR	No details available		NGPP ☐
45a	1958	Vauxhall Victor	Dark Red body, Silver trim, BB, MW. 61 mm.	£500	GP ☐
		Colour change	Yellow body, Metal wheels	£35	GP ☐
		Wheel change	Yellow body, Grey or Silver plastic wheels	£15	NC ☐
45b	1965	Ford Corsair with Boat	Cream body, Green boat, Red S and H, BGPW. 67 mm.	£6-£8	MPR ☐
45c	1970	Ford Group Six	Met Green body, Cream S, RN '7', CW, SF. 75 mm.	£4-£6	MPR ☐
	1973	Colour change	Lime Green body, TW, RN '45'	£2-£4	MPR ☐
	1974	Colour change	Red body RN '45', TW	£2-£4	MPR ☐
45d	1976	B.M.W. 3.0 CSL	Red body, Yellow int, *BMW,* SF/OD. 74 mm.	£2-£4	MPR ☐
	1979	Colour change	Orange body, *BMW*	£2-£4	MPR ☐
45e	1982	Kenworth	White/Blue body, Amber TW, SF. 71 mm.		NRP ☐
	1984	Colour change	Silver Grey body, '45' TPD		NRP ☐
	1986	Colour change	Red body, Yellow/White/Orange design, CCC.		NRP ☐
		US Issue	'Chef Boyardee'	£12	NC ☐
45f	1988	Skip Truck	Yellow body, Grey/Orange Skip		NRP ☐
46a	1958	Morris Minor 1000	Brown body, No WDS, WWPTL, CA/MW. 51 mm.	£250	GP ☐
		Colour change	Blue/Green body, MW/GPW	£100	GP ☐
		Colour change	Blue body, GPW	£100	GP ☐
		Colour change	Green body, MW	£25	GP ☐
46b	1960	'PICKFORDS' Long Distance Removal Truck	Dark Blue body, White ORD, *Removers & Storage, Branches in all Large Towns* in White on three lines, GSPW. 67 mm.	£24	NC ☐
		Changed Logo	'Pickfords Removers & Storage' on two lines	£100	GP ☐
		Colour change	Green body with logo three lines	£24	NC ☐
		'BEALES-BEALSON'	Light Brown body, White decals, PRM.	£250	GP ☐
46c	1968	Mercedes 300 SE	Green body, Cream S, OD/OBT/BPW. 73 mm.	£6-£8	MPR ☐
	1969	Colour change	Metallic Blue body, BPW	£4-£6	MPR ☐
	1970	Colour change	Gold body, SF	£2-£4	MPR ☐
		Colour change	Silver body, SF	£15	NC ☐
		Overseas issue	Met Blue or Red body (Bulgarian), SF	£16	NC ☐

Ref. No.		Model Type	Matchbox Miniatures continued	Price and Rarity Grading	
46d	1973	Stretcha Fetcha	White body, Red BP/Cross, Blue TW and 2FL. 70 mm.	£2-£4	MPR ☐
		Window change	With Amber window	£3-£5	MPR ☐
		Design change	With small Red cross label	£12	NC ☐
		Overseas issue	Red body (German)	£12	NC ☐
			NB. Many other variations exist.		
46e		'Viper' Van	No details	£2-£4	MPR ☐
46f	1979	Ford Tractor and Harrow	Blue body, Silver E, Yel harrow and S, H. 52 mm.	£2-£4	MPR ☐
	1984	Sanber Group 'C' Racer	Red body, Black SPE, BASF, CCC.		NRP ☐
	1986	Colour change	White body, Black RN '61'		NRP ☐
46g	1987	Hot Chocolate	US issue	£4-£6	MPR ☐
46h	1987	'Big Blue'	Met Blue lift up body, RN '39', VW body	£4-£6	MPR ☐
47a	1958	Trojan Van	Red body, STR/MW/GPW, 'BROOKE BOND TEA'.	£24	NC ☐
47b	1963	Commer Mobile Shop	Met Blue body, MLCD decals, 'LYONS MAID' BPW.	£50	GP ☐
		Colour change	Non Metallic Blue body, BGPW.	£20	NC ☐
		Colour change	Cream body, BPW	£20	NC ☐
47c	1969	DAF Tipper CNTT	Sea Green body, Grey roof, Yel CNT, BPW. 77 mm.	£10	NC ☐
	1972	Colour change	Silver body, Yellow CNT, Red BP, BPW.	£6-£8	MPR ☐
47a	1974	Beach Hopper	Met Blue body, Yel D and EM, Or S, SF/RLM. 66 mm.	£2-£4	MPR ☐
47e	1980	'G.W.R.' Pannier Locomotive	Green/Black body, gold decals, 0-6-0, H. 77 mm.	£2-£4	MPR ☐
47f	1982	Jaguar SS100	Red body, Silver trim, Beige S/SW, SF. 76 mm.		NRP ☐
	1986	Colour change	Blue body, Grey BN, White seats, CCC		NRP ☐
47g	1988	School Bus	Yellow body, USIM, 'School District'		NRP ☐
	1988	Army version	Celebrates U.S.A. Matchbox Clubs 7th Anniversary — Olive Green		NRP ☐
48a	1958	Meteor Sports Boat on Trailer	Blue/Cream boat, Black trailer, MGPW. 66 mm.	£15	NC ☐
48b	1962	Sports Boat and Trailer	Red deck, Cream or White hull, Dk Blue TRL.	£12	NC ☐
	1964	Colour change	White deck, Red hull, Lt Blue TRL	£12	NC ☐
48c	1967	Dodge Dumper Truck	All Red body, Silver trim, BPW/SF. 76 mm.	£4-£6	MPR ☐
	1970	Colour change	Blue cab and CH, Yellow tipper	£2-£4	MPR ☐
48d	1973	Pie Eyed Piper	Met Blue body, Silver EE, MLCD decal, SF/TW. 75 mm.	£3-£5	MPR ☐
48e	1978	White Lightning	U.S. issued model.	£3-£5	MPR ☐
48f	1978	Sambron Jacklift	Yel forklift and body, Blk CH, arms adjust. 78 mm.	£2-£4	MPR ☐
48g	1983	(Mercedes) Unimog	Yel/White/Blk body, Red Rescue. SNP/SF. 64 mm.		NRP ☐
			With White blade	£9	NC ☐
48h	1986	Astra GTE	Red body, OD, Black Int, CCC.		NRP ☐
	1987	Decal change	With A.C. Delco TPD.		NRP ☐
48i		Red Rider	US issued model	£3-£5	MPR ☐
49a	1958	Army Halftrack	MG body, White star, Grey tracks, MW & MR	£16	NC ☐
		Roller change	With SPR and GPW	£40	GP ☐
		Roller change	With SPR and BPW	£12	NC ☐
		Track change	With Green tracks, BPW.	£12	NC ☐
49b	1967	(Mercedes) Unimog	Tan body, Green CH and TW/H/SPW/BPW. 62 mm.	£6-£8	MPR ☐
	1968	Colour change	Blue body, Red chassis	£4-£6	MPR ☐
49c	1973	Chop Suey	Met Red body, Silver E and handlebars. 72 mm.	£2-£4	MPR ☐
	1974	Colour change	Met Red body, Red handlebars	£2-£4	MPR ☐
49d	1977	Crane Truck	All Yel body, Grn TW, Blk STB, Red PH. 76 mm.	£2-£4	MPR ☐
		Colour change	Red/Yellow body (GIM)	£35	NC ☐
	1981	Colour change	Yellow body, Black jib	£2-£4	MPR ☐
49e	1983	'SAND DIGGER'	Green body, EE, Yel logo, BPW	£2-£4	MPR ☐
	1985	'DUNE MAN'	Red body, Yellow design on bonnet		NRP ☐
49f	1987	Peugeot Quasar	White body, Chrome Int, CCC		NRP ☐
	1988	Colour change	Maroon body, Yellow design, EE		NRP ☐
50a	1958	Commer Pick Up	Pale Brown body, MW or GPW. 64 mm.	£12	NC ☐
		Colour change	Light Brown body, GPW or SPW	£50	GP ☐
	1961	Colour change	Red body, Cream cab, SPW	£100	GP ☐
	1962	Colour change	Red body, Grey cab, SPW, GPW or BPW	£30	NC ☐
50b	1964	John Deere Lanz Tractor	Green body, Silver/Yellow trim, GBPW/H. 54 mm.	£5-£8	MPR ☐
50c	1969	Kennel Truck	Met Green body in VS, ASM/4WPD/BPW/SF. 70 mm.	£6-£8	MPR ☐
50d	1974	Articulated Truck	Yellow body, Blue TRL, WW Yel FL, SF/TW. 78 mm.	£2-£4	MPR ☐
		Colour change	Red cab, Blue trailer	£8	NC ☐
50e	1981	Harley Davidson Motor Cycle	Met Brown body, Silver E, Black S and HB. 70 mm.	£2-£4	MPR ☐
	1982	Colour change	Met Plum body, Brown rider, Black S/forks		NRP ☐
50f	1985	Chevy Blazer	Red/White body, 'Sheriff' Crest, 'ISP7'.		NRP ☐
50g	1988	Dodge Dakota	Red pick up body, side stripes, 2SL		NRP ☐

Ref. No.		Model Type	Matchbox Miniatures continued	Price and Rarity Grading	
51a	1958	Albion Chieftain	Yellow body, Beige load, MW, 'PORTLAND CEMENT'	£35	GP ☐
		Logo change	SAPM with 'BLUE CIRCLE' added, MW or GSPW.	£20	NC ☐
	1962	Colour change	Light Brown body, GPW or BPW	£24	NC ☐
51b	1964	Tipping Trailer	Green body, 3 Brown barrels, Yel W, GBPW. 67 mm.	£2-£4	MPR ☐
51c	1969	AEC Tipper	Orange, cab and CH, Silver tipper, 'DOUGLAS'	£11	NC ☐
		Colour change	Yellow cab and chassis 'DOUGLAS'	£7-£9	MPR ☐
	1970	Logo Change	Yellow cab and CH, Green/Yel label, 'POINTER'	£7-£9	☐
51d	1973	Citroen SM	Met Red body, Cream seats, OD/CW/SF. 78 mm.	£2-£4	MPR ☐
			Metallic Orange body	£2-£4	MPR ☐
			Metallic Blue body	£2-£4	MPR ☐
			Green, Gold or Blue body (Bulgarian)	£15	NC ☐
	1977	Colour change	Blue body, Red flash RN '8'	£2-£4	MPR ☐
51e	1978	Combine Harvester	Red body, Yellow moving parts. Non SF or SF PW.	£2-£4	MPR ☐
	1982	Midnight Magic	Black/Silver, Chrome Int, USIM	£4-£6	MPR ☐
51f	1983	Pontiac 'FIREBIRD'	Red body, White decals, Tan seats, SF. 76 mm.		NRP ☐
	1984	Colour change	Black body, Grey CH		NRP ☐
	1986	'MAACO'	Red body, MLCD labels, USIM/PRM	£4-£6	MPR ☐
51g	1988	Ford Ltd Police Car	No details known		NRP ☐
52a	1958	Maserati 4 CLT	Red body, Cream D, No RN or RN '52', BPW.	£15	NC ☐
		Wheel change	Red body, RN '52' wire wheels	£55	GP ☐
		Colour change	Yellow body, RN '5' or '3' wire wheels	£30	GP ☐
52b	1965	B.R.M. Racing Car	Blue body, RN '5', Yel W, BPT. 70 mm.	£5-£7	MPR ☐
		Colour change	Red body, RN '5'	£8-£11	MPR ☐
52c	1970	Dodge Charger Mk III	Red body, Blk/Yel FL, LMS/SF. 76 mm.	£2-£4	MPR ☐
	1973	Colour change	Purple body, no decal	£2-£4	MPR ☐
			Purple body with RN '5' label	£10	NC ☐
	1974	Colour change	Green body, no decal	£2-£4	MPR ☐
52d	1977	'POLICE' Launch	Blue and White boat, Blue TW, 2 PM. 77 mm.	£2-£4	MPR ☐
52e	1981	BMW MI	Silver body, Black RN '52', Red S, SF. 75 mm.	£2-£4	MPR ☐
	1983	Colour change	White body, Black RN '52', Red *BMW MI* SF		NRP ☐
	1984	Design change	Red/Yellow body, RN '5'		NRP ☐
	1985	Design change	Black body, RN '59'		NRP ☐
	1986	Design change	Yellow/White body, Red RN '11'		NRP ☐
	1988	Design change	Red body, Blue/Red/White design		NRP ☐
53a	1958	Aston Martin	Met Green body, WWPTL, MWGPW. 66 mm.	£15	NC ☐
		Colour change	Met Red body, GPW/BPW	£15	NC ☐
		Colour change	Non Met Red body, BPW	£50	GP ☐
53b	1963	Mercedes Benz 220SE	Maroon body, Cream seats, BB, SGBPW. 69 mm.	£12	NC ☐
		Colour change	Dark Red body, GPW or BPW	£9	NC ☐
53c	1968	Ford Zodiac Mk IV	Met Blue body, Cream S, OBN/SPW/BPW. 70 mm.	£12	NC ☐
	1970	Colour change	Met Green.	£5-£7	MPR ☐
		Colour change	Lime Green body.	£14	NC ☐
53d	1973	Tanzara	Orange body, Clover leaf decal, TW/SF. 76 mm.	£2-£4	MPR ☐
	1976	Colour change	White body, Blue/Red stripes, RN '53', SF	£2-£4	MPR ☐
53e	1977	CJ6 Jeep	Red body, Fawn seats and roof, SF. 75 mm.	£2-£4	MPR ☐
		Seat change	With Black seats	£7	NC ☐
		Colour change	Green body, with Black seats	£7	NC ☐
		Colour change	Yellow body, with Brown roof	£5	NC ☐
	1981	Colour change	Green body, Yellow seats, Fawn roof	£2-£4	MPR ☐
53f	1982	Flareside Pick-Up	Orange body, White S, *Baja Bouncer, 326,* SF. 76 mm.	£2-£4	MPR ☐
	1986	Design change	Yellow/Blue body, 'FORD'		NRP ☐
54a	1958	Army Saracen Carrier	Olive Green body, RGT, 6 Black PW, CRA/RTR. 56 mm.	£10	NC ☐
54b	1965	Cadillac Ambulance	White body, Red cross and SL, TW, BPW/SF. 73 mm.	£5-£7	MPR ☐
54c	1971	Ford Capri	Red body, Black OBN, White seats, SF. 77 mm.	£2-£4	MPR ☐
	1974	Colour change	Met Purple body, White seats	£2-£4	MPR ☐
54d	1977	Personnel Carrier	Green body, Brown figures and RGT, SF. 76 mm.	£2-£4	MPR ☐
	1980	Mobile Home	Green body, Orange interior, Brown OD, SF. 76 mm.	£2-£4	MPR ☐
54e	1982	'NASA' Tracking Vehicle	White body, Blue/Red decal, WW *Space Shuttle* logo.	£2-£4	MPR ☐
	1984	Airport Unit	Red/White body, Black/White design		NRP ☐
	1985	Design change	Red/Yellow body, 'METRO', 2 Blue FLL		NRP ☐
55a	1958	D.U.K.W. Amphibian	Olive Green body, MGPW. 70 mm.	£12	NC ☐
55b	1963	'POLICE' Car	Dark Blue body, BNB & DBG, BPW.	£30	GP ☐
		Colour change	Metallic blue body, BPW	£14	NC ☐
		Wheel change	With SPW or GPW	£20	NC ☐
55c	1966	'POLICE' Car	White body, Red/Blue PCR, SL, BPW. 73 mm.	£10	NC ☐
55d	1968	Mercury 'POLICE' Car	White body, Red/Bl PCR, SL/ASM/2PS/BPW/SF.	£7-£9	MPR ☐
55e	1971	Mercury 'POLICE' Estate Car	White body, WW, PCR, 2SL/No PS/SF. 77 mm.	£4-£6	MPR ☐
55f	1976	Hell Raiser	White body, Silver EE, Red seats. 75 mm.	£1-£3	MPR ☐
	1978	Colour change	Met Blue body, stars and stripes decal	£1-£3	MPR ☐
55g	1980	Ford Cortina 1600 GL	Met Green body, Red seats OD/SF. 75 mm.	£2-£4	MPR ☐
	1981	Colour change	Met Red body, Yel seats, OD/SF	£2-£4	MPR ☐
	1982	Colour change	Met Bronze and White body, Yellow seats, MOV.	£2-£4	MPR ☐
55h	1983	Ford Sierra XR4i	Met Silver and Black body, Red seats, SF. 76 mm.	£2-£4	MPR ☐
	1984	Colour change	Silver/Grey body, Red/Black design		NRP ☐
	1985	Colour change	Silver/Red body, Red 'XR4i' design		NRP ☐
	1986	Ford Sierra 'XR4 × 4'	Yellow body, Black CH/SPL/TPD		NRP ☐
		Colour change	Yellow body, Red Interior	£8	NC ☐

Ref. No.	Year	Model Type	Description	Price	Rarity
56a	1958	Trolley Bus 'DRINK PEARDRAX'	Red body, 2 Red or Black roof poles. Decal in Red/White/Black, MGPW/CRA. 66 mm.	£25	NC
56b	1966	Fiat 1500	Green body, Red seats, Brown LG, BPW/H.	£9	NC
		Colour change	Red body, Light Brown luggage	£35	GP
56c	1969	B.M.C. 1800 Pininfarina	Gold body, White seats, OD/BPT. 70 mm.	£2-£4	MPR
	1970	Colour change	Orange body, White S, WDW/SF	£2-£4	MPR
	1971	Colour change	Bronze body, White seats, SF	£3-£5	MPR
	1973	Colour change	Orange body, THW/SF	£3-£5	MPR
56d	1975	Hi-Tailer	White body, Blue/Orange D, 'TEAM MATCHBOX'	£3-£5	MPR
		Logo change	SAPM with Red base, 'MARTINI RACING'	£3-£5	MPR
56e	1980	Mercedes 450 SEL	Met Blue body, Tan or Red Int, CW.	£2-£4	MPR
	1981	Taxi version	Cream body, Red *Taxi* on roof	£2-£4	MPR
	1983	Policecar version	Green and White body, *Polizei*, 2 Blue SL, SF	£2-£4	MPR
56f	1982	Peterbilt Tanker	Blue/White body, 'MILKS THE ONE'	£2-£4	MPR
56g	1985	VW Golf GTi	Red body, opening bonnet		NRP
	1986	TPD change	SAPM, White, 'GTI' design		NRP
	1987	'QUANTUM'	Blue/White body, RN '66', PRO.		NRP
57a	1958	Wolseley 1500	Pale Green body, WWPTL/CRA/GPW/BB/OC. 55 mm.	£15	NC
57b	1961	Chevrolet Impala	TT Blue body, CW. SPW/H. 70 mm.	£25	GP
		Wheel change	With knobby or fine GPW, Green WDS.	£17	NC
	1964	Wheel change	With Black plastic wheels, Green WDS.	£12	NC
57c	1966	Land Rover Fire Truck	Red body, Yellow logo, 'KENT FIRE BRIGADE' BPW.	£12	NC
		Wheel change	SAPM with Grey plastic wheels	£20	NC
57d	1970	Eccles Caravan	Pale Yel body, Orange RF, Mrn stripe, SF. 75 mm.	£5-£7	MPR
	1971	Colour change	Off White body, flower decal	£5-£7	MPR
	1973	Colour change	Cream body, flower decal	£3-£5	MPR
57e	1974	Wild Life Truck	Yellow body, *Ranger* decal, RLM, CPC. 70 mm.	£2-£4	MPR
	1981	Colour change	White body, Black stripes	£2-£4	MPR
57f	1982	Carmichael Vehicle	White body, Black roof, *Police Rescue*.	£2-£4	MPR
57g	1983	Carmichael 'FIRE' Vehicle	Red/White body, Black plastic ladder		NRP
		'Mountain Man'	Blue body, 'CIBIE', '4x4 USIM	£4-£6	MPR
57h	1986	Mission Helicopter	Blue body, White rotor/tail		NRP
	1987	Colour change	Red body, 'SHERIFF' TPD		NRP
58a	1958	AEC Coach 'BEA'	Dark Blue body, White logo, GPW. 65 mm.	£25	NC
		Decal change	SAPM with 'BEA' panel in Red at front, GSBPW	£15	NC
	1959	Decal change	With 'BEA' Red panel at rear. GSBPW	£15	NC
58b	1962	Drott Excavator	Red or Orange body, BPW, Green RT, OC. 67 mm.	£5-£8	MPR
58c	1968	DAF Girder Truck	Cream body, Red girders, TW/BPW/ST. 76 mm.	£4-£6	MPR
58d	1973	Woosh-N-Push	Yellow body, RN '2' SF. 77 mm.		NRP
		Design change	Yellow body with flower label	£10	NG
		Design change	Purple body with '8' label	£3-£5	MPR
58e	1977	Faun Dumper	Yellow body, Black CH, *Cat* SF. 71 mm.		NRP
58f	1983	'RUFF TREK' (Pick Up)	Gold/Brown body, Red trim, Blk load, SPW. 74 mm.		NRP
	1985	Design change	White body, Red/Yellow TPD, RN '217'		NRP
58g	1988	Mercedes 300e	No details known		NRP
59a	1958	Ford 'SINGER' Van	Light Green body, Red Seats and logo, GPW. 57 mm.	£27	NC
		Wheel change	With Silver plastic wheels	£45	GP
		Colour change	Mid Green body and GPW	£27	NC
		Wheel change	With Silver plastic wheels	£75	GP
59b	1963	'FIRE CHIEF' Car	Red body, Yel logo, SL on roof, BPW. 65 mm.	£14	NC
		Wheel change	With Silver plastic wheels	£20	NC
		Wheel change	With Grey plastic wheels	£17	NC
59c	1966	'FIRE CHIEF' Car	Red body, Yel logo, Blue SL, BPW/SF/H/D. 73 mm.	£8-£11	MPR
59d	1971	'FIRE CHIEF' Car	Red body, Yel logo, D and PS, Blue SL, SF. 73 mm.	£5-£8	MPR
59e	1976	Planet Scout	TT Green body, TW, Silver trim, 2SL. 70 mm.	£3-£5	MPR
	1979	Colour change	Red body, Cream chassis	£2-£4	MPR
	1981	Colour change	Green/Black body, Purple WDS.	£6	NC
	1983	Colour change	Met Blue with Purple WDS.	£15	NC
59f	1980	Porsche 928	Met Brown body, *Porsche,* OD/SF. 75 mm.	£2-£4	MPR
	1981	Colour change	Blue body	£2-£4	MPR
	1982	Colour change	Black body, White stripes, crest on BN	£2-£4	MPR
	1984	Colour change	Grey/Blue body, 'PORSCHE'		NRP
	1985	Colour change	Black with Tan interior	£5	NC
	1986	Colour change	Silver/Blue body, Blue 'PORSCHE'		NRP
	1988	Porsche '944 Turbo'	All Red body, Yellow design		NRP
60a	1958	Morris J2 Pick Up	Light Blue body, Red and Black logo, with cab rear window, GPW. 'BUILDERS DIRECT SUPPLY'	£75	GP
		Logo change	SAPM with Red and White logo, GSBPW.	£15	NC
		Casting change	Without cab window, GPW or BPW	£45	GP
60b	1966	Truck with Site Office	Blue body, Yel/Green office, BPW/SF. 65 mm.	£6-£8	MPR
60c	1972	Lotus Super Seven	Light Brown body, Black seats, BPW. 74 mm.	£5-£7	MPR
	1976	Colour change	Yellow body, Red stripes RN '60'	£2-£4	MPR

Ref. No.		Model Type	Matchbox Miniatures continued	Price	Grade	
60d	1977	Holden Pick-Up	Red or Blue body, 2 Yel MC, *500* decal, SF. 77 mm.	£2-£4	MPR	☐
	1981	Colour change	White body, 2 Red MC, *Superbike*	£2-£4	MPR	☐
60e	1983	'TOYOTA RACING'	White body, Black OHB, RN '41' in Red SF. 76 mm.	£2-£4	MPR	☐
	1985	Logo change	SAPM with 'SUPRA' logo		NRP	☐
60f	1986	Ford Transit Van	Red body, Blue design 'MOTORSPORT'		NRP	☐
	1987	Design change	With 'AMBULANCE' logo		NRP	☐
	1987	'UNICHEM'	No details known		NRP	☐
	1988	'XP'	White body, Yellow/Green design		NRP	☐
		GT ORMOND ST HOSPITAL APPEAL	Promotional — no details at time of printing but buy a model and help save the Hospital.		NRP	☐
61a	1959	Military Scout Car	Olive Green body, Tan driver, SPW/BPW. 57 mm.	£12	NC	☐
61b	1966	Alvis Stalwart 'BP'	White body, Yellow DTC, Green hubs, BPT. 66 mm.	£8	NC	☐
		Wheel change	SAPM with Yellow wheel hubs	£12	NC	☐
61c	1972	Blue Shark	Met Blue body, White D, Sil EE, RN '86' SF. 77 mm.	£2-£4	MPR	☐
		Design change	With 'Scorpion' Label	£10	NC	☐
		Design change	With '69' Label	£10	NC	☐
		Design change	'86' Label with Silver/Grey base	£6	NC	☐
61d	1978	Wreck Truck	Red body, 2 White jibs, 2 Red H and SL, SF. 76 mm.	£2-£4	MPR	☐
	1981	Colour change	Yellow body, 2 Red jibs, 2 Black hooks	£2-£4	MPR	☐
61e	1982	Wreck Truck	Red body, 2 Blk jibs, *Eddies Wrecker* SF/6W. 77 mm.	£2-£4	MPR	☐
	1983	Colour and decal change	White body, 2 Blk jibs, *9* and *Dial 911*, SF	£2-£4	MPR	☐
	1984	Colour change	SAPM with Blue jibs		NRP	☐
	1985	'POLICE SFPD'	SAPM with Orange jibs, CCC.		NRP	☐
	1988	T-Bird Turbo	All Red body, Black band.		NRP	☐
62a	1959	General Service Lorry	Olive Green body, tow hook, 6BPW. 68 mm.	£14	NC	☐
62b	1963	TV Service Van 'RENTASET'	Cream body, Red logo, plastic ladder, TV aerial and 3 TV's, White ORS, GPW/BPW. 64 mm.	£12	NC	☐
	1967	'RADIO RENTALS'	SAPM with changed logo in Green	£50	GP	☐
62c	1969	Mercury Cougar	Cream body, White int, BPW, EE, SF, 76 cm.	£35	GP	☐
		Colour change	Met Green body, Red int, BPW	£10	NC	☐
62d	1970	'RAT ROD' Dragster	Lime Green body, Red decal, Sil EE, SF. 76 mm.	£2-£4	MPR	☐
		Design change	With 'WILD CAT' design	£10	NC	☐
62e	1974	Renault 17 TL	Red body, White seats, Blue TW, RN '9', SF. 76 mm.	£2-£4	MPR	☐
62f	1980	Chevrolet Corvette	Met Red body, White flashes and int, SF. 74 mm.	£2-£4	MPR	☐
	1983	Colour change	White body, Orange/Black stripes, RN '09'	£2-£4	MPR	☐
	1985	Colour change	Blue body, Red/White/Yel design		NRP	☐
	1986	Volvo 760	Pale Green body		NRP	☐
	1988	Colour change	Red body, opening windows		NRP	☐
63a	1959	Service Ambulance (Ford)	Olive Green body, Red crosses, BPW. 67 mm.	£15	NC	☐
63b	1964	Fire Fighting Crash Tender	Red body, White PLD, Silver hosepipe.	£35	GP	☐
		Hose change	With Gold hosepipe	£15	NC	☐
63c	1969	Dodge Crane Truck	Yellow body, Rotating Crane Jib, Red hook, BPW/SF.	£2-£4	MPR	☐
63d	1973	Freeway Gas Tanker Series	Red cab, White/Red tank			
		i) 'BURMAH'	Black logo Red/White company motif TW/AV/SF. 78 mm.	£1-£3	MPR	☐
		ii) 'ARAL' (German issue)	Blue cab, Blue and White logo, SF	£10	NVE	☐
		iii) 'SHELL'	White/Yellow body, Red logo, SF	£2-£4	MPR	☐
		iv) 'CHEVRON'	Red cab, Red/White/Blue logo, SF	£2-£4	MPR	☐
		v) 'BP SUPER'	White cab, White/Grn tank, Yel logo, SF	£2-£4	MPR	☐
		vi) 'EXXON'	US issued model	£4-£6	MPR	☐
		vii) Army issue	Dark Military Green, French Flag	£30	GP	☐
		viii) Army issue	Military Green '95 High Octane'	£3-£5	MPR	☐
		ix) 'CASTROL'	Red/White body	£30	GP	☐
63e	1982	4×4 Pick-Up	Yellow body, Orange panels RN '24'. 71 mm.		NRP	☐
	1986	Design change	White/Blue body, RN 63		NRP	☐
63f		Dodge Challenger	USIM, Green body	£4-£6	MPR	☐
64a	1959	Scammell Breakdown Truck	Olive Green body, metal or P hook, BPW. 67 mm.	£15	NC	☐
64b	1966	MG 1100	Green body, White seats, BPW/D/dog. 66 mm.	£6-£8	MPR	☐
	1970	Colour change	Metallic Blue body	£4-£6	MPR	☐
64c	1972	Slingshot Dragster	Pink body, Silver/Black EE, RN '9' D/SF. 76 mm.	£6	NC	☐
	1974	Colour change	Green body, Silver/Red exposed engine	£6	NC	☐
		Colour change	Orange body	£50	GP	☐
		Colour change	Metallic Green body, RN '3'.	£12	NC	☐
	1975	Colour change	Blue body, Silver/Red exposed engine	£2-£4	MPR	☐
64d	1976	Fire Chief Car	Red body, Yel/Blk *Fire*, Blue TW. 77 mm.	£2-£4	MPR	☐
64e	1982	Bulldozer	Black/Yellow/Silver body Blk PT, H		NRP	☐
64f	1984	Dodge Caravan	Silver body, Red seats, SLD, CTR		NRP	☐
	1985	Colour change	SAPM with Yellow/White bands		NRP	☐
	1985	Colour change	White body		NRP	☐

Ref. No.		Model Type	Matchbox Miniatures continued	Price	Rarity	
65a	1959	Jaguar 3.4 litre	Blue body, WW PTL/CRA/GPW/BB. 61 mm.	£18	NC	☐
		Colour change	Metallic Blue body, CRA/GPW	£65	GP	☐
65b	1962	Jaguar 3.4 Sedan	Metallic Red body, RB/BB/STR/TW/SPW. 68 mm.	£15	NC	☐
		Colour change	Non Met Red body, no RB, BGSPW	£12	NC	☐
65c	1968	Combine Harvester	Red body, Yellow RCB and wheels, BPT. 76 mm.		NRP	☐
65d	1973	Saab Sonnet	Met Blue body, Orange seats and TW, OTG/SF. 73 mm.	£2-£4	MPR	☐
65e	1978	Airport Coach	Metallic Blue lower body with White plastic upper body, Amber or clear windows, Yellow or Ivory interior, SF. 78 mm.			
		'BRITISH AIRWAYS'	Red, White and Blue labels.	£3-£5	MPR	☐
		'AMERICAN AIRWAYS'	Red, White and Blue labels.	£3-£5	MPR	☐
		'LUFTHANSA'	Black, Blue, Orange and White labels.	£3-£5	MPR	☐
	1980	Colour change	Metallic Red lower body, White upper body, Yellow interior, Amber windows			
		'TWA'	Red logo on White label.	£3-£5	MPR	☐
		'QUANTAS'	White logo on Red labels.	£3-£5	MPR	☐
	1982	Colour changes				
		'ALITALIA'	Green, Red, Black body	£3-£5	MPR	☐
		'SCHULBUS'	Orange lower body, White upper body, GIM	£2-£4	MPR	☐
		'PAN AM'	White body	£2-£4	MPR	☐
		'GIROBANK'	Blue/White body, 'SIMPLY MORE CONVENIENT'		NGPP	☐
		'STORK SB'	White/Blue body, AUSTRALIAN ISSUE	£5	NC	☐
65f		Bandag Bandit	Black body, (USIM)	£3-£5	MPR	☐
65g		Indy Racer	Yellow body, (USIM)	£2-£4	MPR	☐
65h	1985	Plane Transporter	Yel body, Red/White plane, 'RESCUE' CCC.		NRP	☐
	1987	Cadillac Allante	Silver body, Red seats, OD.		NRP	☐
66a	1959	Citroen DS 19	Yellow body, Silver trim, GPW. 64 mm.	£18	NC	☐
		Wheel change	SAPM with Silver plastic wheels	£40	GP	☐
66b	1962	Harley Davidson	Met Bronze body, 3 SPKW, BPT. 67 mm.	£38	NC	☐
66c	1967	'GREYHOUND' COACH	Silver body, clear windows, BPW, 76 mm.	£40	GP	☐
		Window change	SAPM with Amber windows	£6-£8	MPR	☐
66d	1972	'Mazda' RX500	Orange body, White BP, TW, OREC.SF. 74 mm.	£2-£4	MPR	☐
	1976	Colour change	Red body, White baseplate, 'CASTROL'	£10	NC	☐
		Colour change	Dark Green body, Yellow RN '66'	£15	NC	☐
		Colour change	Red body, 'RN77' & RX500' design	£10	NC	☐
		Colour change	Gold body — Bulgarian issue	£15	NC	☐
66e	1978	Ford Transit Pick Up	Orange body, Yel or Green int. Tan crate crago, 'FRAGILE' & 'SPARES' logo, Green TW	£2-£4	MPR	☐
		Window change	SAPM with Amber tinted windows	£2-£4	MPR	☐
	1980	Colour change	Pale Orange body	£2-£4	MPR	☐
66f	1983	Tyrone Malone	White body, Red Blue design 'SUPERBOSS' SF.		NRP	☐
66g	1957	RR Silver Spirit	Brown body and interior, OD/SF		NRP	☐
67a	1959	Saladin Armoured Car	Olive Green body, RGT/6BPW. 57 mm.	£10-£12	MPR	☐
67b	1968	Volkswagen 1600 TL	Red body, White seats, opening doors, BPT.*	£12	NC	☐
		Colour change	Metallic Purple body BPT*	£12	NC	☐
			*NB. 50% less for models with SF wheels			
	1968/9	RACE N RALLY G.S.	Red body, Maroon roof rack, BPT		NGPP	☐
		Wheel change	Same model with SF wheels	£4-£7	MPR	☐
	1970	Column change	Pink body, SF	£4-£7	MPR	☐
67c	1974	Hot Rocker	Met Green body, Sil EE, White S, SF/RLM. 77 mm.	£2-£4	MPR	☐
	1976	Colour change	Red body	£2-£4	MPR	☐
67d	1979	Datsun 260 Z	Met Pink, Yellow interior, H/SF. 75 mm.	£2-£4	MPR	☐
	1981	Colour change	Met Silver body, Red interior, SF	£2-£4	MPR	☐
	1982	Colour change	SAPM plus Red/Blk flashes *Datsun 2+2*	£2-£4	MPR	☐
	1983	IMSA 'FORD MUSTANG'	Black body, Red/White/Blue stripes TW/SF	£2-£4	MRP	☐
	1985	Window change	SAPM with LMG windows		NRP	☐
	1986	'IKARUS' Coach	White body, 'GIBRALTAR' (Spanish)	£4-£6	MPR	☐
	1986	Design change	White body, Orange RF, 'VOYAGER' CCC.	£2-£4	MPR	☐
	1988	Design change	White with Green stripes, 'TOURIST CITY LINE'		NRP	☐
68a	1959	Austin Radio Truck	Olive Green body, Black plastic wheels, CRA. 64 mm.	£10-£12	MPR	☐
68b	1965	Mercedes Coach	Turquoise body, White PUS and int, BPW.	£150	GP	☐
		Colour change	With Orange body, White PUS, BPW.	£5-£7	MPR	☐
68c	1970	Porsche 910	Metallic Red, White seats RN '68', SF/TW. 76 mm.	£2-£4	MPR	☐
		Design change	With '68' labels on sides	£10	NC	☐
		Colour change	White body	£15	NC	☐
68d	1976	Cosmobile	Metallic Blue and Yellow body, Silver trim TW. 73 mm.	£2-£4	MPR	☐
	1979	Colour change	Metallic Red and Brown body	£1-£2	MPR	☐
		Colour change	Green/Black body.	£6	NC	☐
		Colour change	Blue/Black body.	£15	NC	☐
68e	1980	Chevrolet Van	Orange body, Red and Blue flashes SF. 77 mm.	£2-£4	MPR	☐
	1981	Colour change	Green body, Orange flash, *Chev.* SF	£2-£4	MPR	☐
	1982	Colour change	Sil body, Blk/Bl/Red flashes *Vanpire* SF	£2-£4	MPR	☐
	1983	Colour change	White body, Orange flashes, *Matchbox Racing*	£2-£4	MPR	☐
		Colour change	Orange body, *Matchbox Collectors Club*	£8	NC	☐
		Colour change	White body, *Adidas* (German)	£7	NC	☐
		Logo change	White body with *USA* logo	£5	NC	☐
		4x4 Chevy Van	*Castrol* (Australian)	£8	NC	☐
68f	1987	Camero Iroc-Z	Blue or Pale Green body, CCC.		NRP	☐
	1988	Design change	Yellow body, Blue/Red design		NRP	☐

Ref. No.		Model Type	Matchbox Miniatures continued	Price	Rarity
69a	1959	Commer 'NESTLES' Van	Maroon body, Yellow logo, PSD/D/GPW. 57 mm.	£20	NC ☐
		Colour change	Red body	£20	NC ☐
69b	1965	Hatra Tractor Shovel	Orange body, BPT, shovel lifts. 80 mm.	£5-£7	MPR ☐
	1967	Colour change	Yellow body, Black plastic tyres	£3-£5	MPR ☐
69c	1970	Rolls Royce Silver Shadow	Met Blue body, Red S, Tan HD, OBT/TW/SF BP in VS.	£3-£5	MPR ☐
	1973	Colour change	Met Gold body, White seats, Black hood, BP in VS	£3-£5	MPR ☐
69d	1974	Turbo Fury	Red body, MLCD FL, RN '69', White D, SF/RLM.	£2-£4	MPR ☐
		Decal change	SAPM with '86' label	£10	NC ☐
69e		Security Truck	Metal body, plastic roof. SF. 73 mm.		
	1979	'WELLS FARGO'	Red body, White roof & logo, SL/SF.	£2-£4	MPR ☐
	1980	'DRESNER BANK'	Green body, White roof, GIM	£5-£8	MPR ☐
	1983	83 Corvette	Silver body, Red bands '83 Vette'		NRP ☐
	1984	Colour change	Red/Grey body, 'Vette' on BN		NRP ☐
69f		Willys Street Rod	Black body, RN '313' (USIM)	£4-£7	MPR ☐
69g	1988	Volvo 480 ES	All White body, '480 ES'		NRP ☐
70a	1959	Ford Thames Estate Car	Green and Yellow body, GPW, No WDS. 55 mm.	£15	NC ☐
		Window change	With clear WDS and GPW or SPW	£20	NC ☐
		Window change	With Green WDS, GPW, SPW or BPW	£15	NC ☐
70b	1966	Ford Grit Spreader	Red/Yellow body, Lemon hold, Green TW. 67 mm.	£12	NC ☐
		Colour change	Red/Yellow body, Yellow hold (container)	£6-£8	MPR ☐
70c	1972	Dodge Dragster	Pink body, snake decal, LOB/EE/SF. 78 mm.	£3-£5	MPR ☐
70d	1977	SP Gun	Olive Green body, Black gun, Tan tracks. 68 mm.	£2-£4	MPR ☐
70e	1981	Ferrari 308 GTB	Orange body, Black flash, Black int, SF. 75 mm.	£2-£4	MPR ☐
	1982	Colour change	Same colours with Ferrari decal, SF	£2-£4	MPR ☐
	1983	Colour change	Red body, White chassis, SF	£2-£4	MPR ☐
	1985	Colour change	Red/Blue body, RN '39', Pioneer		NRP ☐
71a	1959	200 Gallon Water Truck	Olive Green body, BPW. 61 mm. with badge	£25	NC ☐
			Without Matchbox Collectors badge	£10-£12	NC ☐
71b	1964	Jeep Gladiator Pick-UP	Red body, White interior, OD/BPW. 67 mm.	£6-£9	MPR ☐
		Colour change	SAPM with Green interior	£20	NC ☐
71c	1969	Ford 'ESSO' Wreck Truck	Red cab/jib, White body, Amber TW, Red/Yel H	£8-£11	MPR ☐
		Window change	SAPM with Green tinted windows, BPW.	£8-£11	MPR ☐
		Colour change	Military Green, Black hubs	£4-£6	MPR ☐
		Component change	SAPM with Chrome hubs	£8	NC ☐
		Colour change	Blue body	£60	GP ☐
71d	1973	Jumbo Jet Motor Cycle	Met Blue body, Lt or Dk Blue handlebars.	£3-£5	MPR ☐
71e	1977	Dodge Cattle Truck	Bronze cab, Yellow cage, 2 Black cows.	£2-£4	MPR ☐
	1979	Colour change	Red cab, Yellow cage, 2 Black cows	£2-£4	MPR ☐
	1981	Colour change	Red cab, White cage, 2 Black cows	£15	NC ☐
	1982	Colour change	Yellow cab, Brown cage, 2 Brown cows	£3-£5	MPR ☐
		Colour change	Metallic Orange cab, Yellow cage, 2 Brown cows	£6	NC ☐
		Colour change	Non Metallic Green cab, Brown cage, 2 Brown cows	£14	NC ☐
		Colour change	Metallic Lime Green, Cream cage, 2 Brown cows	£3-£5	MPR ☐
			NB. Many other variations exist e.g. with either Amber, Orange, Red, Blue, Purple or Green windows!		
	1983	Colour change	Green and White body, 2 Brown P cows, SF	£2-£4	MPR ☐
71f	1985	Scania T142	White/Blue body, Black bumper		NRP ☐
	1987	Colour change	Blue body		NRP ☐
71g	1987	Corvette	Blue, Red or White body (USIM)	£3-£5	MPR ☐
71h	1987	Blue Flame Vette	White body (USIM)	£3-£5	MPR ☐
71i	1988	GMC Wrecker	White Red body, 'FRANKS', FUB.		NRP ☐
72a	1959	Fordson Tractor	Blue body, STR, GPW at front, Orange hubs at rear with GPW. 50 mm.	£14	NC ☐
		Wheel change	BPW front & rear, Orange rear hubs	£16	NC ☐
		Wheel change	Orange front hubs & GPT with same at rear	£16	NC ☐
		Wheel change	Yellow front hubs & GPT with same at rear	£16	NC ☐
		Wheel change	SAPM with BPT at front, GPT at rear	£14	NC ☐
72b	1967	Standard Jeep	Yellow body, Red seats, SPW/BPT/H. 61 mm.	£6-£9	MPR ☐
	1970	Colour change	With Yellow and Orange body. SF	£5-£8	MPR ☐
72c	1972	'SRN6' Hovercraft	White/Red/Black body, union jack. 77 mm.	£2-£4	MPR ☐
72d	1979	B omag (Road Roller)	Yellow body, Red engine and interior, SF. 71 mm.	£2-£4	MPR ☐
		Wheel change	With Silver rear hubs	£9	NC ☐
72e	1982	Dodge 'PEPSI' Truck	Red and White body, Red/Wh/Blue decal, SF. 72 mm.		NRP ☐
	1984	'KELLOGGS'	Red and White body	£2-£4	MPR ☐
		Wheel change	With Gold hubs	£8	NC ☐
	1984	'SMITHS CRISPS'	With crisp packet design	£8	NC ☐
	1984	'STREETS ICE CREAM'	Australian issue	£8	NC ☐
	1985	'HERTZ'	All Yellow body		NRP ☐
	1986	'ROYAL MAIL'	Red body		NRP ☐
	1987	'RISI'	All Yellow body		NRP ☐
	1987	'JETPRESS'	White body, Australian	£8	NC ☐
	1988	'YORKIE'	Blue body, Red/Yellow design. PRM		NRP ☐
	1988	'KIT KAT'	Red Body, Red/White design. PRM		NRP ☐
72f	1986	Sand Racer	(USIM)	£3-£5	MPR ☐
72g	1986	Ford 'SUPERVAN 2'	White/Blue body & TPD, CCC.		NRP ☐
	1987	Colour change	Med or Dark Blue body		NRP ☐
	1988	Design change	White body, Blue/Red design 'STARFIRE'		NRP ☐

Ref. No.	Year	Model Type	Description	Price	Rarity	
73a	1960	R.A.F. 10 ton Refueller	Blue body, R.A.F. roundel, GPW. 65 mm.	£24	MPR	☐
73b	1963	Ferrari Racing Car	Red body, Grey or White driver RN '73', BPT.	£5-£8	MPR	☐
73c	1969	Mercury Commuter	Metallic Lime Green, CW/BPT	£6-£8	MPR	☐
	1972	Colour change	Red body version	£2-£4	MPR	☐
73d	1974	Weasel	Met Green body, Black RGT/SF/RLM. 72 mm.	£2-£4	MPR	☐
		Colour change	Dark Military Green body	£50	GP	☐
		Colour change	Light Military Green, Chrome hubs	£10	NC	☐
73e	1980	Model A Ford Series	Cream body, Green CH/TW, WW SPW and WDS, SF.	£5-£8	MPR	☐
	1981	Colour change	TT Green body and CH, WW SPW and WDS, TW/SF	£4-£6	MPR	☐
	1982	Colour change	Cream/Blk body, Brown CH, Orange TW, SF	£2-£4	MPR	☐
	1984	Colour change	Brown body, Black LWB & roof	£2-£4	MPR	☐
	1985	Colour change	Red body, otherwise SAPM		NRP	☐
	1986	Colour change	Black body, Yellow/Red fire design		NRP	☐
		Code & PRM	Met Green/Green 'CLIMAT' label	£25	GP	☐
74a	1960	Mobile 'REFRESHMENTS' Bar	White body, Pale Blue base, Blue interior, opening hatch, GPW/H. 67 mm.	£50	GP	☐
		Colour change	Cream body, GPW	£50	GP	☐
		Colour change	Pink body, GPW	£100	GP	☐
		Colour change	Silver body, Green base, SPW or GPW	£18	NC	☐
		Colour change	Silver body, Blue base, VS	£15	NC	☐
74b	1966	Daimler Fleetline Double Decker Bus 'ESSO EXTRA'	Cream body, Red/White/Blue labels, BPW. 76 mm.	£15	NC	☐
	1968	Colour change	Green body otherwise SAPM	£15	NC	☐
	1969	Colour change	Red body, BPT & SF.	£12	NC	☐
		Variants	With 'INN ON THE PARK' logo	£50	GP	☐
			Pink body, Red or Pink base	£12	NC	☐
74c	1973	Toe Joe Breakdown Truck	Met Green body, 2 Red PH, 2 SL, SF. 75 mm.	£2-£4	MPR	☐
		Colour change	Green/White body	£50	GP	☐
		Colour change	Yellow/Red body, 'HITCH HIKER'	£50	GP	☐
			NB. Many other variations exist.			
74a		'Orange Peel'	White/Orange body, RN '70' (USIM)	£4-£6	MPR	☐
74e	1979	Cougar Villager	Met Green body, Yellow interior. 76 mm.	£2-£4	MPR	☐
		Variants	Met Blue body, Orange/Yellow int	£14	NC	☐
			Met Blue with Black int (Bulgarian)	£15	NC	☐
			Met Green with Black int (Bulgarian)	£15	NC	☐
			NB. Many other variations exist.			
74f	1982	'FIAT' Abarth	White body, *Matchbox Toys*, RN '45', SF. 76 mm.	£1-£3	MPR	☐
	1983	Design change	White body, RN '3', *'ALITALIA'*		NRP	☐
74g		Mustang	(USIM) Orange body, 'GT' logo	£4-£6	MPR	☐
74h		'TOYOTA' MR2	White body, 'MR 2', 'PACE CAR', CCC.		NRP	☐
75a	1960	Ford Thunderbird	Cream body, Peach front sides, Green TW, Blue base in VS, SPW. 67 mm.	£20	NC	☐
		Base change	SAPM with SPW & Black base	£12	NC	☐
		Base & wheel change	SAPM with GPW or BPW	£12	NC	☐
75b	1965	Ferrari Berlinetta	Met Green body, Silver base, BPW.	£12	NC	☐
		Colour change	SAPM with unpainted base	£10	NC	☐
		Colour change	Red body, White seats, BPW	£3-£5	MPR	☐
75c	1971	Alfa Carabo	Pink body, Yellow BP, SF. 76 mm.	£2-£4	MPR	☐
		Colour change	Red body, Streetcar design, Yellow BP	£2-£4	MPR	☐
			NB. There are many other variations.			
75d	1977	Seasprite Helicopter	Red and White body, *Rescue* Blk Rotors. 74 mm.	£2-£4	MPR	☐
75e	1982	'MB TV NEWS' Helicopter	Orange/White body, TW. 76 mm.		NRP	☐
75f	1983	'POLICE' Helicopter	Black/White body, Black rotors		NRP	☐
	1984	Colour change	Orange body, *Rescue* logo		NRP	☐

Miscellaneous models from around the world and the prices asked

Ref. No.	Model Type	Description	Price	Rarity	
76	Mazda	Australian issue	£6	NC	☐
77	Toyota Celica	Australian	£6	NC	☐
77	Helicopter	Japanese issue	£6	NC	☐
78	Datsun	Australian issue	£6	NC	☐
78	Porsche	Turbo-Red Japanese issue	£6	NC	☐
79	Mitsubishi Galant	Australian issue	£6	NC	☐
	Toyota Celica	Red *Sunburner* US issue	£6	NC	☐
	Challenger	Green *Hot Points* US issue	£6	NC	☐
	Datsun Fairlady	Black Phantom, US issue	£10	NC	☐
	Code Red	Helicopter, US issue	£6	NC	☐

124

Matchbox Gift Sets

The first presentation set was sold in the USA in 1957 and consisted of an enlarged normal 'Matchbox' containing eight of the sixty-four models that Lesney manufactured at that time. The first sets not being sold in the UK until 1959.

1957					
	PS1 Presentation Set	Contains 1—8 only available in USA	£500	NPE	☐
	PS2 Presentation Set	Contains 9—16 only available in USA	£500	NPE	☐
	PS3 Presentation Set	17—24 only available in US	£500	NPE	☐
	PS4 Presentation Set	25—32 only available in USA	£500	NPE	☐
	PS5 Presentation Set	33—40 only available in USA	£500	NPE	☐
	PS6 Presentation Set	41—48 only available in USA	£500	NPE	☐
	PS7 Presentation Set	49—56 only available in USA	£500	NPE	☐
	PS8 Presentation Set	57—64 only available in USA	£500	NPE	☐

1959					
	PS1 Private Owner Set	Contains 19 MGA, 43 Hillman Minx, 45 Vauxhall Victor A-3 Garage	£100	NPE	☐
	PS2 Transporter and 4 Cars Set	Contains 30 Ford, 31 Ford Station Wagon, 33 Ford Zodiac, 36 Austin A50, A2 Transporter	£125	NPE	☐
	PS3 Transporter and 6 Cars Set	Contains 22 Vauxhall Cresta, 32 Jaguar XK, 33 Ford Zodiac, 43 Hillman Minx, 44 Rolls Royce Silver Cloud, 45 Vauxhall Victor A2 Transporter	£150	NPE	☐
	PS4 Commercial Vehicle Set	Contains 5 Bus, 11 Petrol Tanker, 21 Long Distance Coach, 25 Dunlop Van, 35 Horse Box, 40 Bedford Tipper, 47 Brooke Bond, 60 Morris Pickup	£350	NPE	☐
	PS5 Army Personnel Carrier Set	Contains M3 Personnel Carrier, 54 Saracen, 55 DUKW, 61 Ferret, 62 General Service Lorry, 63 Ambulance, M3 Tank Transporter	£125	NPE	☐

NB. The packaging for the first UK issued sets consisted of a frail blue box with a yellow lid panel on which were displayed in red, the models which made up the set. Sets in similar packaging were issued for the German market. See photo.

G-1	1960/1	Commercial Motor Set	Contains 5b 'PLAYERS PLEASE' GPW, 57 mm. 47a 'BROOKE BOND' Van, GPW; 69a 'NESTLES' Van, GPW; 60a 'BUILDERS SUPPLY COMPANY' Pick Up, RWDS/GPW; 37a 'COCA COLA' Lorry, Even Load, GPW; 59a Ford 'SINGER' Van GPW; 20a 'EVER READY' Truck, GPW; 51a Albion 'PORTLAND CEMENT' Lorry, GPW	£300	GP	☐
G2	1960/1	Car Transporter Set	Contains A2, 22, 25, 33, 39, 57 & 75	£150	GP	☐
G3	1960/1	Building Constructors Set	Contains 2, 6, 15, 16, 18, 24, 28 & M1	£125	GP	☐
G4	1960/1	Farm Set	Contains 12, 23, 31, 35, 50, 72 & M7	£100	GP	☐
G5	1960/1	Military Vehicles	Contains 54, 62/3/4, 67/8 & M3	£125	GP	☐
	1960/1	Garage Set 'C'	Contains 8 various models, a garage, R1 (roadway) A1 Esso pumps, A2 Transporter, M6 'Pickfords'	£300	NPE	☐
G1	1962/3	Commercial Vehicle Set	Contains 5c Visco-Static, 10c, 12b, 13c, 14c, 21c, 46b, 74a	£250	GP	☐
G2	1962/3	Car Transporter Set	Contains 25b, 30b, 31b, 39b, 48b, 65b, Accessory Pack No 2	£200	GP	☐
G3	1962/3	Constructional Plant Set	Contains 2, 6, 15, 16, 18, 24, 28 & M1	£200	NPE	☐
G4	1963	Agricultural Implements and Farm Vehicles Set	Contains 12, 23, 31, 35, 50, 72, M7	£200	NPE	☐
G4	1963	Grand Prix Set	Contains 13c, 14b, 19c, 41b, 47b, 52a, 32b, 73b, Major Pack No 1 R4 Racetrack	£250	NPE	☐
G5	1963	Army Gift Set	Contains 54a, 62a, 63a, 67a, 68a, 64a, Major Pack No 3	£125	GP	☐
G10	1963	Service Station Set	Contains Service Station, 13c, 25b, 31b, and Accessory Pack No 1	£45	GP	☐
G1	1965	Motorway Set	Contains 6, 10, 13, 33, 34, 38, 48, 55, 71, R1 layout	£100	NPE	☐
G2	1965	Car Transporter Set	Contains 22c, 28c, 36c, 75b, Major Pack 8b	£65	GP	☐
G3	1965	Vacation Set	Contains 12c, 23c, 27d, 42b, 45b, 56b, 68b, and Sports Boat on Trailer	£65	GP	☐
G4	1965	Racetrack Set	Contains 13d, 19d Green, 19d Orange, 41c White, 41c Yellow, 52b Blue, 52b Red, 54b, Major Pack M6 29c	£65	GP	☐
G5	1965	Army Gift Set	Contains 12, 49, 54, 61, 64, 67, M3	£125	GP	☐
G5	1965	Fire Station Set	Contains Fire Station, 29c, 54b, 59c	£155	GP	☐
G6	1965	Commercial Trucks Set	Contains 6, 15, 16, 17, 26, 30, 58, 62	£65	GP	☐
G9	1965	Service Station Set	Contains 13, 33, 71, A1, MG1	£45	GP	☐
G10	1965	Fire Station Set	Contains MF1, 14, 59, 2 of No 9	£55	GP	☐
G1	1967	Service Station Set	Contains Service Station, 32c, 13d, 64b	£40	NC	☐
G2	1967	Transporter Set	Contains Transporter, 14d, 24c, 31c, 53c	£45	NC	☐
G3	1968	Farm Set	Contains 12c, 37d, 40c, 43c, 65c, 72b, 47c, 39c	£45	NC	☐
G4	1968	Race 'N Rally Set	Contains 19d Orange, 19d Green, 52b Blue, 52b Red, 29d, 3c, 41c, 67b, 25d, 8e	£65	NC	☐
G6	1970	Truck Set	Contains 1e, 10d, 21d, 30c, 60b, 70b, 49b, 26c	£55	NC	☐
G1	1970	Service Station Set	Contains 13e, 32d, 15e and Service Station	£35	NC	☐
G2	1970	Transporter Set	Contains Transporter and 5 SF models	£35	NC	☐
G3	1970	Racing Specials Set	Contains 5e, 20d, 45c, 56c, 52c, 68c	£35	NC	☐
G4	1970	Truck Superset	Contains 47c, 63d, 58d, 49c, 16d, 21e, 11d, 51d	£45	NC	☐
G2	1973	Transporter Set	Contains Transporter and 5 SF models	£35	NC	☐

Ref. No.		Model Type	Gift Sets continued	Price and Rarity Grading	
G3	1973	'WILD ONES' Set	Contains 5 Superfast Cars	£35	NC ☐
G4	1973	Team Matchbox Set	Contains Racing Car Transporter and 4 Racing Cars	£30	NC ☐
G6	1973	Drag Race Set	Contains 5 Superfast Cars	£30	NC ☐
G7	1973	Ferry Boat	Contains Plastic Boat and 4 SF Cars	£15	NC ☐
G11	1978	Strike Force Set	Contains 6 Army Vehicles	£45	NC ☐
G12	1978	Rescue Set	Contains 6 Rescue Vehicles	£20	NC ☐
G13	1978	Construction Set	Contains 6 Construction Vehicles	£20	NC ☐
G14	1978	Grand Prix Set	Contains Transporter and 4 Racing Cars	£20	NC ☐
G15	1978	Transporter Set	Contains Transporter and 5 SF Cars	£20	NC ☐
G7	1978	Car Ferry Set	Contains 3 Cars and Sports Boat	£15	NC ☐
G1	1981	Transporter Set	Contains Transporter and 5 SF Cars	£15	NC ☐
G2	1981	Railway Set	Contains 43f, 2×4 4f, 25g	£10	NC ☐
G3	1981	Racing Car Set	Contains Transporter and 4 Racing Cars	£10	NC ☐
G4	1981	Military Assault	Contains, Landing Craft and 6 Models	£10	NC ☐
G5	1981	Construction Set	Contains 5 Construction Models	£10	NC ☐
G6	1981	Farm Set	Contains 6 Farming Models	£10	NC ☐
G7	1981	Emergency Set	Contains 5 Rescue Models	£10	NC ☐
G1	1984	Transporter Set	Contains K10 plus, 4 Cars	£6-£9	MPR ☐
G7	1984	Emergency Set	Contains Models 8, 12, 22, 57, 75	£6-£9	MPR ☐
G8	1984	Turbo Charged Set	Contains Turbo Charger plus 7, 9, 52, 60, 68	£6-£9	MPR ☐
G10	1986	'PAN-AM'	Contains 10, 54, 64, 65 & Sky Buster Boeing		NGPP ☐
G11	1986	'LUFTHANSA'	Contains 30, 54, 59, 65 & Skybuster A300 Airbus		NGPP ☐
G3	1987	JCB Gift Set	Contains 32, 60, 75 & Skybuster Lear Jet		NGPP ☐
	1988	40 years Set	Contains Aveling Barford Road Roller, London Bus, Horse Drawn Milk Float, Massey Harris Tractor, Dennis Fire Engine		NGPP ☐

N.B. These models may be distinguished from the original issues for they display 'Made in Macau' on the underneath of the body.

Miscellaneous Sets

C6		Japanese Emergency Gift Set	All Japanese Set	£12	NC ☐
C11		Japanese Airport Gift Set	Japanese Foam Pump, Ikarus Coach & Aircraft	£15	NC ☐
		Japanese Cars Gift Set	JPS Lotus, VW, Gold RR & Mercedes	£25	NC ☐
		Las Vegas Dodge Set	Car and Van	£120	GP ☐

Early Accessory Packs

1a	1957	'ESSO' Petrol Pump Set	Red pumps, White figure	£11	NC ☐
b	1963	'BP' Petrol Pump Set	White pumps, Yel/White decal	£11	NC ☐
2	1957	'MATCHBOX CAR TRANSPORTER'	All blue body, Silver trim, GMW	£25	NC ☐
3	1957	Garage	Yellow/Green/Red, opening doors, all metal	£10	NC ☐
4	1960	Road Signs Set	Eight Red/White/Black signs *Lesney* on BP	£5	NC ☐
5	1960	'HOME STORES'	Food shop with window display, OD	£11	NC ☐

N.B. In 1959 the first of a continuing series of 'MATCHBOX GARAGES' was issued (MG1A). In 1963 a 'MATCHBOX FIRE STATION' was issued (MF1A). Models made of Plastic £28 NC (Both).

1976—1981 'TWO PACK MODELS' — 'TP' SERIES

TP1	1976	Mercedes Truck and Trailer	Blue/Yellow body, 'IMS' logo (Nos. 1e & 2d)	£7	NC ☐
			Red/Yellow body, 'TRANSCONTINENTAL'	£5	NC ☐
TP2	1976	Mod Tractor and hay trailer	Red tractor, Yellow trailer (Nos 25e & 40c)	£5	NC ☐
TP2	1979	Police Car and Fire Engine	Either 22e or 35c with 59d	£7	NC ☐
TP2	1981	'EXXON' Tanker	Red Cab & chassis, Red White tank	£6	NC ☐
TP3	1976	Javelin & Pony Trailer	Green Javelin, Orange or Cream trailer, 2HS	£6	NC ☐
TP3		French issue	Jeep and pony trailer	£8	NC ☐
TP4	1976	Car and Caravan	Met Blue car, Yellow/Red caravan No. 57	£6	NC ☐
TP5	1976	Car towing boat	Orange Ford Capri and others	£6	NC ☐
	1981	Colour change	Blue car 'PHANTOM, and Blue boat & TRC	£6	NC ☐
TP5	1976	Lotus Set	2 Black JPS Lotus Cars	£12	NC ☐
TP6	1976	Breakdown Set	Nos. 61 or 74 with 15d VW or 65d Saab or 2ve Range R	£6	NC ☐
TP7	1976	Emergency Set	Strecha Fetcha No. 46 with either 59d or 64d	£6	NC ☐
TP7	1978	Jeep and Glider Set	Yellow jeep No. 38c plus trailer	£5	— ☐
	1981		Red jeep and trailer	£5	— ☐
TP7	1978	Escort & Glider Set	No. 9f plus trailer	£5	— ☐
TP8	1976	Bus & Hovercraft	No. 17d (CARNABY ST. Labels) & No. 72c	£5	NC ☐
TP8	1977	Field Car & Motorcycle	Orange No. 18c with Silver base plus Honda 38c	£6	NC ☐
	1981	Colour change	Yellow car and TRC, Green M/C	£6	NC ☐
TP9	1978	Field Car & Racing Car	No.18c with Team Matchbox No.24	£8	NC ☐
	1981	Colour change	Orange car and racing car	£6	NC ☐
TP10	1978	M'cedes AMB & Fire Chief	With fire labels No.59d with 3c	£6	NC ☐
TP11	1977	Jeep and Motorcycle	Military Green No.38c with 'JEEP' or BP plus 18f	£25	NC ☐
		Model change	SAPM with No.2c plus 18f Hondaroma	£6	NC ☐
TP11	1979	Tractor & Hay Trailer	Red tractor and trailer Nos.25e and 40c		NC ☐
	1981	Colour change	Green tractor, Yellow trailer	£5	NC ☐
TP12	1977	Military Police & Field Car	Dark Military Green 'POLICE' labels Nos.20e & 18c	£25	NC ☐
			SAPM with 'AMBULANCE' labels	£25	NC ☐
TP12	1977	Field Car & VW Ambulance	Military Green	£25	NC ☐

Ref. No.		Model Type	'TP' Series continued	Price and Rarity Grading		
TP13	1977	Weasel & Stoat	Dark Military Green	£100	GP	☐
TP13	1978	Unimog & Gun	Nos.49b in Military Green plus 32e	£6	NC	☐
TP14	1977	Tanker & Badger	Dk Military Green (French flap on tanker)	£50	GP	☐
TP14	1978	M'cedes AMB & Staff Car	Military Green No.3c plus MG No.46	£5	NC	☐
TP15	1977	M'cedes Truck & Tri	Military Green Nos.1e and 2d, 'USA 48350' labels	£35	NC	☐
TP16	1977	Dump Truck & Bulldozer	In Dark Military Green — 28d Mack truck	£30	NC	☐
		Colour change	In normal Military Green livery	£6	NC	☐
TP16	1979	Wreck Truck & Stalwart	Military Green finish Nos.71c and 61b	£6	NC	☐
TP16	1980	Artic Truck & Trailer	Yellow/Blue body for each model	£5	NC	☐
		Colour change	Red/Silver body for each model	£12	NC	☐
TP17	1979	Tanker and Trailer	Red/White body 'CHEVRON' logo No.63	£5	NC	☐
		Colour change	White/Yellow body 'SHELL' logo No. 63	£5	NC	☐
TP18	1979	Water Sporter	Red 7e VW Golf, Red/White 5f	£6	NC	☐
TP19	1980	Cattle Truck & TRC	Red/Cream body for each model, 2 cows	£5	NC	☐
TP20	1980	Shunter & Side Tipper	Cream/Red 24c, Red or Black side tipper	£6	NC	☐
	1981	Colour change	Yellow/Red bodies, 'D1496-RF' logo	£5	NC	☐
TP21	1980	Datsun & M/C Trailer	Met Blue 24f, 3 Cream or Red bikes	£6	NC	☐
TP21	1980	Citroen & M/C Trailer	Met Blue 12f, RR, 3 Red or Cream bikes	£6	NC	☐
TP22	1980	Container Truck	Met Red cab, Cream containers	£4	NC	☐
	1981	With logo	SAPM with 'OCL' logo in Blue	£6	NC	☐
TP23	1980	Covered Truck	Red/White body, AV, 'FIRESTONE'	£4	NC	☐
TP24	1980	Box Truck	All Red body, 'FIRESTONE' in White 8w	£8	NC	☐
		Colour change	Cream cab, Yellow box, 'KODAK' 8w	£150	GP	☐
		Colour change	Cream cab, Red trailer base 'MATCHBOX'	£4	NC	☐
		Colour change	Cream cab, Black trailer base 'MATCHBOX'	£8	NC	☐
		Colour change	Red cab, Red trailer base	£8	NC	☐
TP25	1980	Pipe Truck	Met Green cab, Black TRL base, 3 Red pipes	£4	NC	☐
		Colour change	Yellow cab version	£16	NC	☐
TP26	1981	Boat Transporter	Blue cab, Silver TRL, Red/Cream boat	£4	NC	☐
TP27	1981	Steam loco & Caboose	Green/Black logo, Green/Cream/Black Caboose	£4	NC	☐
TP28	1982	Cortina & Caravan	Bronze/White 25d, Red/White 'SUN SET' caravan 57d	£6	NC	☐
TP29	1982	Flareside Pickup & boat	Blue 57f plus Blue/White boat	£6	NC	☐
TP30	1982	Datsun and speed boat	Silver/Red 24f, Yellow/Black 5f	£5	NC	☐
TP31	1982	Citroen & M/C Trailer	Yellow 12f and trailer with 3 Red bikes	£5	NC	☐
TP32	1982	Wreck Truck & Dodge 1g	Green 61d, Orange/Blue 'REVIN REBEL'	£6	NC	☐
TP102	1984	Escort & Pony TRL	Green Escort and 'SEAGULL' trailer	£5	NC	☐
TP103	1984	Cattle Truck & TRL	Yellow cab and chassis, Brown cages, 4 cows	£4	NC	☐
TP104/5		No issues				
TP106	1984	Renault 5 & M/C TRL	Black car, Yel/Red panels, Yel/Red M/C TRG	£4	NC	☐
TP107	1984	Datsun & Caravan	Silver/Blue car, White caravan	£4	NC	☐
TP108	1984	Tractor & Hay TRL	Blue tractor, Red/Black trailer	£4	NC	☐
TP109	1984	Citroen & boat	White/Blue car, Black/White boat, Red TRL	£4	NC	☐
TP110	1984	Matra Rancho & boat	Black rancho, Yel log, Orange inflatable	£4	NC	☐
TP111	1984	Cortina & Horsebox	Red car, Yellow 'SILVERSHOES' horsebox, 2HS	£4	NC	☐
TP112	1985	Unimeg & Trailer	Yellow body, White covers, Red 'ALPINE RESCUE'	£4	NC	☐
TP113	1985	Porsche & Caravan	Black car, White/Orange caravan	£4	NC	☐

NB. Two Pack Models were only issued on blister cards.

Major Series Models

M1 a)	1960	Caterpillar Excavator	Yellow body, Silver MW, BPT. 99 mm.	£10-£14	MPR	☐
b)	1963	'BP' Petrol Tanker	Green/Yellow/White MB, CEM, BPW/TW. 102 mm.	£10-£14	MPR	☐
M2 a)	1960	Bedford Articulated Truck 'WALLS ICE CREAM'	Light Blue cab, Cream box TRL, Red and Blue logo, MW or GPW, No WDS, BB. 101 mm.	£28	GP	☐
b)	1963	York Trailer 'DANES TYRES'	Red cab, Grey box TRL, Silver trim, Yel/Black/Red decals, AV/10BPW/WDS/ORD. 117 mm.	£18	NC	☐
c)	1966	LEP International Transport	Silver cab, Maroon box trailer, Yel/Black/Red decals, AV/10BPW/WDS/ORD. 117 mm.	£16	NC	☐
M3	1960	Centurion Tank with Transporter	Olive Green TRPT and tank, BPW and Green RTR, MRW, DDR AV/10 wheels. 155 mm.	£20	NC	☐
M4 a)	1960	'RUSTON BUCYRUS'	Brown/Yel MB and jib, Green RTR, PRW. 99 mm.	£14	NC	☐
b)	1966	'FREUHOF' Hopper Train	Maroon TRL, 2 Sil hoppers, Red W, BPT. 286 m.	£20	NC	☐
M5	1966	'MASSEY FERGUSON' Combine	Red MB, Tan D, Yel blades, 2BPT/2SBPW. 117 mm.	£20	NC	☐
M6 a)	1960	'PICKFORDS' 200 Ton Transporter	Blue tractor (6W), Red/Blue TRL (12W), BPW. 279 mm.	£30	GP	☐
b)	1966	'BP RACING TRANSPORTER'	Green MB, Yel/Grn decal, Red hubs, BPT. 127 mm.	£14	NC	☐
M7	1960	'Jennings' Cattle Truck	Red tractor, Tan trailer, GBPW, DDR. 121 mm.	£14	NC	☐
M8 a)	1960	'MOBILGAS' Petrol Tanker	Red MB, Silver trim, Blk/Wh decal, GBPW. 99 mm.	£30	GP	☐
M8 b)	1964	Car Transporter 'FARNBOROUGH MEASHAM'	Blue cab, Orange TRL, Silver trim, DDR *Car Auction Collection* Orange hubs, GPT. 209 mm.	£16	NC	☐
M9	1962	'COOPER JARRETT' Freighter	Blue tractor, 2 TRL, 34 BPW, Yel/Blk, DCS. 289 mm.	£20	GP	☐
M10	1963	Dinkum Rear Dumper	Yellow MB and Dumper *DD70* Red hubs, BPT. 108 mm.	£6-£8	MPR	☐

Gift Set

G9	1963	Major Series Set	Contains Major Packs 1, 2, 4, 6	£75	GP	☐

'KING SIZED' Models — The Early Issues

Following the successful sales of Major Series Lesney Products decided to further develop the range by introducing a larger scale toy and a suitable name was KING size. Ultimately the popular Major Models were themselves built into the King Size series when the Major Model series was discontinued in 1966.

K1a	1960	Hydraulic Shovel	All Yellow body, Grey plastic wheels, 'WEATHERILL'	£18	NC	☐
b	1963	Tipper Truck	Red cab and chassis, Orange tipper, 8W, 'HOVERINGHAM'	£18	NC	☐
c	1970	Excavator	Red body, Silver shovel, TW, 'O & K' logo, BPT	£10	NC	☐
K2a	1960	Dumper Truck	Red body, 'MUIR HILL 14B', Black or Green, MW	£8	NC	☐
b	1964	Dumper Truck	Yellow body, 'KW DART' logo, 6 Red wheels, BPT.	£15	NC	☐
c	1968	Scammell Wreck Trucks	White body, Red jib & wheels, Grey H, 'ESSO' logo	£15	NC	☐
		Colour change	Gold body version	£15	NC	☐
K3a	1960	Caterpillar Bulldozer	Yellow body, Red engine, Grey metal rollers	£15	NC	☐
		Colour change	SAPM with Red metal rollers	£10	NC	☐
		Colour change	SAPM with Yellow metal rollers	£10	NC	☐
b	1965	Tractor Shovel	Orange body, Red wheels 'HATRA'	£15	NC	☐
c	1970	Tractor & Trailer	Each has Red body, Yellow trim, 'MASSEY FERGUSON' logo	£10	NC	☐
K4a	1960	Tractor	Red body, Green wheels, 'McCORMICK INTERNATIONAL'	£20	NC	☐
		Colour change	SAPM with Orange or Red wheel hubs	£15	NC	☐
b	1967	G.M.C. Tractor & Hoppers	Dark Red cab, 2 Silver hoppers, 'FRUEHAUF' logo	£20	NC	☐
c	1969	Leyland Tipper	Dark Red cab and chassis, Silver tipper 'W. WALES'	£15	NC	☐
		Colour change	SAPM with Yellow/Green body colours	£15	NC	☐
		Colour change	With Red cab and chassis, Green tipper	£15	NC	☐
		Colour change	With Blue cab and chassis, Silver tipper 'miner' label	£15	NC	☐
		Colour change	With Silver tipper and LE TRANSPORT logo	£20	NC	☐
K5a	1961	Tipper Truck	Yellow body and tipper, Red wheels, FODEN logo	£15	NC	☐
b	1967	Racing Car TPTR	Green body, Silver drop down rear door, Red wheels	£25	NC	☐
c	1970	Tractor and Trailer	Each has Yellow body, Red wheels, 'MUIR HILL'	£12	NC	☐
K6a	1961	Earth Scraper	Orange body, Red engine, 'ALL IS CHALMERS'	£15	NC	☐
b	1967	Mercedes Ambulance	White body, Silver grille, Red badge, man/stretcher	£15	NC	☐
K7a	1961	Rear Dumper	Yellow body, Red engine, 'CURTISS-WRIGHT'	£12	NC	☐
b	1967	Refuse Truck	Red body and wheels 'CLEANSING DEPARTMENT'	£10	NC	☐
		Colour change	Blue body version	£10	NC	☐
K8a	1962	Prime Mover & TPTR with Crawler Tractor	Each has Orange body with Yellow crawler 'LAING' logo in Black on Yellow panels (6x6w)	£45	GV	☐
b	1967	Guy Warrior Car TPTR	Blue cab, Yellow TPTR 'FARNBOROUGH MEASHAM'	£20	NC	☐
		Colour change	Orange cab, Orange or Yellow TPTR	£20	NC	☐
c	1970	'CATERPILLAR TRAXCAVATOR'	Yellow body and shovel, Blue or White driver	£20	NC	☐
K9a		Diesel Road Roller	Green body, Red wheels and driver 'AVELING BARFORD'	£10	NC	☐
b	1967	Combine Harvester	Red body, Yellow blades and wheels, 'CLAAS'	£15	NC	☐
		Colour change	Green body, Red blades and wheels 'CLAAS'	£15	NC	☐
K10a	1963	Tractor Shovel	Blue Green body, Red seat and wheels 'AVELING BARFORD'	£16	NC	☐
b	1966	Pipe Truck	Yellow body, Red wheels, 6 Grey pipes	£15	NC	☐
		Colour change	Super King issue — Purple body, Grey or Yellow pipes	£12	NC	☐
K11a	1963	Tractor & Trailer	Blue tractor, Grey/Blue trailer 'FORDSON SUPER MAJOR'	£25	NC	☐
b	1969	DAF Car TPTR	Yellow body, Yellow/Red decks, 'D.A.F.' logo	£14	NC	☐
		Colour change	Metallic Blue body, Gold trailer decks	£14	NC	☐
K12a	1963	Breakdown Truck	Green body, Yellow jib, 'MATCHBOX SERVICE STATION'	£25	NC	☐
b	1969	Scammell Crane Truck	Yellow body and chassis, 'LAING' on crane	£10	NC	☐
K13	1963	Concrete Truck	Orange body and barrel, 'READYMIX' logo	£16	NC	☐
		Logo change	SAPM with 'RMC' logo	£16	NC	☐
K14	1964	Jumbo Crane	Yellow body and crane, 'TAYLOR JUMBO CRANE'	£10	NC	☐
K15A	1964	Merryweather Fire Engine	Red body, Silver ladder, 'KENT FIRE BRIGADE'	£15	NC	☐
K15B	1973	THE LONDONER DOUBLE DECKER BUS				
i)	1973	Red body	'SWINGING LONDON' CARNABY STREET' labels	£15	NC	☐
ii)	1977	Silver body	'SILVER JUBILEE', '1952 EIIR 1977' labels	£15	NC	☐
iii)	1978	Red body	'ENTER A DIFFERENT WORLD — HARRODS' labels	£10	NC	☐
iv)	1978	Red body	'HAMLEYS THE FINEST TOY SHOP' labels	£10	NC	☐
v)	1979	Red body	'TOURIST LONDON — BY BUS' labels	£10	NC	☐
vi)	1980	Red body	'VISIT THE LONDON DUNGEON' labels	£10	NC	☐
vii)	1981	Red body	'LONDON DUNGEON MUSEUM' labels	£10	NC	☐
viii)	1981	Silver body	'THE ROYAL WEDDING 1981' labels	£10	NC	☐
ix)	1985	Red/White body	'NESTLE MILKY BAR' labels	£5-£10	MPR	☐
x)	1986	Red body	'LONDON WIDE TOUR BUS' labels	£5-£10	MPR	☐
K16	1966	Tractor & twin tippers	Green cab, Yellow tippers, 'DODGE TRUCKS' in Red.			☐
		Colour change	Yellow cab, Blue tippers same logo (22w)	£35	GV	☐

Ref. No.		Model Type	'King Sized' Models continued	Price and Rarity Grading		
K17	1967	Low Loader & Bulldozer	Green cab and loader, Red/Yel Bulldozer	£25	NC	☐
K18	1966	Artic Horse Box	Red cab, Brown box, 4 White horses 'ASCOT STABLES'	£15	NC	☐
K19	1967	Scammell Tipper	Red body, Yellow tipper, Silver trim	£14	NC	☐
K20	1968	Tractor Transporter	Red body, Yellow rack, 3 Blue tractors (39c)	£24	NC	☐
		Colour change	SAPM with Orange tractors	£24	NC	☐

N.B. After 1970 the KING SIZE range developed into the larger SUPER KING Series.

G8 — Gift Sets

Ref. No.		Model Type	Model Features and Size	Price and Rarity Grading		
	1963	King Size Set	Contains K1a, K2a, K3a, 5a, K6a	£60	GV	☐
	1965	Construction Set	Contains K16, K7a, K10a, K13 Concrete Truck, K14 Crane	£75	GV	☐
	1966	King Size Set	Contains K16, K11a, K12a, K15	£40	GV	☐

The Early Lesney Toys

Lesney Products first produced diecast toys in 1948. Whilst production ceased during the Korean war period (1950-52) the models produced formed the basis from which the 1—75 series was launched in 1953. The models were sold in boxes under the name of 'MOKO' who were ultimately to also market all the early 1—75 series models.

Ref. No.	Model Type	Model Features and Size	Price and Rarity Grading		
i)	Road Roller	All Green body and flywheel, unpainted wheels	£250	GP	☐
	Colour change	SAPM with Red roller wheels and Yellow flywheel	£200	GP	☐
	Casting change	With a driver and without a flywheel	£200	GP	☐
	Casting change	Without both a driver and flywheel	£200	GP	☐
ii)	Cement Mixer	All Green body, Red wheels	£100	GP	☐
	Colour change	Pale Green body, Red mixer and wheels	£100	GP	☐
	Colour change	Dark Green body, Red mixer and wheels	£100	GP	☐
	Colour change	Red body, Green mixer and wheels	£100	GP	☐
iii)	Caterpillar Tractor	Orange body, Red roller wheels, Black rubber tracks driver	£100	GP	☐
iv)	Caterpillar Bulldozer	Green on Red body, driver, Black rubber tracks	£100	GP	☐
	Colour change	Yellow body, Red dozer blade and wheels	£100	GP	☐
v)	Prime Mover 'BRITISH ROAD SERVICES'	Orange body with Green removable engine covers & 6GPW/H. Blue trailer with 6GPW plus Red/Yellow bulldozer	£750	GP	☐
vi)	'MASSEY HARRIS' Tractor	Red body, Cream hubs, Black rubber tyres	£750	GP	☐
vii)	Excavator	Red lower body, Yellow upper body, Black rubber tracks and scoop '10RB' cast on	£150	GP	☐
viii)	Builders Crane	Blue or Grey versions exist — lattice work construction	£40	GP	☐
ix)	Small Farm Cart	Green body and shafts, 2 Yellow, 12 spoke wheels, Silver-Grey horse, Brown harness and standing man, plus 1 Cream basket load	£750	GP	☐
x)	Hayrake	Red frame, Blue rake and solid wheels			
xi)	Milk Cart	Orange body, White driver and 6 crates Black horse, GPW, with 'PASTEURISED MILK' cast into cart sides	£440	GP	☐
	Colour change	SAPM with Grey Silver horse	£440	GP	☐
	Colour change	Blue body, Black horse	£440	GP	☐
		N.B. Model sold at Lacy Scotts, Bury St. Edmunds auction Feb. 1988 for £440.			
xii)	Breadbait press	Red body with unpainted butterfly press	£25	NC	☐
xiii)	Quarry Truck	Yellow body, Black tyres, 'LAING'	£350	NPE	☐
xiv)	Covered Wagon with Barrels	Green body, White cover, 2 Red barrels, six mid Brown horses, White tails with straight rider and wagon driver	£200	GP	☐
xv)	Covered Wagon without Barrels	SAPM with Chocolate Brown horses and no barrels	£200	GP	☐
xvi)	Merchants Cart	Yellow body and shafts, Red spoke wheels — large (13) small (9), Black horse, Brown driver, 7 pieces of junk, 'RAG & BONE MERCHANT' cast in.	£1000	GP	☐
xvii)	Scooter and rider	Brown or Grey scooter, Blue/Red rider	£200	NPE	☐
xviii)	Soap box roller	Brown box, Grey spoke wheels (16 and 9), Dark Blue boy with Pink face	£750	NPE	☐
xix)	Large Coronation Coach	Gold coach with King and Queen, eight White horses, Gold/Red trappings, 4 Red riders. 200 issued	£750	GP	☐
xx)	Large Coronation Coach	Gold, Silver or Gilt coach with just the Queen inside. Horses and riders SAPM	£150	GP	☐
xxi)	Small Coronation Coach	Silver or Gold coach, 8 White horses with Red/Gold trappings, 4 Red riders, 'A MOKO TOY BY LESNEY' cast into horsebar (1000000 sold)	£75	NC	☐

OTHER EARLY LESNEY TOYS
Collectors should be aware that in addition to diecast models some tinplate items were also produced namely:- a clockwork 'JUMBO elephant, Muffin the Mule, 'PEREGRINE' puppet, a Red drummer boy

MODELS OF YESTERYEAR

Whilst prices for models at the rarefied top end of the market do appear to have reached a plateau, there have been steady if not spectacular rises in the price levels of most other collectable models. Demand for some of the 'DIFFICULT' to find models being particularly strong and resulting in large increases for certain models eg Y12-3 ARNOTTS for which the price has doubled.

PRICE AND RARITY CHANGES

		1981-83 Survey		1985 Survey		1988 Survey*
Y3-1	London Tramcar	£28	NC	£45	NC	£50-£65
Y5-1	Le Mans Bentley	£35	NC	£50	NC	£55-£70
Y8-1	Morris Cowley	£32	NC	£50	NC	£55-£70
Y12-1	Horse Drawn Bus	£40	NC	£50	NC	£55-£65
Y16-1	Pale Yellow Spyker	£14	NC	£20	NC	£17-£24
Y1-2	Red Model T Ford	£10-£13	MPR	£20	NC	£20-£25
Y4-2	Shand Mason 'KENT' Fire Engine	£88	GV	£110	GV	£125-£135
Y5-2	Metallic Apple Green Bentley	£120	GV	£250	GV	£325-£375
Y6-2	Blue Bugatti	£16	NC	£29	NC	£30-£38
Y12-2	Thomas Flyabout. Blue body, Yellow seats (the rare one)		NGPP	£1000	GV	£1000-£1250
Y2-3	Prince Henry Vauxhall. Red Seat version		NGPP	£1000	GV	£1000-£1250
Y12-3	Model T Ford Van 'COCA COLA'	£25		£35	NC	£35-£40
Y12-3	Model T Ford Van 'ARNOTTS'	£45		£75	NC	£150-£175
Y13-3	R.A.F. Tender	£12-£15	MPR	£35	NC	£35-£40
Y3-4	'ZEROLENE' Model T Ford Tanker	£25		£35	NC	£45-£50
Y4-4	Duesenburg — White body, Yellow Hood and Seats (the rare one)		NGPP	£1300	GV	£1350-£1500

*N.B. Price grading system changed for 1988 Survey. All prices shown on a Market Price Range basis.

The model listings have been prepared by reference to the renowned Matchbox 'Models of Yesteryear' collectors manual 'THE COLLECTION' by the kind permission of Matchbox International Ltd. 'THE COLLECTION' is the Bible for all 'Models of Yesteryear' collectors, for it contains full colour pictures of all the models and boxes, plus a full listing of the fascinating range of model variations. Furthermore an annual supplement ensures the information is kept fully up to date. The manual may be obtained by contacting your nearest Matchbox Toys official stockist or if in difficulty from the 'Matchbox International Collectors Association', (MICA) at 42 Bridge Street Row, Chester, England CH1 1NQ.

The listings in this catalogue therefore are not intended to replace in any way 'THE COLLECTION' listings, but have been solely prepared to provide Models of Yesteryear collectors with an idea of the amount they might reasonably expect to pay for all the normal models plus the better known variations. For those collectors requiring information about all the other variations plus pictures of the models and boxes described in these listings, a copy of 'THE COLLECTION' is an absolute must. Nevertheless for collectors without this book ample information has been provided to enable them to build up an excellent collection.

MODEL IDENTIFICATION

To ensure present owners of 'THE COLLECTION' can easily follow the model listings the same 'CODE' reference numbers have been employed. In addition to avoid any possible confusion which might arise by using this catalogues 'Price and Rarity Grading System', the same 'SCARCITY CATEGORIES' as used in 'THE COLLECTION' have been adopted as follows:-

SCARCITY CATEGORIES
EXTREMELY RARE   less than twenty known examples
VERY RARE   models that come onto the market very occasionally and command a very high premium.
RARE   models that come onto the market occasionally and command a high premium.
SCARCE   models that are on the market and command a premium.
DIFFICULT   models that are on the market but are hard to find.

MARKET PRICE RANGE
Alongside each model is shown the price range which indicates the likely asking price level. For recent issues or models that have yet to obtain a premium the normal retail price (NRP) grading has been given. This would normally indicate an asking price within the Market Price Range of £3-£5.

N.B. No price information has been given alongside models prone to being easily faked.

Common Features
Many models have common identifying features and these are shown below to avoid unnecessary repetition in the Features Column.

Models of Yesteryear
and **Made in England by Lesney**
All models issued prior to the end of 1982 have the above stamped onto their base-plates/chassis. With the change of ownership this was replaced by Matchbox Intl Ltd.

Wheels
All the wheels prior to 1970 were of metal construction.
   From 1972 approximately plastic wheels were used on all models. Nevertheless the models issued at this changeover period are to be found with either metal or plastic wheels. The varieties of wheels are:—
   Metal Spoke Wheels
   Metal or Plastic Spoke Wheels
   Plastic Bolt Head Wheels
   Plastic Spoke Wheels
   Solid Spoke Wheels

Scale Sizes
These are not all made to the same scale ranging from 34:1 to 130:1. The sizes are shown with the boxes which makes for easy reference.

Logos and Designs
The early models had waterslide transfers (WSTR). Labels have also been used and currently models display the latest types of attractive tempo print designs. (TPD).

Catalogue Listings
Do not place too much reliance on the model colours shown in catalogues. Very often the pictures shown are from mock-ups in colours never actually issued. E.g. the 1969 catalogue showed a picture of a Blue Y-5 (c) Peugeot when it was issued in Yellow. Similarly the 1973 catalogue showed a Silver Hispano Suiza when it was issued in Red.

Model Number and Name
It has been assumed that all models have both shown on the baseplate or chassis.

Bumpers, Dashboards, Headlights,
Radiator Shells and Windscreens
All assumed to be of metal construction prior to approx. 1974 after which time plastic was increasingly used.

Tyres
All assumed to be treaded Black Plastic unless otherwise indicated.

Country of Origin
Models 'Made in Macau' from 1987 onwards and shown on base plate eg Y1 SS Jaguar (Yellow)

Box Types
1956-60 i)   All card box with line drawing of model used for first 15 models issued.
        ii)   Same box with a blue number shown on a white circle on end flap.
1960-61
        iii)   Same as previous with a red number.
        iv)   All card box with coloured picture of the model — 3 varieties of this box exist.
        v)   All card box with model pictures on the box end flaps.
1968-69
        vi)   Window box — Pink/Yellow design.
1968-70
        vii)   SAPM — with hanging cards as developed in the U.S. market and led to the U.S. Blister pack design.
1969-70
        viii)   Window Box — Mauve/Purple stripe issue.
1974-78   'Woodgrain' window box.
1979-83x)   'Straw' window box.
1984   xi)   'Red' window box

N.B. Full details of which models were issued in which boxes are given in 'THE COLLECTION'.

LIST OF MODEL TYPES AND LOGOS

1st Issues

Y1-1 1925 Allchin 7NHP Steam Traction Engine
Y2-1 1911 'B' Type Bus
Y3-1 1907 'E' Class Tram
Y4-1 Sentinel Steam Wagon
Y5-1 1929 Le Mans Bentley
Y6-1 1916 A.E.C. 'Y' Type Lorry
Y7-1 Four ton Leyland Lorry — 'W & R JACOBS & CO'
Y8-1 Morris Cowley 1926 'BULLNOSE'
Y9-1 1924 Fowler 'BIG LION' Showman's Engine

Y10-1 1908 'GRAND PRIX' Mercedes
Y11-1 Aveling & Porter 1920 Steam Roller
Y12-1 1899 Horse Drawn Bus
Y13-1 1862 USA 'SANTE FE' Locomotive
Y14-1 1903 'DUKE OF CONNAUGHT' Loco'
Y15-1 1907 Rolls Royce Silver Ghost
Y16-1 1904 Spyker Veteran Automobile
Y17-1 1938 Hispano Suiza
Y18-1 1937 Cord 812
Y19-1 1933 Auburn Speedster
Y20-1 1937 Mercedes 540K
Y21-1 1930 Ford Model 'A' Wagon
       Woody Wagon
       'A & J BOX GENERAL STORES'
       'CARTERS'

Y22-1 1930 Ford Model 'A' Van
       'OXO'
       'MAGGI SOUPS'
       'TOBLERONE'
       'PALM TOFFEE'
       'POSTES CANADA POST'
       'SPRATTS'
       'LYONS TEA'

Y23-1 1922 A.E.C. 'GENERAL' 'S' Type
Omnibus
       'SCHWEPPES'
       'R.A.C.
       'MAPLES'
       'HAIG EXPRESS'
       'RICE KRISPIES'

Y24-1 1927 Bugatti T44
Y25-1 1910 Renault Type
       AG 'PERRIER'
       'JAMES NEALE'
       'DUCKHAMS OIL'
       'EAGLE PENCILS'
       'TUNNOCKS'
       'RED CROSS' AMBULANCE
       'DELHAIZE'

Y26-1 Crossley Delivery Truck
       'LOWENBRAU'
       'ROMFORD BREWERY CO'
       'GONZALEZ BYAS'

Y27-1 1927 Foden Steam Lorry
       'PICKFORDS'
       'HOVIS'
       'TATE & LYLE'
       'SPILLERS'
       'FRASERS'

Y28-1 Unic Taxi

Y29-a Walker Electric Van
       'HARRODS'
       'JOSEPH LUCAS'
       'HIS MASTER'S VOICE'

Y30-1 1930 Mack Truck
       'ACORN STORAGE'
       'CONSOLIDATED MOTORLINES'
       'ARCTIC ICE CREAM CO'
       'KIWI BOOT POLISH'

2nd Issues

Y1-2 1911 Model 'T' Ford car
Y2-2 1911 Renault Two Seater
Y3-2 1910 Benz Limousine
Y4-2 Shand Mason Horse Drawn Fire Engine
      i) Kent Fire Brigade
      ii) London Fire Brigade
Y5-2 1929 4½ Litre 'BLOWER' Bentley
Y6-2 1923 Type 35 Bugatti
Y7-2 1913 Mercer Raceabout
Y8-2 1914 Sunbeam Motorcycle & Sidecar
Y9-2 1912 Simplex
Y10-2 1928 Mercedes Benz 36/220
Y11-2 1912 Packard Landaulet
Y12-2 1909 Thomas Flyabout
Y13-2 1911 Daimler
Y14-2 1911 Maxwell Roadster
Y15-2 1930 Packard Victoria
Y16-2 1928 Mercedes Benz Coupe
Y17-2 No model issued
Y18-2 1918 Atkinson 'D' Type Steam Wagon
       'LAKE GOLDSMITH'
       'BLUE CIRCLE'
       'BASS & CO'
       'BURGHFIELD MILLS'
Y19-2 Showmans Engine

LIST OF MODEL TYPES AND LOGOS

3rd Issues

Y1-3 1936 SS100 Jaguar
Y2-3 1914 Prince Henry Vauxhall
Y3-3 1934 Riley MPH
Y4-3 1909 Opel Coupe
Y5-3 1907 Peugot
Y6-3 1913 Cadillac
Y7-3 1912 Rolls Royce
Y8-3 1914 Stutz
Y9-3 1920 3 ton Leyland Lorry
Y10-3 1906 Rolls Royce 'SILVER GHOST'
Y11-3 1938 Lagonda Drophead Coupe
Y12-3 1912 Ford Model 'T' Van
  'COLMANS MUSTARD'
  'ENJOY COCA COLA'
  'SUZE A LA GENTIANE'
  25th 'MODELS OF YESTERYEAR'
  'SMITHS POTATO CRISPS'
  'ARNOTTS BISCUITS'
  'BIRDS' Custard Powder
  'CEREBOS TABLE SALT'
  'HARRODS EXPRESS DELIVERY'
  'SUNLIGHT SEIFFE'
  'ROYAL MAIL'
  'CAPTAIN MORGAN BLACK LABEL'
  'HOOVER'
  'PEPSI COLA'
  'MOTOR 100'
  'IMBACA'
  H.J. HEINZ & Co'
  'ROSELCA'

Y13-3 1918 Crossley Wagon
  'R.A.F.' Tender
  'EVANS BROS COAL AND COKE'
  'CARLSBERG'
  'WARINGS'
  'KOHLE & KOKS'

Y14-3 1931 Stutz Bearcat

Y15-3 Preston type tram
  'SWAN MATCHES'
  'SWAN SOAP'
Y16-3 Ferrari Dino 246/V12
Y17-3 No model issued
Y18-3 1918 ATKINSONS STEAM WAGON
Y19-3 Morris Cowley Van
  'BRASSO'
  'MICHELIN'

4th Issues

Y1-4 No issue as yet
Y2-4 1930 4½ Lt Bentley

Y3-4 1912 Ford Model 'T' Tanker
  'BP'
  'ZEROLENE'
  'EXPRESS DAIRY'
  'CARNATION PRODUCTS'
  'MOBIL OIL'
  'CASTROL'
  'RED CROWN'
Y4-4 1930 Duesenberg Model 'J' Town Car
Y5-4 1927 Talbot Van
  'LIPTONS TEA' Royal Crest
  'LIPTONS TEA — CITY ROAD'
  'CHOCOLAT MENIER'
  'TAYSTEE BREAD'
  'NESTLES MILK'
  'CHIVERS & SONS LTD'
  'WRIGHTS SOAP'
  'EVER READY BATTERIES'
  'DUNLOP TYRES'
  'ROSES LIME JUICE'
Y6-4 1920 Rolls Royce Fire Engine
Y7-4 1930 Ford Breakdown Truck
Y8-4 1945 MG TC.
Y9-4 No issues
Y10-4 1957 Maserati 250F
Y11-4 1932 Bugatti Type S1
Y12-4 1937 GMC Van
Y13-4 No issues
Y14-4 1936 ERA R1B
Y15-4 No model issued
Y16-4 Scania Half Track Bus
Y17-4 No model issued
Y18-4 No model issued
Y19-4 No model issued
Y20-4 No model issued
Y21-4 1955 B.M.W. 507

5th Issues

Y1-5 No model issued
Y2-5 No model issued
Y3-5 No model issued
Y4-5 No model issued
Y5-5 No model issued
Y6-5 1932 Mercedes Benz Truck
  'STRUTTGART HOFFBRAU'
Y7-5 No model issued
Y8-8 Yorkshire Steam Wagon
  'JOHNNIE WALKER WHISKY'
Y9-5 No model issued
Y10-5 Diddler Trolley Bus
  RONUK/JEYES
Y11-5 No model issued
Y12-5 1937 GMC Van
  'GOBLIN'

Gift Sets
Codes 2 & 3 Models
Plated Model Issues — Giftware

Ref. No.		Model Type	Model Features and Size		Price Grading	

N.B.: The references to code numbers refer to the model variations listed in 'The Collection' book and should not be confused with the model codes described in the introductory pages.

Y1-1   **ALLCHIN TRACTION ENGINE**

	1956	Code 1	Mid-Green engine body, Dark Red spoke wheels with 10 at front and 16 at rear with unpainted 'straight across' treads and copper boiler door SCARCE	£175-£200	☐
		Code 2	Same as (1) but rear wheels with unpainted 'diagonal' treads	£55-£70	☐
	1983	Code 7	Mid-Green engine body, Gold boiler door, all smooth tread on rear wheels EXTREMELY RARE	£300-£400	☐
			All other codes	£55-£70	☐

Y2-1   **1911 'B' TYPE LONDON BUS**

	1956	Code 1	Post Office Red body, Grey spoke wheels, 8 front, 16 rear. Silver radiator shell, 4 small window frames over 4 larger window frames SCARCE	£130-£150	☐
		Code 2	Same as 1 but 8 small window frames above 4 large window frames	£55-£70	☐
			All other codes	£55-£70	☐

Y3-1   **1907 'E' CLASS TRAMCAR**

	1956	Code 1	Post Office Red body, Cream roof, Silver trim, thin Grey cow-catcher and unpainted wheels, cut out in luggage area beneath the stairs. RARE	£165-£195	☐
		Code 2	Same as 1 with double thick cow-catcher SCARCE	£90-£110	☐
		Code 3	Same as 2 with Powder Grey base plate, Silver or Gold trim VERY RARE	No Prices Available	☐
		Codes 5-9	With no cut out area beneath the stairs	£50-£65	☐

Y4-1   **SENTINEL STEAM WAGON — 'SAND & GRAVEL SUPPLIES'**

	1956	Code 1	Bright Blue body, cab and box, Black chassis & boiler, Grey metal spoke wheels. Yellow logo with Red border VERY RARE	No Prices Available	☐
		Codes 2 & 3	As 1 but with Gold box	£55-£70	☐
		Code 4	As 2 but with Black plastic wheels (24 treads) RARE	£160-£190	☐

Y5-1   **1929 LE MANS BENTLEY**

	1958	Code 1	British Racing Green body, same colour tonneau but with Grey rear end. Silver solid spoke wheels. Black knobbly tyres, spare wheel on near side, all Silver radiator, Black racing number '5', Red metal seats SCARCE	£100-£125	☐
		Code 2	As 1 but with Green radiator grille SCARCE	£10-£125	☐
		Code 3	As 2 but with Gold radiator surround RARE	£165-£190	☐
		Code 4	As 3 but with an all Green tonneau	£55-£70	☐
			All other codes	£55-£70	☐

Y6-1   **1916 A.E.C. 'Y' TYPE LORRY — 'OSRAM LAMPS'**

	1957	Code 1	Duck Egg Blue body, Grey metal spoke wheels (8 front/16 rear) White logo. EXTREMELY RARE	£700-£900	☐
		Codes 2 & 3	As 1 but with Light Grey body — with or without painted bonnet handles	£60-£85	☐
	1959	Codes 4 & 5	As 2 & 3 but with Dark Grey body — with or without painted bonnet handles SCARCE	£145-£165	☐
	1961	Code 6	As 4 & 5 but with unpainted bonnet handles and Black plastic wheels (24 treads front/30 treads rear) EXTREMELY RARE	£700-£900	☐

Y7-1   **FOUR TON LEYLAND —'W & R JACOB & Co.Ltd', 'by Royal appointment to His Majesty the King'.**

	1957	Codes 1 & 2	Dark Brown body with White or Cream roof, solid Grey metal wheels, Silver radiator. Yellow logo	£60-£85	☐
		Code 3	As 1 & 2 but with Light Brown body	£60-£85	☐
		Code 4	As 3 but without 'By Royal Appointment' etc logo EXTREMELY RARE	£600-£800	☐
		Code 5	As 3 but with Redish/brown body and radiator surround	£60-£85	☐
		Code 6	As 4 but with Black plastic wheels (24 treads front/32 treads rear) EXTREMELY RARE	£1000-£1200	☐

Y8-1   **1926 MORRIS COWLEY 'BULLNOSE'**

	1958	Code 1	Tan main body, Dark Brown lower body, unpainted metal spoke wheels (10), spare wheel on offside	£60-£80	☐
		Code 2	With Dark Tan body	£60-£80	☐

Ref. No.		Model Type	1st Issues continued	Price Grading
Y9-1		**1924 FOWLER SHOWMANS ENGINE — 'LESNEYS MODERN AMUSEMENTS'**		
	1958	Code 1	Dark Maroon body with a Cream roof, Gold cylinder block & chimney, smooth Orange/Yellow metal wheels. Copper boiler door. Brass canopy supports RARE	£150-£180 ☐
		Codes 2 & 3	As 1 but with Dark Maroon cylinder block with or without Gold boiler door	£60-£80 ☐
		Codes 4 & 5	Pale Maroon body with or without Silver boiler door	£60-£80 ☐
		Code 6	Bright Red body with White roof & Silver boiler door.	£60-£80 ☐
			All other codes	
Y10-1		**1908 'GRAND PRIX' MERCEDES**		
	1958	Code 1	Cream body, 2 spare tyres on rear, Green seats	£50-£70 ☐
		Code 6	With pure White body SCARCE	£100-£125 ☐
			All other codes	£50-£70 ☐
Y11-1		**AVELING & PORTER 1920 STEAM ROLLER**		
	1958	All Codes	Mid-Green body, Brown or Black flywheel, Black or Green canopy supports	£60-£80 ☐
Y12-1		**1899 HORSE DRAWN BUS — 'LIPTONS TEA'**		
	1959	All Codes	Red body, Black metal spoke wheels (16), Beige driver and metal seats. 'VICTORIA & KINGS CROSS'	£60-£80 ☐
Y13-1		**1862 'SANTE FE' Locomotive**		
	1959	Code 1	Dark Green and Maroon body, Black metal spoke wheels (12), Gold trim on condensers, boiler, smoke stack & headlight-lens	£55-£70 ☐
		Code 3	As (1) with Silver headlight lens and no Gold trim	£55-£70 ☐
		Code 6	Light Green body, Maroon headlight lens, no Gold trim EXTREMELY RARE	£700-£900 ☐
			All other codes	£55-£70 ☐
Y14-1		**'DUKE OF CONNAUGHT' locomotive**		
	1959	Code 1	Dark Green & Brown body, Brown metal spoke wheels (12), Gold trimmed sandbox on walkway not joined to main wheel arch. Gold trim on other main features DIFFICULT	£100-£125 ☐
		Code 3	As 1 but walkway sandbox with no Gold trim is not joined to main wheel arch	£55-£70 ☐
			All other codes	£55-£70 ☐
Y15-1		**1907 ROLLS ROYCE SILVER GHOST**		
	1960	Code 1	Metallic Silver Green body, Silver metal spoke wheels (12), Grey knobbly tyres, Brass radiator, Black seats, Silver number plate and Red rear lights DIFFICULT	£35-£45 ☐
		Code 2	As 1 but Metallic Silver Green rear lights and number plate DIFFICULT	£35-£45 ☐
		Code 3	As 2 but with Black knobbly tyres	£20-£25 ☐
		Code 7	With Gold spoke wheels (12), Black smooth tyres and Green seats SCARCE	£45-£55 ☐
			All other codes	£20-£25 ☐
Y16-1		**1904 SPYKER VETERAN AUTOMOBILE**		
	1961	Code 1	Pale Cream body, Silver spoke wheels (12), Grey knobbly tyres, Gold radiator surround, Green seats, spare wheel RARE	£200-£250 ☐
		Code 2	As 1 but with Pale Yellow body	£16-£22 ☐
		Code 3	As 2 but with Black knobbly tyres	£16-£22 ☐
		Code 4	As 3 but with without 'MODELS OF YESTERYEAR No.16' on baseplate and two unthreaded holes RARE	£100 ☐
		Code 5	As 4 but four braces on Gold wheels with fine tread tyres	£15-£20 ☐
		Code 6	As 5 but with Maroon body EXTREMELY RARE	£1200-£1400 ☐
		Codes 7 & 9		£15-£20 ☐
Y17-1	1974	Code 1	Metallic Red body, Black chassis, mudguards and roof	£10-£15 ☐
	1980	**1938 HISPANO SUIZA** Code 2	Two tone Metallic Silver Blue body, chassis and mudguards, Chrome 24 spoke wheels, Black textured roof	£5-£8 ☐
		Code 3	As 2 but with Black chassis and mudguards	£5-£8 ☐
	1981	Code 4	As 3 but with Silver solid wheels & whitewall tyres	£5-£8 ☐
		Code 5	As 4 but with Metallic Silver chassis & mudguards	£5-£8 ☐
	1986	Codes 6 & 7	Emerald Green body, Brass spoked wheels, Black roof, Black or Green radiator grille	NRP ☐

135

Y18-1   **1937 CORD 812**

1979	Code 1	Bright Red body, Chrome spoke wheels (24), whitewall tyres, White plastic roof and seats, Chrome trim	£6-£9 ☐
1983	Code 4	Plum Purple body, White roof, Chrome solid wheels	NRP ☐
	Codes 2 & 3		£6-£9 ☐

N.B. Whilst a White pre-production model is shown in 'THE COLLECTION', no price information has been given as this would set a precedent for the many other pre-production models known to exist, but which are not included in the 'THE COLLECTION'.

Y19-1   **1936 AUBURN SPEEDSTER**

1979	Codes 1 & 2	Light Brown main body, mid or Dark Brown lower body, Red solid wheels, White wall tyres, Chrome trim, Red seats	£6-£9 ☐
1983	Code 3	As 1 & 2 with Light Cream body, Black lower body	£5-£8 ☐
1985	Code 4	White body, Blue side panels, wheels and seats	NRP ☐

Y20-1   **1937 MERCEDES BENZ 540K**

1981	Code 1	Metallic Silver main body, Black lower body, Chrome trim, spare wheel at rear, opening dicky seat	£7-£10 ☐
	Code 2-5		£7-£10 ☐
1985	Code 6	White body with Red side stripe, seats and wheels	NRP ☐
1987	Code 7	Bright Red body, Beige seats, Chrome chassis	NRP ☐

Y21-1   **FORD MODEL 'A' WOODY WAGON**

1981	Code 1	Bright Yellow bonnet, Dark Brown lower body, Black roof, Red seats	£5-£8 ☐
	Codes 2 & 3		£5-£8 ☐
	Code 4	As 1 but with Black lower body, Orange seats and 'FORD MODEL A' on baseplate DIFFICULT	£30-£40 ☐
	Code 5	As 4 but with Dark Brown lower body, Dark Orange bonnet.	£12-£16 ☐

Y22-1   **FORD MODEL 'A' VAN**

The model features an all metal body with spoke wheels and spare wheel on nearside. Chrome trim

1982	'OXO' Code 1	Red main body, Black lower body and roof, Chrome wheels, Whitewall tyres, Blue/White logo	NRP ☐
	Codes 2-5		NRP ☐
1984	'MAGGI SOUPS' Code 1	Yellow main body, Black lower body, Red roof & 'MAGGIS' Chrome spoke wheels, Whitewall tyres	NRP ☐
	Codes 2-4		NRP ☐
1984	'TOBLERONE' Codes 1 & 2	Beige main body, Black lower body, Red roof & logo, Whitewall tyres, Chrome spoke wheels (24)	NRP ☐
1984	'PALM TOFFEE' Code 1	Off-White main body, Red lower body and roof, Gold spoke wheels (24), Red/Black logo	NRP ☐
1984	'POSTES CANADA POST' Code 1	Bright Red main body, Black lower body and roof, in special North American presentation box	£25-£35 ☐
	Code 2	As 1 but packed in normal Red box	NRP ☐
1986	'SPRATTS' Code 1	Reddish-Brown main body, Dark Brown lower body, White roof and logo, Chrome spoke wheels (24)	NRP ☐
1987	'LYONS TEA' Code 1	Dark Blue main body, Black lower body, Chrome spoke wheels (24), White roof, White/Orange logo	NRP ☐
	Code 2 As 1	But with Light Gold wheels DIFFICULT	£35-£45 ☐

Y23-1   **1922 AEC GENERAL**

The model features a metal lower body, with a plastic staircase, upperdeck, seats, safety bars and spoke wheels (12) on smooth Black tyres.

1983	'SCHWEPPES' Code 1	Red main body and wheels, Black lower body, Dark Brown seats and safety bars. Logo in Red on White label with round ends. RARE	£35-£45 ☐
	Code 2	As 1 but with Black and White label	£7-£10 ☐
	Codes 3 & 4	As 2 with either Mid or Light Brown safety bars	£5-£8 ☐
	Code 5	With White logo on Yellow label and single Red handrail	NRP ☐
	Code 6	As 5 but with unplated radiator surround DIFFICULT	£18-£24 ☐
1985	'R.A.C.' Code 1	Red main body, Black lower body, Blue/White label	NRP ☐
1985	'MAPLES' Code 1	Red main body, Black lower body, Green/White label (issued in gift set)	NRP ☐
1986	'HAIG' Code 1	Dark Brown lower body, off White upper body/staircase. Red wheels & logo	NRP ☐
	Codes 2 & 3		NRP ☐
1987	'KELLOGGS' Code 1	Red main body, Black lower body	NRP ☐

Ref. No.		Model Type	1st Issues continued		Price Grading
Y24-1		**1928 BUGATTI T44**			
	1983	Codes 1 & 2	Black main body, with Yellow door panels, Chrome spoke wheels (24) and trim, Tan or Brown plastic seats, 2SPW		NRP ☐
		Code 3	As 1 but with Green plastic seats	RARE	£35-£45 ☐
		Code 4	As 3 but with White plastic seats	RARE	£35-£45 ☐
		Code 9	With Black body line stripe on side windows and Black plastic seats	DIFFICULT	£18-£26 ☐
		Code 11	Light Grey main body with Red lower body		NRP ☐
			All other codes		NRP ☐
Y25-1		**1910 RENAULT TYPE 'AG' VAN**	The model features an all metal main body, with a plastic roof rack, seats and spoke wheels (12)		
	1983	'PERRIER'			
		Code 1	Two tone Green main body, White roof and logo, 3 struts at rear of roof rack	RARE	£125-£140 ☐
		Code 2	As 1 but with 4 struts at rear of roof rack		NRP ☐
		Codes 3 & 4			NRP ☐
	1985	'JAMES NEALES'			
		Code 1	Yellow main body & wheels, Blue lower body, White roof, Gold logo, Brass trim		£19-£25 ☐
		Code 3	As 1 but with 'open' grab handles	SCARCE	£45-£55 ☐
		Code 5	As 1 but with Navy Blue lower body	SCARCE	£45-£55 ☐
		Code 6	As 5 with 'open' grab handles	RARE	£70-£80 ☐
			Other codes		£19-£25 ☐
	1985	'DUCKHAMS OILS'			
		Code 1	Metallic Silver main body, Blue lower body, White roof, Red wheels		NRP ☐
		Code 2	As 1 but with 'open' grab handles		£35-£45 ☐
	1985	'EAGLE PENCILS'			
		Code 1	All Blue body, White roof, Brass trim and 'open' grab handles		NRP ☐
		Code 2	As 1 but with 'closed' grab handles	RARE	£35-£45 ☐
			Other codes		NRP ☐
	1986	'AMBULANCE'			
		Codes 1 & 2	Green main body, Black lower body, White label with Red cross and logo		NRP ☐
	1987	'TUNNOCKS'			
		Code 1	Red main body, Black lower body, White roof		NRP ☐
	1987	'DELHAIZE'			
		Code 1	Dark Green main body, White roof, Grey/White van sides with Gold logo		NRP ☐
Y26-1		**CROSSLEY DELIVERY TRUCK**	The model features a metal body with a plastic cab canopy and a plastic three barrel load.		
	1984	'LOWENBRAU LAGER'			
		Code 1	Blue main body, Black lower body, Tan canopy, Chocolate Brown barrels, Y13 on baseplate	DIFFICULT	£17-£23 ☐
		Code 2	As 1 but with Y13-26 cast on baseplate	VERY RARE	£90 ☐
		Code 3	As 1 but Y25 cast on baseplate	DIFFICULT	£17-£23 ☐
		Code 4	As 2 but canopy in Light Tan plastic		NRP ☐
	1986	Code 5	As 2 but very Light Tan canopy and very Dark Brown load	DIFFICULT	£17-£23 ☐
			N.B. Cab canopies and barrel loads are easily inter-changeable.		
	1986	'ROMFORD BREWERY'			
		Code 1	Black main body & canopy, Red/Brown lower body, Brass wheels, Gold logo, Brown seats		NRP ☐
		Code 2	As 1 but with Ruby Red seats	DIFFICULT	£18-£24 ☐
	1987	'GONZALEZ BYASS'			
		Code 1	White body, Red canopy, lower body & logo		NRP ☐
		Codes 2 & 3	As 1 with 'SHERRY' in White on load		NRP ☐
Y27-1		**1922 FODEN STEAM LORRY**	The model features a metal main body with a plastic canopy and cab roof, Gold smoke stack, daisy effect wheels		
	1984	'PICKFORDS'			
		Code 1	Blue truck body, Red lower body, Grey cab roof and canopy, Red wheels		NRP ☐
		Code 2	As (1) but truck body extends to 5 mm from bottom of cab panel.	SCARCE	£32-£39 ☐
		Code 3	As (2) but extension carries to bottom of cab panel		NRP ☐
			Variation with tow hook		£25-£30 ☐
	1985	'HOVIS'			
		Code 1	Dark Brown truck body, Black lower body, Light Brown cab roof & canopy		NRP ☐
	1986	'TATE & LYLE'S'			
		Code 1	Light Brown truck body, Black lower body, with side panel dividing strut under TATE 'E'	DIFFICULT	£17-£24 ☐
		Code 2	As 1 but with smoother side panel		NRP ☐
	1986	'FRASERS'			
		Code 1	Dark Green truck and trailer bodies, White canopies and cab roof, Red lower body		£13-£18 ☐
	1987	'SPILLERS'			
		Code 1	Off-White truck body, Dark Green lower body and cab roof, Pale Green sides, Deep Cream sack load		NRP ☐

137

Ref. No.		Model Type	1st Issues continued	Price Grading
Y28-1		**1907 UNIC TAX**	The model features a metal body with a plastic roof. Red spoke wheels (12) and spare wheel.	
	1984	Code 1	Dark main body, with Black lower body & roof, Red wheels, Tan seats, Brass trim	NRP ☐
		Code 5	As 1 but with Maroon spoke wheels (12)	NRP ☐
	1986	Code 6	Dark Blue main body with Black lower body & roof	NRP ☐
		Code 7	As 6 but with Maroon spoke wheels (12)	NRP ☐
		Other codes		NRP ☐
Y29-1		**1919 WALKER ELECTRIC VAN**	The model features a metal body with a plastic canopy and tilt and solid wheels.	
	1985	'HARRODS'		
		Code 1	Green body, Cream canopy and tilt, Gold logo	£7-£10 ☐
	1986	'JOSEPH LUCAS'		
		Bright Green body, canopy and tilt, White logo		NRP ☐
	1988	'HIS MASTERS VOICE'	Mid-Blue body, Grey canopy	NRP ☐
Y30-1		**1920 MACK TRUCK**	The model features a metal body with a plastic van roof, plastic spoke wheels (5), Gold trim.	
	1985	'ACORN STORAGE Co'		
		Code 1	Blue main body, Grey cab and van roof, Dark Blue lower body. '1984 MADE IN ENGLAND on baseplate	NRP ☐
		Code 2	As 1 but with Grey lower body DIFFICULT	£18-£27 ☐
		Code 4	As 1 but 1985 MADE IN ENGLAND on baseplate DIFFICULT	£18-£27 ☐
		Other codes		NRP ☐
	1985	'CONSOLIDATED'		
		Code 1	Yellow main body, Dark Brown lower body, Tan canopy, Red wheels	NRP ☐
	1987	'ARCTIC ICE CREAM'		
		Code 1	Cream main body, Dark Green lower body, Cream roof & wheels	NRP ☐
	1988	'KIWI POLISH'	Red main body, Brown roof, Gold trim	NRP ☐

Ref. No.		Model Type	Model Features and Size		Price Grading	
Y1-2		**1911 MODEL 'T' FORD**	The model features a metal body and spoke wheels (12) with a plastic roof and seats.			
	1964	Code 1	Bright Red body and steering wheel, smooth Black roof and seats, twin lever handbrake, Brass trim	SCARCE	£60-£80	☐
		Code 2	As 1 but with single lever handbrake		£18-£24	☐
		Code 3	As 1 but with a Black steering wheel		£18-£24	☐
		Code 4	As 3 but with Black textured roof	RARE	£125-£145	☐
	1973	Code 5	Cream body, Red roof, lower body and seats		£18-£24	☐
		Code 6	As 5 but with Black textured roof	RARE	£125-£140	☐
		Code 7	White body on Red chassis and lower body		£13-£18	☐
	1984	Code 8	Gloss Black body, Gold wheels, Black textured roof engraved 'LIMITED EDITION'		£6-£9	☐
Y2-2		**1911 RENAULT TWO SEATER**				
	1963	Code 1	Metallic Green body, Brass trim, Red plastic seats		£12-£18	☐
			Other codes		£12-£18	☐
Y3-2		**1910 BENZ LIMOUSINE**	The model features an all metal body with Dark Green or Dark Red seats and Brass trim			
	1965	Code 1	Cream body, Dark Green roof, metal steering wheel		£24-£29	☐
		Code 2	As 1 but with 'Chartreuse' Yellow roof	VERY RARE	£325-£375	☐
	1969	Code 3	Light Green body, Dark Green roof, Brass trim	VERY RARE	£325-£375	☐
		Code 4	As 3 with 'Chartreuse' roof		£24-£29	☐
		Code 5	As 4 with Black plastic steering wheel		£24-£29	☐
		Code 6	As 5 with Matt Black roof	SCARCE	£40-£45	☐
		Code 7	Metallic Dark Green body with Matt Black roof		£15-£20	☐
		Code 8	Black body and roof, Blue side panels, 'LIMITED EDITION' on baseplate		£6-£9	☐
Y4-2		**SHAND MASON FIRE ENGINE**	The model features an all metal body and two horses with 3 plastic firemen, metal spoke wheels (13 front/15 rear). Gold pump and boiler appliance			
	1960	'KENT FIRE BRIGADE' Code 1	Bright Red body, 2 Grey horses with grey manes, 2 locating hose locker ribs. Three firemen with Gold helmets and breastplates	EXTREMELY RARE	£350-£400	☐
		Code 2	As 1 but with White horses		£125-£145	☐
		Code 3	As 2 but firemen have only Gold helmets		£125-£145	☐
	1963	'LONDON FIRE BRIGADE No.72'. Code 4	As 3 with new logo as above and no locating hose locker ribs	RARE	£145-£175	☐
		Code 5	As 4 but Black horses with White manes		£125-£145	☐
		Code 6	As 5 but Brown horses with White manes, fireman with no Gold trim		£325-£375	☐
			Codes 7, 8, 9		£125-£135	☐
Y-5-2		**1929 4½ LITRE BENTLEY**	The model features a metal body with plastic seals and tonneau. It displays Union Jacks and racing numbers on its sides. It has Chrome trim, a folded down windscreen, a metal steering wheel and Silver spoke wheels (24), plus a spare wheel on drivers side.			
	1962	Code 1	Metallic 'Apple Green' body, Dark Green seats and rear tonneau, Black '3' or '5' on White circle.	VERY RARE	£325-£375	☐
		Code 2	As 1 but with Dark Red seats and rear tonneau.	VERY RARE	£350-£400	☐
		Code 3	As 1 but British Racing Green body plus additional baseplate holes		£35-£45	☐
		Code 4	As 3 but with Dark Red seats and rear tonneau	SCARCE	£45-£55	☐
		Code 5	As 4 but seats and tonneau in bright Red plastic		£20-£27	☐
		Code 6	As 5 but Red racing number '6' in White circle	SCARCE	£70-£80	☐
			Codes 7 and 8		£20-£27	☐
Y6-2		**1926 TYPE 35 BUGATTI**	The model features an all metal body and seats, with Gold 8 spoke wheels. It has a spare wheel on nearside and a black baseplate plus Red racing numbers '6' or '9' on a White circle on rear sides.			
	1961	Code 1	Light Blue body, Grey tyres, Red floor, dashboard and No. '6', Gold radiator	RARE	£100-£125	☐
		Code 2	As 1 but with Black tyres		£30-£38	☐
		Code 2A	As 2 with unplated 8 spoked wheels	RARE	£100-£120	☐
		Code 3	As 2 but with Blue radiator	DIFFICULT	£45-£55	☐
		Code 5	As 2 with White dashboard and floor	VERY RARE	£225-£275	☐
	1965	Code 6	Bright Red body, White dashboard and floor, Red No. '6'	£30-£38		☐
		Code 8	As 6 but Black dashboard and floor	VERY RARE	£225-£275	☐
			Codes 4 & 7		£30-£38	☐
Y7-2	1961	**1913 MERCER RACEABOUT** Code 1	Lilac body, Brass spoke wheels (12), Brass trim, 2 spare wheels on boot	DIFFICULT	£29-£35	☐
			Codes 2, 3 & 4		£29-£35	☐
		Code 5	Yellow body with Silver spoke wheels and trim		£22-£27	☐

Ref. No.		Model Type	2nd Issues continued	Price Grading
Y8-2		**1914 SUNBEAM MOTORCYCLE AND SIDECAR**		
	1962	Code 1	All Silver machine and sidecar, Black M/cycle seat, Dark Green S/car seat	£55-£70 ☐
		Code 2	As 1 but all Gold machine and sidecar VERY RARE	£500-£600 ☐
		Code 3	As 1 but Emerald Green sidecar seat VERY RARE	£200-£250 ☐
	1967	Code 4	As 1 but Black plastic sidecar seat EXTREMELY RARE	£600-£700 ☐
Y9-2		**1912 SIMPLEX**	The model features a metal body with a plastic roof and seats. It has 12 spoke wheels and spare wheel on offside.	
	1968	Code 1	Lime Green body, smooth Tan roof, brass wheels, Red seats and radiator grille, brass trim	£13-£18 ☐
		Code 2	As 1 with textured tan roof	£13-£18 ☐
	1970	Code 3	As 1 but medium Green body and textured Tan roof SCARCE	£30-£35 ☐
		Code 4	Metallic Gold main body, Dark Red lower body, seats and grille, Black roof	£19-£24 ☐
		Code 5	As 4 but with Chrome spoke wheels	£19-£24 ☐
	1973	Code 6	Bright Red body, Black textured roof, brass trim	£13-£18 ☐
	1979	Code 7	Dark Red main body, Black lower body and roof, Yellow seats and grille	£6-£9 ☐
	1986	Code 8	Yellow main body, Black lower body and roof, brown seats, Black grille	NRP ☐
		Code 9	As 8 but with Yellow textured roof	NRP ☐
Y10-2		**1928 MERCEDES BENZ 36/220.**	The model features a metal body with one or two spare wheels, plastic seats and tonneau and Chrome wire spoke wheels.	
	1963	Code 1	White body, Black seats and tonneau, 2 spare wheels, Gold trim, 2 holes in baseplate VERY RARE	£140-£180 ☐
		Code 2	As 1 with Red seats and tonneau DIFFICULT	£28-£36 ☐
		Code 3	As 2 but one spare wheel	£18-£24 ☐
Y11-2		**1912 PACKARD LANDAULET**	The model features a metal body with plastic seats and spare wheel on offside, brass 12 spoke wheels.	
	1962	Code 1	Bright Red body, Black seats, unplated metal components	£13-£18 ☐
		Code 5	Orange/Red body, Black plastic steering wheel DIFFICULT	£32-£38 ☐
		Code 6	Cream main body, Dark Brown lower body and roof, Chocolate Brown seats	£7-£9 ☐
Y12-2		**1909 THOMAS FLYABOUT**	The model features a metal body with a plastic roof and seats, spare wheel on offside, Black plastic steering wheel	
	1967	Code 1	Metallic Blue body, smooth Tan roof, brass 12 spoke wheels, seats and radiator grille in Bright Yellow plastic EXTREMELY RARE	£1000-£1200 ☐
		Code 2	As 1 but Dark Red plastic seats and radiator grille	£12-£18 ☐
		Code 4	As 1 with roof seat pin attachments and textured roof DIFFICULT	£32-£39 ☐
		Code 5	Metallic Purple body, Black textured roof, White seats and grille	£9-£12 ☐
Y13-2		**1911 DAIMLER**	The model features a metal body and 26 spoke wheels with plastic seats, SPW on offside	
	1966	Code 1	Yellow main body, Black lower body, 2 lines on baseplate, '1911 DAIMLER', 'No. Y13', Black seats DIFFICULT	£32-£37 ☐
		Code 2	As 1 but with Dark Red Seats	£12-£16 ☐
		Code 6	With 3 lines on BP, '1911', 'DAIMLER', 'No. Y13'.	£12-£16 ☐
			Codes 2-5	£12-£16 ☐
		Code 7	Mid-Blue main body, Light Blue lower body 'LIMITED EDITION' on baseplate	£6-£9 ☐
Y14-2		**1911 MAXWELL ROADSTER**	The model features a metal body, petrol tank and 12 spoke wheels with spare wheel on boot. It has plastic seats and roof.	
	1965	Code 1	Turquoise body, smooth Black roof, Red seats, Brass wheels, Gold petrol tank RARE	£120-£150 ☐
		Code 2	As 1 but with Copper petrol tank	£12-£17 ☐
		Code 3	As 2 with textured roof	£12-£17 ☐
	1984	Code 4	Dark Cream body, Dark Green lower body, Black textured roof — 'LIMITED EDITION'	£6-£9 ☐
Y15-2		**1930 PACKARD VICTORIA**	The model features a metal body, 12 or 24 spoke wheels, with 2 spare wheels on running boards. It has a plastic roof and luggage trunk. Components are easily interchangeable — many combinations exist — both fake and genuine.	
	1969	Code 1	Metallic Brown Gold main body, Dark Brown lower body, Maroon grille and trunk	£10-£15 ☐
			Codes 2-5	£10-£15 ☐
	1974	Code 6	Metallic Green/Gold main body, Dark Brown lower body, Maroon grille and trunk	£10-£15 ☐
			Codes 7-9	£10-£15 ☐
		Code 10	As 6 but with raised coachline round body rear, Black seats, Maroon grille RARE	£125-£150 ☐
		Code 11	As 10 but with Black chassis RARE	£125-£150 ☐
		Code 12	Black body with Red side panels, Black roof, Dark Red seats	£6-£9 ☐
			Codes 13 & 14	£6-£9 ☐
		Code 15	With White textured roof and Bright Red seats SCARCE	£40-£45 ☐

140

	Code 16	Cream main body, Dark Brown lower body, Cream seats, Brown roof, Red wheels	£6-£9	☐
		Codes 17-21 inclusive	£6-£9	☐
Y16-2	**1928 MERCEDES BENZ SS COUPE**	The model features a metal body, 24 or 12 spoke wheels, 2 spare wheels on running boards, a plastic roof and luggage trunk exposed manifold exhaust pipes in brass		
1972	Codes 1 & 2	Metallic Silver main body, Metallic Red lower body, Black textured roof	£32-£37	☐
1974	Codes 3 & 4	Metallic Lime Green body, Black textured roof, boots and seals	£13-£18	☐
	Code 5	Metallic Lime Green main body with 'Stutz Bearcat', Green lower body, Chrome 12 spoke wheels RARE	£130-£165	☐
	Code 6	As 3 with Dark Green roof, seats, grille and boot DIFFICULT	£40-£45	☐
	Code 9	With Black seats, roof, grille and boot plus cast in exhaust pipes DIFFICULT	£40-£45	☐
1979	Code 11	White body, Black textured roof, Chrome 24 spoke wheels and exhaust pipes. WWT	£7-£10	☐
	Code 12	As 11 but with Black chassis VERY RARE	£180-£220	☐
	Code 13	Mid-Blue body, Grey side panels, Black textured roof, Chrome wheels	£7-£10	☐
	Code 14	As 13 but with Duck Egg Blue side panels RARE	£50-£60	☐
	Code 15	As 13 but with Fawn side panels DIFFICULT	£12-£17	☐
1985	Code 16	Bright Red main body, Silver lower body	NRP	☐
Y17-2		No model issued yet.		
Y18-2	**1918 ATKINSON 'D' TYPE STEAM WAGON**	The model features a metal body on a plastic underframe. It has a chrome smoke stack and boiler, smooth Grey plastic wheels with 8 spokes.		
1985	'LAKE GOLDSMITH'	Code 1 Emerald Green truck body and wheels, Red underframe, Black mudguards, Yellow logo	NRP	☐
1986	'BLUE CIRCLE'	Code 1 Pale Yellow body and wheels, Black underframe and Blue logo	NRP	☐
	Code 2	Deeper Yellow body, Darker Blue logo	NRP	☐
1987	'BASS & Co'	Code 1 Blue truck body, Black underframe, Red chain drive and pipes. Tan flat bed with 7 barrels retained by Gold chain	£7-£10	☐
1988	'BURGHFIELD MILLS'	Code 1 Red truck body, Black underframe, Deep Cream sack load	NRP	☐
Y19-2	**'SHOWMANS ENGINE'**	'Hey Ho Come To The Fair'		
1986	Code 1	Royal Blue body, flywheel and baseplate, Black front assembly and chimney, White roof with Red edge, Red/Yellow spoke wheels, smooth Grey plastic tyres	£24-£30	☐
Y20-2		No model issued		
Y21-2	**FORD MODEL 'A' WOODY WAGON**	The model features a metal bonnet and chassis with a plastic wagon body and roof. It has whitewall tyres with a spare wheel on the nearside, Chrome trims.		
1983	'A & J BOX'			
	Code 1	Copper bonnet, Dark Brown lower body, two tone Brown wagonsides, Black roof, White seats	NRP	☐
	Code 2	As 1 but windscreen surround is Chrome DIFFICULT	£18-£24	☐
	Code 3	As 2 but Dark Orange bonnet	£9-£12	☐
	Code 4	As 2 with bright Yellow bonnet and bright Red seats	£11-£16	☐
	Codes 5-7		NRP	☐
1985	'CARTERS SEEDS'			
	Code 1	Blue bonnet, Black lower body, Cream and Blue wagon sides, Black room	NRP	☐
	Codes 2 & 3		NRP	☐

Models of YesterYear
3rd Issues

Ref. No.		Model Type	Model Features and Size		Price Grading
Y1-3		**1936 SS 100 JAGUAR**	The model features a metal bodied sports car with seats and folded down hood in Black plastic. It normally has Chrome 24 spoke wheels and a spare wheel on the petrol tank. The radiator surround and headlights etc. are Chrome trimmed.		
	1977	Code 1	White body and chassis with small sidelights (2mm) on front mudguards	RARE	£125-£145 ☐
		Code 2	As 1 but with large sidelights (4mm) on front mudguards		£14-£19 ☐
	1978	Code 3	Grey/Blue body and chassis, large sidelights	SCARCE	£30-£40 ☐
	1979	Code 4	Steel Blue body and chassis, large sidelights with or without whitewall tyres		£6-£9 ☐
		Codes 5 & 6			£6-£9 ☐
	1981	Code 7	Dark Green body and chassis, whitewall tyres		£6-£9 ☐
	1986	Code 8	Talbot Yellow body and chassis, whitewall tyres	VERY RARE	£250-£300 ☐
		Code 9	As 8 with Green body and chassis		NRP ☐
		Code 10	Darker Yellow body and chassis than Code 8		NRP ☐
Y2-3		**1914 PRINCE HENRY VAUXHALL**	The model features an open car with a metal body and plastic seats and steering wheel. The radiator surround headlights, windscreen and toolbox are Gold trimmed. It has 24 spoke wheels with a spare on the offside unless described differently		
	1970	Code 1	Red body with Silver bonnet, Red radiator grille, Brass wheels, Gold petrol tank		£14-£19 ☐
		Code 2	As 1 but with Copper petrol tank		£300-£350 ☐
		Code 3	As 1 with Black radiator grille		£14-£19 ☐
	1973	Code 4	Metallic Blue body with Silver bonnet, Red seats, Black grille, Copper petrol tank	EXTREMELY RARE	£1000-£1250 ☐
	1979	Code 8	Red body, Black lower body, Silver bonnet, Red 12 spoke wheels, whitewall tyres		£9-£13 ☐
		Codes 5, 6 & 7			£9-£13 ☐
Y3-3		**1934 RILEY MPH**	The model features a sports car with a metal body and plastic seat and steering wheel. It has a Chrome radiator surround, windscreen, headlights and 24 spoke wheels unless described differently		
	1973	Code 1	Deep Purple/Red body and chassis with Black seats and grille	RARE	£100-£125 ☐
		Code 2	As 1 but seats and grille in White		£10-£15 ☐
		Code 3	As 1 but Reddish Purple body and chassis		£10-£15 ☐
		Code 4	As 2 but with Dark Red body and chassis		
		Code 5	As 4 with Red seats and grille	SCARCE	£70-£90 ☐
		Code 6	As 4 but with Green seats and grille	SCARCE	£70-£90 ☐
		Code 7	As 4 but with Dark Red seats and grille		£10-£15 ☐
		Code 8	As 4 but with seats and grille in Yellow		£70-£90 ☐
		Code 9	As 4 with Chrome 12 spoke wheels		£10-£15 ☐
	1979	Codes 10 & ·11	Light Blue body and chassis, White seats and grille, Black No. '6' or '3'		£6-£9 ☐
Y4-3		**1909 OPEL CAR**	The model features an open fronted metal bodied car with plastic roof, seats and steering wheel. It has 12 spoke wheels.		
	1967	Code 1	White body and chassis, smooth Tan roof, Brass trim and wheels with Maroon seats and grille		£16-£21 ☐
		Code 2	As 1 with bright Red seats and grille		£16-£21 ☐
		Code 4	As 2 with no body pins and textured roof	SCARCE	£60-£70 ☐
		Code 5	With Tan textured roof with window in rear, Red seats	EXTREMELY RARE	£400-£500 ☐
	1974	Code 6	Orange body with Black chassis and roof, White grille, Maroon seats, brass trim		£12-£15 ☐
		Code 7	Bright Red body with Darker Red lower body, Tan roof with 'LIMITED EDITION':		£6-£9 ☐
Y5-3		**1907 PEUGEOT**	The model features a large metal car with plastic seats, grille and steering wheel. It has 12 spoke wheels and a spare tyre on the offside. The trim is in brass.		
	1969	Code 1	All Yellow body, matt Black roof with Dark Orange windows, Red seats and grille	RARE	£145-£170 ☐
		Code 2	As 1 with Pale Orange windows		£10-£15 ☐
		Code 3	As 1 with clear windows	VERY RARE	£180-£200 ☐
	1974	Code 4	Gold body and roof with matt Black lower body, Red seats and grille	RARE	£145-£170 ☐
		Code 5	As 4 with Black seats and grille		£10-£15 ☐
		Code 6	As 5 with matt Black roof	SCARCE	£125-£150 ☐
		Code 7	As 5 with Orange/Gold body and chassis		£10-£15 ☐

142

Ref. No.		Model Type	Model Features and Size	Price Grading
Y6-3		**1913 CADILLAC**	The model features a metal bodied two seater car with a plastic roof and seats. It has 12 spoke wheels with a spare on the rear	
	1968	Code 1	Light Gold body, Red seats, smooth roof and grille, brass trim, '1913' on baseplate	£14-£19 ☐
		Code 2	As 1 with with '913' on baseplate and darker Gold body DIFFICULT	£35-£45 ☐
		Code 3	As 1 with textured Red roof and darker Gold body SCARCE	£45-£55 ☐
	1974	Code 4	Green body, Black textured roof, Yellow seats and grille, Chrome wheels, brass trim	£12-£16 ☐
		Code 5	As 4 with Green seats and grille and Red wheels DIFFICULT	£35-£45 ☐
		Code 6	As 4 with White seats and grille DIFFICULT	£35-£45 ☐
Y7-3		**1912 ROLLS ROYCE**	The model features a metal bodied large car with an open rear seat and plastic seats. It normally has 12 spoke wheels with a spare tyre on offside and brass trim	
	1968	Code 1	Metallic Silver body with a smooth Red roof, brass wheels and trim, red seats and grille	£13-£18 ☐
		Code 2	As 1 with smooth Grey roof	£15-£19 ☐
		Code 3	As 2 with yellow seats VERY RARE	£300-£350 ☐
		Code 4	As 2 with ribbed rear section to Grey roof RARE	£150-£175 ☐
		Code 5	As 4 but ribbed rear section to Red roof	£13-£18 ☐
		Code 6	As 5 but Gold body with Silver bonnet VERY RARE	£300-£350 ☐
	1973	Code 8	Metallic Gold body with ribbed Red roof, Chrome wheels, Dark Red seats and grille	£10-£14 ☐
	1979	Code 11	Bright Yellow main body, Black lower body and ribbed roof with Red wheels	£10-£14 ☐
			Other codes	£10-£14 ☐
Y8-3		**1914 STUTZ**	The model features a metal bodied two seater car with a plastic roof and seats. It has a metal petrol tank and 12 spoke wheels with a brass trim	
	1969	Code 1	Metallic Red body, smooth Tan roof, Copper petrol tank, Green seats and grille	£13-£18 ☐
		Code 2	As 1 with Tan textured roof SCARCE	£35-£40 ☐
		Code 3	As 1 with Gold petrol tank RARE	£75-£85 ☐
		Code 4	Metallic Blue body, Black textured roof, White seats and grille	£9-£14 ☐
		Code 5	As 4 but with Red seats and grille DIFFICULT	£25-£35 ☐
Y9-3		**1920 3 TON LEYLAND LORRY. 'A LUFF & SONS LTD'**	A model features a metal bodied vehicle with high backed sides and a plastic underframe, mudguards and front bumper, solid wheels and tyres	
	1985	Code 1	Dark Green body and wheels, Red underframe, Brown seats, Black grille, Red logo	NRP ☐
			Codes 2, 3 & 4	NRP ☐
Y10-3		**1906 ROLLS ROYCE SILVER GHOST**	The model features an open topped four seater car with a metal body and plastic seats, steering wheel and grille. It has metal 12 spoke wheels plus a spare tyre on offside	
	1969	Code 1	Metallic Lime body with Metallic Brown lower body, brass trim, Red seats and grille	£13-£18 ☐
	1974	Code 2	White body, Metallic Purple lower body, brass trim, Red seats and grille	£13-£18 ☐
			Codes 3 & 4	£13-£18 ☐
	1979	Code 5	Metallic Silver body, Black seats and grille, Chrome wheels	£6-£9 ☐
		Code 6	As 5 with Red seats and grille	£6-£9 ☐
		Code 7	As 5 with Yellow seats and grille	£6-£9 ☐
Y11-3		**1938 LAGONDA DROPHEAD COUPE**	The model features a four seater tourer with a metal body and plastic grille, seats, folded down roof and trunk. It has spare wheel covers on the running boards, 24 spoke wheels and brass trim.	
	1972	Code 1	Metallic Gold main body, Metallic Purple lower body, Black seats and plastic parts VERY RARE	£600-£750 ☐
		Code 2	As 1 but with Dark Red lower body and front and rear bumper lugs VERY RARE	£300-£350 ☐
		Code 3	As 2 but with 'Strawberry Red' lower body VERY RARE	£300-£350 ☐
		Code 4	As 3 but Dark Maroon lower body	£35-£45 ☐
	1974	Code 5	Metallic Orange main body, Gold lower body, Black seats and plastic parts	£10-£15 ☐
		Code 6	As 5 with Maroon seats and plastic parts	£10-£15 ☐
		Code 7	As 6 with bright Red seats, folded roof, trunk and grille RARE	£100-£120 ☐
	1979	Codes 8 & 9	Beige main body, Black lower body, Red or Black radiator grille, Black plastic parts	£6-£9 ☐
		Code 10	With Chrome solid wheels, Red grille, Black seats DIFFICULT	£30-£40 ☐
	1985	Code 11	All Red body, Black plastic parts, Brass wheels and trim	NRP ☐

Y12-3	**1912 FORD MODEL 'T' VAN**	The model features a metal bodied van with side window lenses and a ribbed roof. It has plastic 12 spoke wheels, seats and LHD steering wheel. Three different types of rear door design were produced as follows

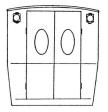

1st Type

2nd Type

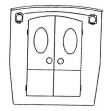

3rd Type cast in

1979	'COLMANS MUSTARD'	Yellow body, Black chassis and White roof.	
	Codes 1-5	Type 1 or 2 doors, Black seats, Red or Chrome wheels	NRP
1980	'COCA-COLA'	Off-White body, Black chassis and roof.	
	Code 1	Type 1 doors in Red, 5 vertical Red body lines, Red wheels	£150-£180
	Code 2	As 1 with only 4 vertical Red body lines	£35-£40
	Codes 3 & 4	As 2 with Chrome 12 or 24 wheels	£45-£55
		See also Code 3 listing.	
1980	'SUZE'	Yellow body, Black chassis and matt Black roof.	
	Code 1	Type 1 doors in Black, Black plastic parts, Red wheels, Black/Red logo	NRP
	Code 2	As 1 with Chrome 24 spoke wheels SCARCE	£30-£40
	Code 4	As 1 with Red rear lights and Type 2 doors DIFFICULT	£20-£30
	Code 5	As 4 with Y12 blanked out on baseplate VERY RARE	£85-£110
	Code 6	As 5 but with red type 2 doors VERY RARE	£85-£110
1981	'SMITHS'	Dark Blue body, White roof, Black chassis, Red wheels, whitewall tyres.	
	Code 1	Type 1 doors and rear lights in White, Black seats with Y12 on baseplate DIFFICULT	£11-£16
	Code 2	As 1 but with Beige seats	
	Code 4	Type 2 doors in White with No. Y12 on baseplate DIFFICULT	£11-£16
	Code 5	As 4 but with Y12 on baseplate VERY RARE	£90-£110
		See also Code 3 listing.	
1981	'25th ANNIVERSARY OF YESTERYEARS'	Two tone Green body, Grey roof.	
	Code 1	Type 2 doors in Grey, Yellow wheels, whitewall tyres, Silver '25' and body line	NRP
	Code 2	As 1 but with Type 1 doors in Grey EXTREMELY RARE	£130-£150
1982	'BIRDS CUSTARD'	Blue body, Yellow roof, Black chassis, Red, White, Yellow design	
	Code 1	Type 2 doors in Yellow, Red wheels, Black seats, brass trim	NRP
	Code 2	As 1 but with a Metallic Blue body RARE	£90-£115
	Code 4	As 1 with Yellow spoke wheels DIFFICULT	£30-£40
	Code 5	Type 3 doors and Tan seats	NRP
	Code 7	With brass radiator and trim plus Black seats RARE	£190-£115
1982	'CEREBOS SALT'	Blue body, Black chassis.	
	Code 1	With Yellow roof and type 2 doors, brass trim, Red 12 spoke wheels RARE	£100-£125
	Code 2	As 1 with Chrome trim and whitewall tyres RARE	£100-£125
	Code 3	As 1 with brass 12 spoke wheels RARE	£100-£125
	Codes 4 & 5	With White roof and Chrome trim, Black or Tan seats	NRP
1982	'ARNOTTS BISCUITS'	Orange/Red body, gloss Black chassis and roof.	
	Code 1	Type 2 doors in Gold, brass trim, label with Cream logo, wheatsheaf & parrot designs	£150-£175
1982	'HARRODS EXPRESS DELIVERY'	Green body Cream side panel and roof, Black chassis.	
	Code 1	Type 2 doors and rear lights in White, Gold logo	£13-£17
	Code 2	As 1 with Green border around Cream side panels and type 3 door	£13-£17
1983	'SUNLIGHT SEIFFE' (SOAP)	Yellow body, Black chassis and roof.	
	Code 1	Type 2 doors and rear lights in Red. Label with mutlicoloured design & Cream logo DIFFICULT	£90-£110
1983	'ROYAL MAIL'	Orange/Red body, Black chassis and roof.	
	Codes 1 & 2	Type 2 doors tampo printed, Yellow rear lights, Red or brass wheels, Black logo, Gold 'GR' & crown RARE	£80-£100
	Code 3	Type 3 doors and a postbox Red body and wheels	NRP
	Code 4	As 3 with brass spoke wheels DIFFICULT	£25-£30
1983	'CAPTAIN MORGAN'	Black body and chassis, White roof, brass wheels.	
	Code 1	Type 3 doors, Black 1 piece label with Gold border, pirate cameo, White logo	NRP
	Code 2	As 1 with 2 piece label	NRP
1983	'HOOVER'	Orange body, Black chassis and roof, Chrome trim.	
	Code 1	Type 3 doors, Black rear lights and wheels, Black logo, lady/cleaner cameo	NRP
		See also Code 2 section.	
1984	'PEPSI-COLA'	White body, Red roof, Blue chassis, Chrome trim	
	Code 1	Type 3 doors, Red rear lights, Chrome wheels, Red logo	NRP
		Codes 2, 3 & 4	NRP
1985	'MOTOR 100'	Metallic Brown body, Dark Brown chassis and roof.	
	Code 1	Type 3 doors, Dark Brown rear lights, Red logo with certificate 1-2300 DIFFICULT	£28-£34

Ref. No.		Model Type	Model Features and Size	Price Grading	
		Code 2	As 1 with no certificate	NRP	☐
	1985	'IMBACH'	A pick-up truck with no van body sides		
		Code 1	Dark Blue body, Black chassis, brass wheels, Tan seats	£6-£8	☐
	1986	'HEINZ'	Mid-Cream body and roof, Green chassis and roof Gherkin.		
		Code 1	Type 3 doors, Cream rear lights, Dark Red wheels, Green seats, Red logo, Red/Green design SCARCE	£18-£24	☐
		Code 3	As 1 but deeper Cream body, Black seats, bright Red wheels	NRP	☐
		Code 5	With MATCHBOX INTL LTD on baseplate and Maroon wheels DIFFICULT	£20-£25	☐
		Codes 2 & 4		NRP	☐
	1987	'ROSELLA	Blue body, Yellow roof, Black chassis.		
		Code 1	Type 3 doors, Yellow rear lights, brass trim, White logo	NRP	☐
		Codes 2-5		NRP	☐
Y13-3		**1918 CROSSLEY R.A.F. TENDER.**	The model features a small metal truck with a plastic cab cover and canopy. It has chrome spoke wheels and a space on the offside. The seats, steering wheel and grille are plastic.		
The models issued as follows:-					
	1979	'R.A.F. TENDER'	Grey/Blue body, Red cross on White square label plus 'R.A.F.' roundel.		
		Code 1	Flat baseplate with 'LTD' complete, Tan cab cover, canopy and grille VERY RARE	£325-£375	☐
		Code 5	As 1 with 'LTD' incomplete on baseplate and Green seats	£35-£48	☐
		Code 7	With 24 spoke wheels and Olive Green cab cover, canopy and grille SCARCE	£75-£90	☐
	1979	Code 8	As 7 with Black cab cover, canopy and grille RARE	£275-£325	☐
		'EVANS BROS COAL & COKE'	Dark Red body, Black lower body, seats and roof.		
		Code 1	With 'CROSSLEY RAF TENDER' on baseplate, Chrome 24 spoke wheels, White logo	£10-£15	☐
		Code 4	With Red 12 spoke wheels and no 'RAF TENDER' on baseplate	NRP	☐
	1983	'CARLSBERG'	Cream body, Black lower body, Green cab cover, canopy and grille.		
		Code 1	With Chrome 12 spoke wheels, brass trim, Maroon seats	£6-£9	☐
		Codes 2, 3 & 4		NRP	☐
	1985	'WARINGS'	Green body, Black lower body, Red logo 'LONDON WG PARIS MADRID'		
		Code 1	White cab cover and canopy with white label DIFFICULT	£10-£12	☐
		Code 2	White cab cover and canopy with Cream label DIFFICULT	£10-£12	☐
		Code 3	Cream cab cover and canopy, White or Cream labels	NRP	☐
	1988	'KOHLE & KOKS'	Yellow body, Black 12 spoke wheels & logo	NRP	☐
Y14-3		**1931 STUTZ BEARCAT**	The model features an open 2 seater tourer with a metal body and plastic seats. It has Chrome 24 spoke wheels and 2 spare wheels set into running boards and is LHD.		
	1974	Code 1	Light Green main body, Metallic Green lower body. Rear bumper open on left hand side, Red seats and grille, '1973' on baseplate RARE	£100-£125	☐
		Code 2	As 1 with rear bumper closed on both sides	£16-£25	☐
		Code 3	As 2 with 1974 on baseplate	£16-£25	☐
		Code 4	As 3 with Maroon seats SCARCE	£30-£35	☐
	1979	Code 5	Cream body sides, Red lower and upper body, Red seats, Maroon or Black grille SCARCE	£30-£35	☐
		Code 8	With Black plastic seats and grille	£12-£16	☐
	1981	Code 10	Cream main body, Emerald Green lower body, Black seats, Black or Red grille	£9-£12	☐
	1985	Code 11	Blue main body, Grey lower body, Tan seats, Black grille	£6-£9	☐
Y15-3		**PRESTON TRAM CAR**	The model features a double decker tram with metal low and upper decks with plastic window sections, chassis, roof, seats and staircase.		
	1987	'SWAN VESTAS'	Code 1 Red body, White window sections, Grey chassis and roof	NRP	☐
	1988	'SWAN SOAP'	Code 1 Blue body, Blue window sections, Blue chassis and roof	NRP	☐
Y16-3		**1960 FERRARI DINO 246/V12**			
	1986	Code 1	Red body, Silver 24 spoke wheels, Grey exhaust pipes, Black No. '17'	NRP	☐
Y17-3			No model issued		
Y18-3			No model issued		
Y19-3		**1929 MORRIS COWLEY VAN**	The model features on all metal van with windows. It has 12 spoke wheels and a spare on nearside		
	1987	'BRASSO	Blue main body, Black lower body, White roof	NRP	☐
	1988	'MICHELIN'	Blue main body, Yellow roof and design	NRP	☐
Y20-3			No model issued		
Y21-3		**AVELING AND PORTER STEAM (ROAD ROLLER)**	'JAMES YOUNG & SONS EDINBURGH'		
	1987	Code 1	Emerald Green body, Yellow/Black bodyline, brass trim, Black chimney, Red front roller housing, Grey roof and roller surfaces DIFFICULT	£14-£19	☐

Models of YesterYear
4th Issues

Ref. No.		Model Type	Model Features and Size	Price Grading
Y1-4		No Model as yet.		
Y2-4	1985	**1930 4½ LITRE BENTLEY.**		
		Code 1	Dark Green body, Green 24 spoke wheels with spare on nearside. Chrome trim, Brown seats and straps. Union Jack on sides	NRP ☐
		Code 5	As with darker Green mudguards SCARCE	No prices available
Y3-4		**1912 FORD MODEL 'T' TANKER.**	The model features a small tanker with an all metal body and tank with brass simulated filler pipes and 12 spoke wheels.	
	1981	'BP'	Dark Green body and bonnet, Black lower body, White roof, Red tank, brass trim	
		Code 1	Gold logo 'BP' on tank with Black shadow effect, '1978 No. Y12' on baseplate VERY RARE	£75-£95 ☐
		Code 3	As 1 but 'No' has been removed, and no shadow effect around 'BP'	NRP ☐
		Code 5	No. Y12 on baseplate and matt Black filler caps SCARCE	£29-£36 ☐
	1982	ZEROLENE'	Code 1 Bright Green body, gloss Black lower body and logo. Brass 12 spoke wheels and trim	£40-£50 ☐
			Code 3 As 1 with Red 12 spoke wheels DIFFICULT	£50-£60 ☐
	1983	'EXPRESS DAIRY'	Code 1 Blue body, Gloss Black lower body, White roof and logo, brass trim	NRP ☐
			Code 2 As 1 with Red 12 spoke wheels	£10-£15 ☐
	1984	'CARNATION'	Code 1 Cream body, Red tank and lower body, White and Red logo	NRP ☐
			Codes 2-4	NRP ☐
	1985	'MOBIL OIL'	Code 1 Blue body and tank, Red bonnet and wheels, White logo, Red design	NRP ☐
	1986	'CASTROL'	Code 1 Dark Green body and tank, White roof, Black lower body, Red logo	NRP ☐
			Codes 2-5	NRP ☐
	1987	'RED CROWN'	Code 1 Bright Red body and tank, Black lower body, White logo	NRP ☐
Y4-4		**1930 DUESENBERG 'J' TOWN CAR**	The model features a superb large car with an open front drivers area and enclosed passenger seats. It has a metal body with a plastic roof, seats and trunk, 24 spoke wheels and two spares set into the running boards.	
	1976	Code 1	White main body, Orange/Red lower body, Yellow roof and seats, small roof window, X shaped roof support EXTREMELY RARE	£1250-£1500 ☐
		Code 2	As 1 but seats and roof in Black EXTREMELY RARE	£1250-£1500 ☐
	1976	Code 3	Metallic Red body, Black roof with larger window, Black seats	£9-£14 ☐
		Code 5	With solid horns and Maroon seats and roof VERY RARE	£150-£200 ☐
	1979	Code 6	Light Green body, Pale Green side and rear panels, Green seats and roof RARE	£60-£75 ☐
		Code 8	As 6 but with Black seats and roof	£9-£14 ☐
		Code 9	Dark Brown lower and upper body, Cream body sides, Beige seats and roof	
			Codes 4, 7, 10, 11 & 12	£9-£14 ☐
	1983	Code 13	As 9 but with Rust Brown seats and roof	£6-£9 ☐
	1986	Code 14	Metallic Silver body, Blue lower body, side panels and wheels	NRP ☐
Y5-4		**1927 TALBOT VAN**	The model features a small van with side windows. It has an all metal body with plastic seats and steering wheel - RHD. It has spoked wheels with a spare on the offside and opening rear doors.	
	1978	'LIPTON'S TEA' WITH ROYAL CYPHER		
		Code 1	Dark Green body with a matt Black roof and lower body, Gold logo and crest	£12-£14 ☐
		Codes 4 & 5	With gloss Black chassis and either 12 or 24 Chrome spoke wheels DIFFICULT	£25-£30 ☐
	1978	'LIPTON'S TEA' WITH NO CREST AND 'CITY ROAD' logo		
		Code 1	Dark Green body with Black roof and lower body, Green 12 spoke wheels, Gold logo	NRP ☐
		Codes 2 & 3	As 1 with Chrome 12 or 24 spoke wheels	£9-£12 ☐
			Codes 4 & 5	NRP ☐
	1979	'CHOCOLATE MENIER'		
		Code 1	Royal Blue body, Black roof and lower body, Yellow logo, Chrome 12 spoke wheels	NRP ☐
		Code 2	As 1 with Chrome 24 spoke wheels	£9-£12 ☐
	1980	'TAYSTEE BREAD'		
		Code 1	Yellow body and lower body, Black roof, Red wheels, whitewall tyres, Red/White design	NRP ☐
		Code 2	As 1 with Black lower body	£6-£9 ☐
		Code 3	As 1 with Red solid wheels	No prices available

Ref. No.		Model Type	4th Issues continued	Price Grading
	1981	'NESTLES'		
		Code 1	Bright Blue body, Black roof and lower body, Red whitewall wheels, White logo, Swiss flag RARE	£95-£120 ☐
		Code 2	As 1 with Dark Grey roof	£19-£22 ☐
		Code 3	As 1 with Light Grey roof	£25-£30 ☐
	1982	'CHIVERS & SONS LTD'		
		Code 1	Cream body and roof, Dark Green lower body & logo, Red whitewall wheels	NRP ☐
	1982	'WRIGHT'S SOAP'		
		Code 1	Dark Brown body with Cream roof, lower body and wheels	NRP ☐
	1983	'EVER READY BATTERIES'		
		Code 1	Dark Blue body, White roof and Black lower body, White/Orange design	NRP ☐
	1984	'DUNLOP TYRES & ACCESSORIES'		
		Code 1	Black body, Yellow roof and upper side panels and wheels, Union Jack/tyre design	NRP ☐
	1985	'ROSES LIME JUICE'		
		Code 1	Light Cream body with Green roof, lower body and logo	NRP ☐
		Codes 2 & 3		NRP ☐
Y6-4		**1920 ROLLS ROYCE FIRE ENGINE**	The model features a metal vehicle body with plastic ladders, brass 12 spoke wheels and trim.	
	1977	Code 1	Bright Red body, White 2 piece ladder, metal crews seat	£6-£9 ☐
		Code 2	As 1 with Dark Brown ladder	NRP ☐
		Code 4	With No. 'Y6' or 'Y7' on baseplate and Red/Brown ladders	NRP ☐
		Code 6	With plastic crews seats and White ladder	NRP ☐
		Code 7	As 6 with drivers seat in bright Red plastic RARE	£200-£250 ☐
Y7-4		**1930 FORD BREAKDOWN TRUCK**	The model is based on the Model 'A' and features a metal body with a plastic roof and lifting gear. It has plastic solid whitewall wheels and a large plastic front bumper.	
	1985	'BARLOW MOTOR SALES'		
		Code 1	Orange body, bumpers and wheels, Black roof and lower body, Green lifting gear	NRP ☐
		Code 2	As 1 with lighter Green crane jib VERY RARE	No prices available
		Codes 3 & 4		NRP ☐
	1988	'SHELL'	Yellow body, Black lower body, Red logo	NRP ☐
Y8-4		**1945 M.G. T.C.**	The model features a metal two seater sports car with a plastic roof and seats. It has Chrome 24 spoke wheels (unless described differently) and a spare at rear.	
	1978	Code 1	Dark Green body and lower body with a Tan roof and seats RARE	£70-£90 ☐
		Codes 2 & 3	With Red seats, with or without Red wheels	£10-£14 ☐
	1981	Code 4	Bright Red body, Black seats, Tan roof	£6-£9 ☐
		Codes 5 & 6		£6-£9 ☐
	1983	Code 7	Mid Blue body, Black seats, Tan roof	£6-£9 ☐
		Codes 8 & 9		£6-£9 ☐
	1984	Code 10	Cream body, Dark Brown lower body, Tan seats and roof	NRP ☐
		Codes 11 & 12		NRP ☐
Y9-4		No model issued		
Y10-4		**1957 MASERATI 250 F**		
		Code 1	Bright Red body, Grey exhaust pipes, Silver 24 spoke wheels, Black No. '12'	NRP ☐
Y11-4		**1932 BUGATTI TYPE 51**		
		Code 1	French racing Blue body with Brown strap, Grey exhaust pipes, Black No. '4'	NRP ☐
Y12-4	1987	**1829 STEPHENSONS ROCKET** Code 1	Yellow ribbed engine, Black chassis and components, Black trim on White smoke stack. Yellow spoke wheels — large 12/small 12. Yellow trailer and barrel with Black trim	£16-£18 ☐
Y13-4		No model issued		
Y14-4		**1936 E.R.A.**		
	1986	Code 1	Black body, Grey plastic exhaust, grille and trim, 'R.I.B.', Black No. '7'	NRP ☐
	1988	Code 2	Blue body, Yellow exhaust pipes 'ROMULUS'	NRP ☐
Y15-4		No model issued		
Y16-4		**SCANIA HALF TRACK BUS**	Swedish Post Office model (1988 issue)	NRP ☐
Y17-4		No model issued		
Y18-4		No model issued		
Y19-4		No model issued		
Y20-4		No model issued		
Y21-4	1988	**1955 BMW 507**	No details available (late 1988 issue)	NRP ☐

Models of YesterYear
5th Issues

Ref. No.		Model Type	Model Features and Size	Price Grading
Y1-5		No model issued		
Y2-5		No model issued		
Y3-5		No model issued		
Y4-5		No model issued		
Y5-5		No model issued		
Y6-5		1932 MERCEDES BENZ TRUCK	'Stuttgart Hofbrau' Late 1988 issue	
Y7-5		No model issued		
Y8-5		YORKSHIRE STEAM WAGON		
	1987	'JOHNNIE WALKER'	Code 1 Red truck & logo, Black components and Cream canopy	NRP ☐
Y9-5		No model issued		
Y10-5		DIDDLER TROLLEY BUS	'RONUK/JEYES' late 1988 issue	
Y11-5		No model issued		
Y12-5		1937 G.M.C. Van - 'GOBLIN'	Black body, White roof	NRP ☐

Models of YesterYear
Gift Sets

Ref. No.			Contents	Rarity and Price Grading
G6	1960	Gift Set.	Contains Nos 1, 2, 5, 10 & 13	£325-£375 ☐
G7	1960	Gift Set.	Contains Nos 3, 8, 9, 12 & 14	£325-£375 ☐
G6	1962	Gift Set.	Contains Nos 6, 7, 10, 15 & 16	£325-£375 ☐
G7	1962	Gift Set.	Contains Nos 3, 4, 11, 12 & 13	£450-£500 ☐
G7	1965	Veteran & Vintage Set.	Contains Y2, Y5, Y10, Y15, Y16	£200-£250 ☐
G7	1966	Gift Set.	Contains Y-1B Model T Ford, Y-3 Benz, Y-11B Packard, Y-14B Maxwell.	£75-£100 ☐
G5	1968	Gift Set.	Contains Y-4C Opel White, Y-6C Cadillac, Y-9B Simplex Yellow Green, Y-9B Simplex Green.	£55-£65 ☐
G5	1970-72	Gift Set.	Contains Y-8C Stutz Red, Y-14 Maxwell, Y-16A Spyker (Dark Yellow), Y-7C Rolls Royce Silver and Red.	£45-£55 ☐
Y-50	1982	Gift Set.	Contains Y-3 BP Tanker, Y-5 Chivers, Y-10 Rolls Royce, Y-12 Model T, Y-13 Crossley Coal.	£14-£18 ☐
	1984	Connoisseurs Collection	Contains Y1/2 Black 1911 Model 'T' Ford, Y4/3 Red/Beige 1909 Opel, Y3/2 Blue/Black 1910 Benz Limousine, Y11/2 White/Black 1912 Packard Landaulet, Y13/2 Blue 1911 Daimler, Y14/2 Beige/Black 1911 Maxwell 30,000 sets issued via Beechwood display case, numbered certificate with each set	£75-£100 ☐
	1985	Connoisseurs Collection	Contains Y11 Red Lagonda, Y23 'MAPLES' Bus, Y25 Renault Van 'DUCKHAMS'	£13-£15 ☐
	1987	30 years Set (A)	Contains Y6/4 R.R. Fire Engine, Y25/1 Eagle Pencils, Y29/1 Harrods Ltd	£13-£15 ☐
	1987	30 years Set (B)	Contains Y4/4 Blue Dusendorf, Y28/1 Red Unie Taxi, Y29/1 Harrods Ltd	£13-£15 ☐
	1987	Starter Kit		
		5 for 4 Set	Australian Gift Set	NGPP ☐

CODE 2 MODELS

Y1-2	1976	**1911 MODEL 'T' FORD CAR** Code 1	With brass trim, 12 spoke wheels All Black body and seats, LHD	VERY RARE	£325-£375	☐
Y5-4	1978	**1927 TALBOT VAN** '2nd A.I.M. CONVENTION' Code 1	With 12 spoke wheels & chrome trim Royal Blue body, Black roof and chains, Green wheels	SCARCE	£85-£100	☐
	1981	'CRAWLEY SWAPMEET 1981' Code 1	Royal Blue body, Black roof & chassis	SCARCE	£130-£150	☐
	1981	'VARIETY CLUB' Code 1	Yellow body, Black roof, Red wheels	RARE	£180-£200	☐
		Code 2	As 1 with Black chassis mudguards etc.	RARE	£180-£200	☐
	1980	'MERITA BREAD' Code 1	Yellow body, Black roof, Red wheels	DIFFICULT	£50-£65	☐
	1980	'LANGENDORF Code 1	Yellow body, Black roof, Red wheels	DIFFICULT	£50-£65	☐
	1980	'TAYSTEE BREAD' Code 1	Yellow body, Black roof, Red wheels and Pale Yellow 'Taystee' letters, no White surround	SCARCE	£90-£110	☐
	1981	'IRONBRIDGE' Code 1	Yellow body with matt Black roof, Red wheels	SCARCE	£140-£160	☐
		Code 2	As 1 with gloss Black chassis and lower body	SCARCE	£140-£160	☐
	1981	'BEES' Code 1	Yellow body, Black roof, Red wheels	DIFFICULT	£85-£100	☐
		Code 2 & 3			£85-£100	☐
	1981	'DUTCH MATCHBOX MEET'	Blue body, Black roof and chassis, Grey van sides	SCARCE	£175-£200	☐
Y7-3	1982	**1912 ROLLS ROYCE — PRINCE CHARLES WEDDING** Code 1	Bright Yellow body, Black roof and chassis, Red wheels, WW	TRARE	£120-£140	☐
Y12-3	1981	**FORD MODEL 'T' VAN** 'BANG & OLUFSEN' Code 1	Red 12 spoke wheels and brass trim White body, Red bonnet, Black roof and chassis, with authenticating certificate	SCARCE	£250-£300	☐
	1981	'RAYLEIGH SWAPMEET' Code 1	Yellow body, Red logo, Black roof and chassis	DIFFICULT	£100-£120	☐
	1982	'CADA TOYS' Code 1	Yellow body, Black roof and side panels	SCARCE	£110-£130	☐
	1982	'DEANS' Code 1	Yellow body, Red logo, Black roof and chassis	DIFFICULT	£100-£120	☐
	1980	'CAMBERLEY NEWS' Code 1	Yellow body, Black roof, chassis and logo	SCARCE	£120-£140	☐
	1983	'HOOVER' Code 1	Blue body, White roof, Black chassis, brass wheels with certificate		£700-£800	☐
		Code 2	As 1 without certificate		£300-£350	☐
Y13-3	1979	**1918 CROSSLEY R.A.F. TENDER. 'U.K. "MATCHBOX" ' CLUB 1979** Code 1	Red body, wheels and logo, Yellow cover and canopy	SCARCE	£250-£275	☐
	1981	'SURREY MODEL FAIR' Code 1	Red body, Grey cover, Black chassis	SCARCE	£140-£160	☐

CODE 3 MODELS

Y22-1		**FORD MODEL 'A' VAN**	"MAGGI SOUPS" with extra 'MAGGI' on rear doors and in special box	£25-£35	☐
Y12-3		**MODEL 'T' VAN** "SMITHS CRISPS"	Smiths issued 500 with 'JUBILEE' logo	£135-£165	☐
		COCA-COLA	2000 with script writing '75th'	£115-£135	☐
Y5		**1927 TALBOT VAN**	"BEAULIEU" Issues		
	1979			£17-£22	☐
	1980			£14-£18	☐
	1981			£12-£15	☐
	1982			£11-£14	☐
	1983			£9-£12	☐

CODE 1
Applies to models which have been totally produced by a manufacturer.
CODE 2
Same as CODE 1 only model labelled outside the factory WITH the permission of the manufacturer. This permission is no longer granted by Matchbox Toys.
CODE 3
Same as CODE 2 only model labelled WITHOUT permission of manufacturer.

Giftware Series

Models specially plated to adorn giftware — eg cigarette boxes, ashtrays, penstands, boxes and pipestands. Non-plated versions of the models listed will also be found with the two baseplate holes used for fixing the plated models to the various items.

SILVER PLATED MODELS

Y1-2	1911	MODEL 'T' FORD
Y2-2	1911	RENAULT 2 SEATER
Y2-3	1914	PRINCE HENRY VAUXHALL
Y3-3	1934	RILEY M.P.H.
Y4-3	1909	OPEL COUPE
Y5-2	1929	4.2 LITRE BENTLEY
Y6-2	1926	TYPE 35 BUGATTI
Y7-2	1913	MERCER RACEABOUT
Y7-3	1912	ROLLS ROYCE
Y10-2	1928	MERCEDES BENZ 36-220
Y10-3	1906	ROLLS ROYCE
Y12-2		THOMAS FLYABOUT
Y13-2	1911	DAIMLER
Y13-3		CROSSLEY
Y14-2	1911	MAXWELL ROADSTER
Y15-1		ROLLS ROYCE SILVER GHOST

GOLD PLATED MODELS

Y1-2	1911	MODEL 'T' FORD
Y2-3	1914	PRINCE HENRY VAUXHALL
Y4-3	1909	OPEL COUPE
Y5-2	1929	4.2 LITRE BENTLEY
Y7-2		MERCER RACEABOUT
Y7-3	1912	ROLLS ROYCE
Y10-2	1928	MERCEDES BENZ 36-220
Y10-3	1906	ROLLS ROYCE
Y12-2		THOMAS FLYABOUT
Y13-2	1911	DAIMLER
Y13-3		CROSSLEY
Y14-2	1911	MAXWELL ROADSTER
Y15-1		ROLLS ROYCE SILVER GHOST

PRICES FOR PLATED MODELS. In general these items are not regarded as quite so collectable as the normal paint finish models. Consequently expect to pay no more than the price shown in the catalogue for the similar model in a standard livery and probably somewhat less. However, as the market for plated models is a very small one, it is very difficult to quote specific price levels for models seen. Consequently especially for the rarer issues, it really is a case of the collector having to pay the price being asked, for he might not see a similar model again for sometime. For pictures of the plated models plus full details of the many interesting variations, see 'THE COLLECTION' manual, as recommended by this catalogue on the Matchbox Collectors Club page.

N.B. Gold plated sets were issued e.g. GOLDEN VETERAN SET with
3 models, Y7-3, Y13-2, Y14-2 — £50-£65 ☐
HERITAGE GIFTS with 2 models Y7-3, Y10-3 — £35-£50 ☐

'Models of Yesteryear' Collectors Passport Scheme

In 1987 Matchbox launched a promotional scheme designed to encourage regular purchases from its nationwide appointed stockists. MOY collectors were issued with a 'passport' which was stamped each time they purchased a model. The purchase of six normal 1987 issues plus three special edition models, qualified the collector to buy a special framed cabinet containing the component parts of the Preston Type Tramcar. This special framed cabinet only being obtainable under the passport scheme. The scheme worked well and was continued in 1988.

The Matchbox International Collectors Association (MICA)

M.I.C.A. was founded in 1985 and provides its members with a bi-monthly magazine which is full of useful information about past, present and future issues across the whole Matchbox range of products.

Furthermore as Matchbox now own the 'Dinky Toys' trade name information on Dinky Toys is also included.

All aspects of collecting are included and cover such topics as new releases, variations, past issues and a members advertisement section etc.

Once a year a convention is held and a special members model is issued to commemorate the event.

Collectors requiring information about joining should contact:—

NORTH AMERICA
The Membership Secretary, Ms Rita Schneider, 585 Highpoint Avenue, Waterloo, Ontario, Canada N2L 423
Tel. c519 885-0529

AUSTRALIA, NEW ZEALAND AND SOUTH PACIFIC
Robert Hill, MATCHBOX TOYS PTY LTD, 5 Leeds St, Rhodes, Sydney, New South Wales 2138.

UNITED KINGDOM, EUROPE AND REST OF THE WORLD
The Membership Secretary, 42 Bridge Street Row, Chester CH1 1NQ.
Tel. 0244 46297.

Please note that all enquiries requiring a response must contain a stamped envelope.

Recommended reading for Matchbox collectors:—

'THE COLLECTION'

Kevin McGimpsey and Stewart Orr the editors of the MICA magazine have joined forces with Matchbox Toys Ltd to produce the ultimate book for 'Models of Yesteryear' collectors. It contains superb colour pictures and information on all the issues and is kept fully up to date by the issue of regular supplements. Details of all the variations are included and really is a must for MOY collectors.

'The History of Matchbox Toys'

This important book is due to be published early in 1989 and will contain chapters on every aspect of Matchbox production since 1947, with MICA members providing much of the technical input.

Copies of both publications may be ordered from your local Matchbox Stockist but if in difficulty write to MICA enclosing a S.A.E. who will be pleased to help you obtain a copy.

CORGI TOYS

Just as the first edition was going to print in 1983 there was an announcement on 31st October that the Mettoy Company PLC had asked its bankers to call in the receivers and that the business would continue for a few months in the hope that a buyer could be found. This statement was published as a footnote in the first edition and what a chilling statement it was. Well, all that is history for following a successful management buy-out the new and totally revitalised Corgi Toys company has made tremendous strides and is currently probably more successful than at any time in its history. The reasons for this success are not difficult to understand for following an in-depth investigation of market needs, the company have produced an excellent range of new products which has culminated in Corgi Toys Ltd winning the coveted 1987 Toymaker of the Year award.

Of all the new products which contributed to the winning of the award the reintroduced range of 'Corgi Classics' models must surely have impressed the judges by the quality of the engineering and superb finish. On behalf of collectors everywhere congratulations to the Corgi management team for mounting such a successful rescue operation.

MARKET SURVEY

It was quite clear from the upward movements recorded in Corgi price levels that the models have become far more sought-after. There was a period when it was possible to purchase four Corgi Toys for the price of one Dinky Toy — nowadays the ratio is closer to two to one. From the chart below it can be seen that prices have risen generally with the largest increases occurring in the commercial vehicle and novelty sections.

PRICE AND RARITY CHANGES

			1981-83 Survey		1985 Survey		1988 Survey	
SALOONS	200M	Ford Consul (mechanical)	£18	NC	£30	NC	£40	NC
	224	Bentley Continental	£11-£14	MPR	£28	NC	£45	NC
	307	'E' Type Jaguar	£16	NC	£30	NC	£50	GP
RACING AND	153	Bluebird Record Car	£17	NC	£30	NC	£45	NC
RALLY CARS	345	M.G.T.	£11-£14	MPR	£25	NC	£40	NC
VANS	421	Bedford 'EVENING STANDARD'	£28	NC	£55	NC	£75	GP
	422	Bedford 'CORGI TOYS'	£30	NC	£70	NC	£80	GP
	447	Ford Thames 'WALLS ICE CREAM'	£14	NC	£27	NC	£41	NC
COMMERCIALS	456	E.R.F. Dropside Lorry 449	£7-£9	MPR	£25	NC	£36	NC
	1100	Bedford 'S' Type Low Loader	£18	NC	£40	NC	£70	NC
	1141	Bedford 'TK' Petrol Tanker	£35	NC	£65	NC	£95	GP
BUSES	468	'CORGI TOYS' Routemaster	£20	NC	£33	NC	£45	NC
	C469/18	'BLACKPOOL TRANSPORT' Open top	£12	NC	£35	NC	£45	NC
NOVELTY	266	'CHITTY CHITTY BANG BANG'	£35	NC	£55	GP	£135	GP
	426	Circus Booking Office	£35	NC	£75	GP	£85	GP
GIFT SET No 1		Transporter and 4 Cars	£65	NC	£125	GP	£150	NPE

Corgi will always be known as 'the ones with windows', as they were the first manufacturer to produce models with windows. In addition some of their first models had a mechanical motor. Independent suspension was introduced from 1959 and was quickly followed in 1960 by the first die-cast model to have an opening bonnet.

The first production models were all based on real cars of the period. Similarly, with the launch of the 'Corgi Major Toys' in 1959, models of real commercial vehicles were available; no doubt issued as Corgi's answer to the Dinky 'Supertoys' range.

During the sixties Corgi produced many very successful film and TV link up models. Probably the best remembered and most successful of these being the 'James Bond' Aston Martin which sold in huge quantities in the autumn of 1965. Indeed, such was the popularity of the model that a version is still available at the time of publication.

During the sixties Corgi introduced many new features such as: jewelled headlights, opening bonnet revealing detailed engine, opening boot revealing spare, self-centring steering, ruby rear lights, etc.

Many heavy commercial vehicles were produced in the sixties and seventies again containing enormous detail and often working parts as well.

One particularly attractive model of the early sixties, which apparently did not sell well at the time, was the Midland Red Motorway Express Coach. The detailed interior even incorporated a toilet! Needless to say good examples of this model are highly sought after by the bus collectors.

Similarly the 'Chipperfields Circus' collection of models were beautifully produced and are highly prized today.

As mentioned earlier Corgi Toys are famous for their innovations and in the late sixties they introduced 'Golden Jacks' which was a built-in jacking system which enabled models to have 'Take Off' wheels.

A further exciting feature was the introduction of 'Trans-O-Lite' whereby light rays were captured and fed through glass tubes to illuminate the headlights.

The seventies saw 'WHIZZWHEELS' and the slightly larger scale of $1/_{42}$ being introduced.

No commentary on the Corgi range would be complete without talking about a market strategy unique to Corgi — launching a replica model car simultaneously with the real car.

To date simultaneous launches have occurred with Austin Metro, Ford Escort, Triumph Acclaim, Ford Sierra and the MG Maestro 1600, which is a unique record. Corgi were the first die-cast manufacturers to introduce the dimensions of light, sound and movement into their models by using the micro-chip in their 'Corgitronic' range. The models 'come alive', for example by just pushing down on the rear axle or, in the case of the Road Repair Unit, by pressing the workman to activate the pneumatic drill sound. Some models such as the Sonic Corgi Truck Set are activated by a remote controlled handset which controls the movements of forward, stop, reverse and swinging round.

Since the new company took over in 1984 the collector has been treated to a succession of delightful new models which have been introduced as part of the 'CORGI CLASSICS' range. Of these new products, the superb Thorneycroft models with their close attention to fine detail and authentic period designs and logos have proved to be a winner, as have the new models of the greatly loved Morris 1000 vans and cars. 1988 will see the launch of the 'TRAMLINES' range based on the Dick Kerr tram of 1901. Corgi have gone to great trouble to ensure that these models will be totally authentic. In addition the packaging will be on a tram theme basis featuring tram tickets, early tram pictures and the like.

Corgi have long been famous for innovation and with their new product range they have more than maintained their reputation.

Common Features

Many models have common identifying features and these are shown below to avoid unnecessary repetition.

a. Base Plates

The early base plates were mostly all of the tinplate variety until about 1960 when they changed to a more realistic diecast type of chassis which became increasingly detailed. The later plastic chassis are indicated where applicable as (PCH).

b. Wheel Hubs

Prior to about 1961 wheel hubs were plain and smooth. After this date they became contoured and more realistic in appearance.

c. Mechanical

All the early Corgi Toys were produced in either the normal form or there was a mechanical friction type flywheel version. The only exceptions being the sports cars and trucks which could not be converted to take the flywheel. The mechanical versions were not all that popular and were phased out in 1959.

d. Model Number and Name

It has been assumed that all models have the name of the model on the base plate or chassis. Unlike Dinky Toys the model numbers are not shown on all models which can make unboxed models a little difficult to categorize at times.

However, models without numbers may be found in the catalogue by looking for them in their own thematic section: e.g. Saloon Car, Novelty, etc.

e. Windows

It goes without saying that all vehicles are assumed to have windows.

f. Construction Materials

All models assumed to be comprised at least in part of a diecast alloy.

g. Corgi Toys

All models have the name shown on the body.

Corgi Toys
Saloons Estates and Sports Cars

Ref. No.		Model Type	Model Features and Size	Rarity and Price Grading	
200	1956-61	Ford Consul	Cream or two tone Green body, OC. 90 mm.	£40	NC
200M	1956-59	Ford Consul	Blue or Green body, FWM. 90 mm.	£40	NC
C200	1976-78	B.L.M. Mini 1000	Blue/Silver body, Red and White arrow. 85 mm.		MPR
201	1956-63	Austin Cambridge	Blue or Cream body, OC/SDL/RB. 90 mm.	£40	NC
201M	1956-59	Austin Cambridge	Cream or Grey body, FWM. 90 mm.	£40	NC
202	1956-60	Morris Cowley	Cream or Green body. 91 mm. OC	£40	NC
202M	1956-59	Morris Cowley	Cream/Green/Grey body, FWM. 91 mm.	£40	NC
202	1970-72	Renault R16	Blue/Silver body. 91 mm.	£7-£9	MPR
203	1956-60	Vauxhall Velox	Red or Cream or Red/Cream. 91 mm.	£40	NC
203M	1956-59	Vauxhall Velox	Red or Yellow body, FWM. 91 mm.	£40	NC
203	1971-72	De Tomaso Mangusta	Green/Gold body, WZW. 99 mm.	£7-£9	MPR
204	1956-60	Rover 90	White or Bronze body. 97 mm.	£40	NC
204M	1956-59	Rover 90	Green or Grey body, FWM. 97 mm.	£40	NC
204	1972-74	Morris Mini Minor	Dark Blue or Orange body, WZW. 73 mm.	£9-£11	MPR
205	1956-61	Riley Pathfinder	Red or Blue body. 97 mm.	£40	NC
205M	1956-59	Riley Pathfinder	Red or Blue body, FWM. 97 mm.	£40	GP
206	1956-60	Hillman Husky Estate	Tan or Blue/Silver body. 86 mm.	£35	NC
206M	1956-59	Hillman Husky Estate	Cream or Blue body, FWM. 86 mm.	£35	NC
207	1957-62	Standard Vanguard III	White/Red or Green/Red body. 95 mm.	£35	NC
207M	1957-59	Standard Vanguard III	Yellow or Green/Red body, FWM. 95 mm.	£40	NC
208	1957-60	Jaguar 2.4 litre. 95 mm.	White body, S/SW/No SS/WS. 95 mm.	£40	NC
208	1957-59	Jaguar 2.4 litre	Dark Blue body, S/SW/No SS/WS/FWM. 95 mm.	£40	GP
208S	1960-62	Jaguar 2.4 litre	Blue or White body, 95 mm.	£35	NC
		Colour change	Lemon body, 95 mm	£45	NPE
210	1957-60	Citroen DS19	Red/Yellow body, LHD/No SS/SW/S. 97 mm.	£38	NC
210S	1960-65	Citroen DS19	Green/Black body, LHD/SS/SW/S. 97 mm.	£35	NC
211	1958-60	Studebaker Golden Hawk	Blue/Gold body, LHD/No SS. 104 mm.	£35	NC
211M	1958-59	Studebaker Golden Hawk	White/Gold body, LHD/No SS. 104 mm.	£35	NC
211S	1960-65	Studebaker Golden Hawk	Blue/Gold body, LHD/SS. 104 mm.	£32	NC
214	1959-62	Ford Thunderbird	Green/Cream body, LHD/No SS. 102 mm.	£32	NC
214M	1959 only	Ford Thunderbird	Pink/Black body, LHD/No SS. 102 mm.	£45	GP
214 S	1962-65	Ford Thunderbird	Green/Cream body, LHD/SS. 102 mm.	£32	NC
215	1959-62	Thunderbird Open Sports	White body, LHD/No SS. 102 mm.	£40	NC
215S	1962-65	Thunderbird Open Sports	White body, LHD/SS. 102 mm.	£35	NC
216	1959-62	Austin A40	Two tone Blue body. AVI red/black. 86 mm.	£35	NC
216M	1959 only	Austin A40	Two tone Blue body. 86 mm.	£45	GP
217	1960-63	Fiat 1800 Saloon	Two tone Blue/Silver body. 95 mm.	£22	NC
218	1960-62	Aston Martin DB4	Red or Yellow body, OBN/SS/DE. 95 mm.	£35	NC
219	1959-62	Plymouth Suburban Sports	Brown/Cream body, LHD/S/SW. 104 mm.	£35	NC
220	1960-62	Chevrolet Impala	Pink or Blue body, LHD/S/SW. 108 mm.	£30	NC
222	1959-60	Renault Floride	Dark Red body, S/SW/WDS/No SS. 91 mm.	£30	NC
222	1960-65	Renault Floride	Blue or Green body, OC/S/SW/SS. 91 mm.	£25	NC
224	1961-66	Bentley Continental	Blue/Silver body, OC/PP/SL/DSPW/SCS/S/OBT. 108 mm.	£45	NC
225	1961-66	Austin 7 Saloon	Red body, WDS/SS/S/SW. 73 mm.	£36	GP
226	1960-71	Morris Mini Minor	Blue or Maroon body, SS/S/SW. 73 mm.	£19	NC
228	1962-66	Volvo P 1800	Gold or Red body, LHD/SL/SW/SS. 95 mm.	£24	NC
229	1961-66	Chevrolet Corvair	Blue or Gold body, LHD/OEC/SS/SW. 97 mm.	£22	NC
230	1962-64	M-Benz 220 SE Coupe	Red body, SS/OBT/SPW. 102 mm.	£24	NC
231	1961-65	Triumph Herald	Blue/White body, SS/SW/OBT/DE. 90 mm.	£41	NC
232	1961-65	Fiat 2100	Red/Yellow body, OC/SS/SL/VB/S/SW. 95 mm.	£42	NC
233	1962-72	Heinkel Trojan	Yellow, Blue or Red body, S/SW. 73 mm.	£33	NC
234	1961-64	Ford Consul Classic	Brown/Pink body, S/SW/SS/OBN/DE. 95 mm.	£33	NC
235	1962-66	Oldsmobile Super 88	Steel Blue/White body, S/SW/SS. 108 mm.	£35	NC
236	1964-69	'CORGI DSC' Austin A60	Blue body D/PS/SS/STC/DI. 95 mm.	£37	NC
238	1962-67	Mk 10 Jaguar	Blue or GRN body, DE/OBB/LG/BOFL. 108 mm.	£37	NC
239	1963-68	VW 1500 Karmann Ghia	Red body, OBT/SS/LG/SPW. 91 mm.	£24	NC
240	1963-65	Fiat 600 Jolly	Blue body, DRF/SS/D/PS/WP/SW. 79 mm.	£24	NC
241	1963-69	Chrysler Ghia L64	Green body, OC/DE/TS/SS/OBT/DD/RVM/PP. 108 mm.	£24	NC
242	1965-66	Fiat 600 Jolly	Yellow body, SS/D/PS no canopy. 79 mm.	£24	NC
245	1964-68	Buick Riviera	Gold or Blue body, OC/TOL/PP/SS/SPKW. 108 mm.	£30	NC
246	1965-68	Chrysler Imperial	Red body, OC D/PS golf clubs ODBB/SPKW. 108 mm.	£35	NC
		Variant	Blue body - RARE	£35	NGPP
247	1964-69	Mercedes Benz Pullman	Met Maroon body, WSW/OWD/DD/PP/SS. 121 mm.	£30	NC
248	1965-67	Chevrolet Impala	Brown/White body, LHD/SS/PP. 108 mm.	£30	NC
249	1965-68	Morris Mini-Cooper	Black/Red body, Wickerwork panels. 73 mm.	£36	NC
251	1963-69	Hillman Imp	Blue or Bronze body, OWD/LG. 83 mm.	£28	NC
252	1963-66	Rover 2000	Blue or Maroon body, SS/SL. 95 mm.	£26	NC
253	1964-68	Mercedes 220 SE Coupe	Met Maroon or Blue body, SS/OBT/LG/SPW. 121 mm.	£26	NC
255	1964-68	Motor School A60	Same as 236 only LHD	£28	NC
C257	1985	Mercedes 500 SEC	White body, MAGIC TOP—fold away roof		NRP
C258	1985	Toyota Celica Supra	Brown body, Black base, ODT, 125 mm		NRP
	1986	Colour change	Blue body, Black base, ODT.		NRP
	1987	Colour change	Blue UPB, Cream LWB, Red line		NRP
259	1966-69	Citroën 'LE DANDY'	Blue or Maroon body, ODBN/SL/TS/SPKW. 102 mm.	£50	NC
260	1969	Renault 16 TS	Met Maroon body, OBNHB/SPW/AS. 91 mm.	£18	NC
262	1967-69	Lincoln Continental	Gold/Black body, ODBB/BOCTV/SL/IS/CPT. 149 mm.	£48	NPE
		Variant	Pale blue and Tan body, RARE		NGPP

Ref. No.		Model Type	Saloons, Estates and Sports Cars continued	Rarity and Price Grading		
263	1966-69	Marlin Rambler Sports	Red/Black body, OD/SS/SPKW/H. 102 mm.	£24	NC	☐
264	1966-69	Oldsmobile Toronado	Blue body, SL/PP/SPKW. 108 mm.	£24	NC	☐
271	1969	Ghia 500 Mangusta	Blue/White/Yellow body, LOB/WZW. 97 mm.	£24	NC	☐
273	1970	Rolls Royce Silver Shadow	Silver/Blue body, GJ/TOW/SPW/PP. 120 mm.	£48	NPE	☐
			Less rare — White/Blue version	£38	NC	☐
274	1970-72	Bentley T Series	Red body, ODBN/SL/DD/DE/PP/WZW. 120 mm.	£33	NC	☐
275	1968-70	Rover 2000 TC	Green body, TP roof/GJ/TOW/SPW opens. 95 mm.	£18	NC	☐
			White body	£35	GP	☐
			Metallic Lime Green body		NGPP	☐
			Dark Green body	£20-£25	MPR	☐
C275	1981-	Mini Metro	Red body, Yellow interior OC/ODHB. 94 mm.	£5-£8	MPR	☐
C276	1982-	Triumph Acclaim	Metallic Blue body, STC. 120 mm.	£5-£8	MPR	☐
276	1968-70	Oldsmobile Toronado	Plum or Gold body, GJ/TOW/SL. 108 mm.	£15	NC	☐
C278	1982-	Triumph Acclaim DSC	Yellow/Black body, STC. 118 mm.	£5-£8	MPR	☐
C279	1979-	Rolls Royce Corniche	Met Maroon or Yellow body, DE/ODBB/TS. 144 mm.	£5-£8	MPR	☐
	1985	Colour change	Cream and Brown body		NRP	☐
	1987	Colour change	Silver/Black body, chrome trim		NRP	☐
C280	1970-78	Rolls Royce Silver Shadow	Gold body, ODBB/SL/DD/DE/PP/WZW. 120 mm.	£38	NC	☐
281	1971-73	Rover 2000 TC	Met Purple/Silver body, clear roof/WZW. 95 mm.	£18	NC	☐
283	1971-74	'DAF CITY' car	Brown/Black body, WZW/SL/ODBN/TS. 73 mm.	£10-£13	MPR	☐
C284	1970-76	Citroen S.M.	Lilac or Yellow body, PP/ODT/WZW. 112 mm.	£18	NC	☐
C285	1975-81	Mercedes-Benz 240 D	Silver or Met Blue body, WZW/H. 127 mm.	£8-£11	MPR	☐
C286	1975-79	Jaguar XJC V-12	Blue/Black or Red/Black, ODBT/WZW/H. 127 mm.	£14	NC	☐
C287	1975-78	Citroen Dyane	Green/Black body, ORD/WZW/duck decal. 115 mm.	£8-£11	MPR	☐
C288	1975-79	Minissima	Green and Cream body, ODBN. 63 mm.	£8-£11	MPR	☐
C289	1977-81	Volkswagen Polo	Green body, ODHB. 97 mm.	£8-£11	MPR	☐
291	1977-78	AMC Pacer	Met Maroon body, LHD/ODHB. 118 mm.	£6-£9	MPR	☐
C293	1977	Renault 5TS	Yellow body, Black trim, ODHB. 97 mm.	£4-£7	MPR	☐
C294	1980	Renault 5TS Alpine	Black body, White stripe, ODHB. 97 mm.	£5-£7	MPR	☐
C299	1982	Ford Sierra 2.3 Ghia	Met Blue body, White int., ODHB/HPS. 124 mm.			☐
		Rare variant	1st issue with Ford badge on box	£100	NPE	☐
	1985	Colour change	Met Silver body	£4-£6	MPR	☐
	1985	Colour change	Red body, White broken ground		NRP	☐
300	1956-63	Austin Healey 100-4	Red/Cream body, PWS/SWCI/DI. 86 mm.	£45	NVE	☐
300	1970-72	Corvette Stingray	Maroon/Black body, OC/SPW/LG/VD/GJ/TOW. 102 mm.	£23	NC	☐
301	1956-59	Triumph TR2	Cream or Green body, PWS/SWCI/DI. Red or WHS. 86 mm.	£50	GP	☐
301	1970-73	Iso Grifo 7 litre	Blue/Black body, ODBN/WZW/SL. 102 mm.	£15	NC	☐
302	1957-64	MG 'A'	Red/Cream or Green/Cream body, WS/DI/SW. 90 mm. AVI Red body and Cream seats	£55	GP	☐
303	1958-60	M-Benz 300 SL Open	Blue/White body, OC/LHD/PWS/No SS/SW. 95 mm.	£38	NC	☐
303 S	1961-66	M-Benz 300 SL Open	Blue/White body, OC/LHD/PWS/SS/SW. 95 mm.	£38	NC	☐
304	1959-61	M-Benz 300 SL Hard Top	Yellow or Yellow/Red body, No SS/SPKW.	£38	NC	☐
304	1971-73	Chevrolet Camaro	Green/Black or Blue/White body, DRF/SL. 102 mm.	£14	NC	☐
305	1960-62	Triumph TR3	Light Green or Cream body, PWS/No SS. 86 mm.	£50	GP	☐
305S	1962-64	Triumph TR3	Light Green or Cream body, PWS/SS. 86 mm.	£50	GP	☐
306	1971-73	Morris Marina 1.8 Coupe	Maroon or Green, ODBN/WZW. 98 mm.	£14	NC	☐
307	1962-64	'E' Type Jaguar	Red or Met Grey body, Red RHT. 95 mm.	£50	GP	☐
310	1963-68	Chevrolet Stingray	Red or Silver body, SL/SS/PP/SPKW. 90 mm.	£17	NC	☐
310	1984	Porsche 924 Turbo	Black body, gold design, Red seats	£5-£7	MPR	☐
		Colour variant	Red body, Porsche badge on RDT	£5-£7	MPR	☐
C311	1970-72	Ford Capri V6	Red/Black body, OD/SS/WZW. 102 mm.	£11-£14	MPR	☐
312	1971-73	Marcos Mantis	Met Plum body, OC/OD/SPKW. 110 mm.	£11-£14	MPR	☐
313	1970-73	Ford Cortina GXL	Blue/Black body, OD, Graham Hill fig. 102 mm.	£23	NC	☐
C314	1976-79	Fiat X1-9	Green or Silver body, OEC/SS/H. 110 mm.	£8-£11	MPR	☐
C314	1982-	Supercat Jaguar XJS-HE	Black body, Red interior, OD. 118 mm.	£7-£10	MPR	☐
C315	1976-78	Lotus Elite	Red/Black body, OD/SS. 120 mm.	£11-£14	MPR	☐
316	1963-66	NSU Sport Prinz	Plum body, S/SW/SS. 86 mm.	£16	NC	☐
318	1965-68	Lotus Elan	Blue or Green/Yellow body, TS/SS/OBN/OWDS.	£20	NC	☐
318	1981	Jaguar XJS	Blue/Cream body with Red line		NRP	☐
318	1988	Colour change	Pale Blue body, Beige seats		NRP	☐
319	1978-82	Jaguar XJS	Met Plum/Black body, OD/SS. 128 mm	£5-£8	MPR	☐
320	1965-67	Ford Mustang Fastback	Met Blue or Green body, OD/SL/SS/CP/OWDS. 95 mm.	£23	NC	☐
321	1978-82	Porsche 924 Saloon.	Green or Red body, Porsche ODHB/H. 118 mm.	£8-£11	MPR	☐
324	1966-69	Marcos Volvo 1800GT.	White/Green body, OD/DE/SPKW/SS. 91 mm.	£26	NC	☐
325	1981-	Chevrolet Caprice.	Met Gold body ODBT/WWT. 150 mm.	£8-£11	MPR	☐
327	1967-68	MGB GT.	Red body OBT/TS/SPKW. 90 mm.	£60	GP	☐
329	1980-	Opel Senator.	Purple or Gold body, OD. 142 mm.	£10-£13	MPR	☐
332	1967-69	Lancia Fulvia Sports.	Met Blue, OC/ODBN/TS/SS/DE. 91 mm.	£24	NC	☐
334	1968-70	Mini Magnifique.	Green or Blue body, Red RF/ODBN/PLE. 73 mm.	£24	NC	☐
C334	1981-	Ford Escort 1.3GL.	Steel Blue or Red body, OD/SS. 112 mm.	£6-£9	MPR	☐
335	1968-69	Jaguar 4.2 litre.	Blue body TS/SPKW/PP/ODBNHB. AVI Red body. 108 mm.	£44	NC	☐
338	1968-70	Chevrolet SS350.	Yellow/Black body, RHT/SS/WS/GJ/TOW. 102 mm.	£20	NC	☐
C338	1980-	Rover 3500.	Blue/Silver body, ODBNHB/WDS/SS.	£5-£8	MPR	☐
341	1968-70	Mini Marcos GT850.	Maroon body, ODBNHB/HLS/GJ/TOW. 86 mm.	£16	NC	☐
342	1969-72	Lamborghini Muira.	Red body, RWS/OEC/WW or GJ/TOW/OBN. 95 mm.	£20	NC	☐
343	1969-73	Pontiac Firebird.	Silver/Black body, OD/TS/PP/GJ/TOW. 102 mm.	£18	NC	☐
343	1980-	Ford Capri 3 litre.	Yellow/Black, 'S' Stripe ODHB. 124 mm.	£7-£9	MPR	☐
C345	1981-	Honda Prelude.	Met Blue/Black body, ORF/OD/SR. 114 mm.	£7-£9	MPR	☐
C346	1982-	Citroen 2CV.	Yellow or Maroon/Black body, OBN/SR. 108 mm.	£4-£6	MPR	☐
C346	1984	Citroen Charleston	Black/Brown body & seats, OSR/CTR	£4-£6	MPR	☐
346	1987	Citroen 2CV Dolly	White/Red body, OSR/CTR			
347	1969-74	Chevrolet Astro.	Blue or Gold body, WS/WZW/2PS. 102 mm.	£15	NC	☐

155

Ref. No.		Model Type	Saloons, Estates and Sports Cars continued	Rarity and Price Grading	
C352	1986	'BMW 325'	White with Black logo, Swiss EXPM		NRP ☐
353/1	1986	BMW 325	Red body, Black trim, opening features		NRP ☐
372	1970-72	Lancia Fulvia.	Red/Black body, ODBN/WZW/SS. 91 mm.	£15	NC ☐
C373	1981-	Peugeot 505.	Metallic Gold body, SS/OD. 127 mm.	£5-£8	MPR ☐
374	1970-76	Jaguar 'E' Type.	Red or Yellow body, TTEC/WZW. 108 mm.	£26	NC ☐
375	1970-72	Toyota 2000GT.	Blue or Purple body, A/WS/WZW. 102 mm.	£20	MPR ☐
377	1970-73	Marcos 3 litre.	Yellow/Black body, OEC/DE/SS/WZW. 91 mm.	£15	MPR ☐
378	1970-72	MGC GT.	Red/Black body, ODHB/WZW. 90 mm.	£38	GP ☐
		Rare Variant	All Orange body — only seen in Gift Set 20	£150	GP ☐
C378	1982-	Ferrari 308GTS.	Red body, pop up HL/OEC. 115 mm.	£4-£6	MPR ☐
380	1970-74	Alfa Romeo P33.	White/Black body, AF/WZW. 95 mm.		MPR ☐
381	1970-74	VW Beach Buggy.	Yellow/MRN body, 2SKIS/WZW/DR. 95 mm.	£7-£10	MPR ☐
382	1970-75	Porsche Targa 911S.	Met Blue or GRN, BLK RF/WZW. 95 mm.	£7-£10	MPR ☐
C382	1981-	Lotus Elite 2.2.	Blue body, *Elite 22* OD/NP. 120 mm.	£5-£8	MPR ☐
383	1971-73	Bertone Barchetta.	Yellow body, Black interior. AF/WZW. 83 mm.	£9-£12	MPR ☐
384	1970-73	Adams Brothers Probe.	Met Maroon body, OC/WZW/TTWDS/OD. 97 mm.	£9-£12	MPR ☐
384	1984	Renault 11	Red body, Black PCH, CTR/OD, 110 mm.		NRP ☐
385	1984	Mercedes 190	Blue body, White seats, RGN/CTR		NRP ☐
	1985	Colour change	Silver body, White seats, RGN/CTR		NRP ☐
386	1971-73	Bertone Barchetta.	Yellow body, Black interior and trim, AF/WZW. 83 mm.	£9-£12	MRP ☐
386	1987	Mercedes 2.3/16	Black body, ARDT/RGN/AF		
387	1970-73	Chevrolet Corvette.	Red/Blue body, OC/RHL/DR/OBN/WZW. 102 mm.	£16	NC ☐
388	1970-74	M-Benz C111.	Orange/Black body, WZW. 104 mm.	£6-£8	MPR ☐
389	1971-74	Reliant Bond Bug 700ES.	Green *Bug* raised HL/body lifts. Also Orange. 67 mm.	£14	NC ☐
391	1971-73	Ford Mustang Mach 1.	Red/Black body, OD/PP/WZW. 113 mm.	£14	NC ☐
392	1973-74	Bertone Shake Buggy.	Yellow body, OC/DE/PP/flag. 89 mm.	£9-£12	MPR ☐
C393	1972-79	M-Benz 350SL.	Metallic Blue body, ODBN/SPKW/PP. 102 mm.	£9-£12	MPR ☐
394	1973-76	Datsun 240Z.	Red/Black body, non rally version. 102 mm.	£10-£13	MPR ☐
C400	1975-77	VW 1200DSC (also 401).	Blue body, STC, *Corgi MSC*. 92 mm.	£18	NC ☐
424	1961-65	Ford Zephyr Estate.	Two Tone Blue, SS/WDS/MLG. 97 mm.	£26	NC ☐
435	1986	Volvo 760 Turbo	Dark Blue body, ARDT		NRP ☐
435/1	1987	Colour change	Silver body		NRP ☐
440	1966-67	Ford Cortina Estate.	Blue/Brown, SL/OTG/SS/2 figs/Golf EQ. 95 mm.	£26	NC ☐
C440	1988	Porsche 944 Saloon	Red body		NRP ☐
C453	1984	Ford 'ESCORT' RS1600i	White body, Red seats, Black TPD, AK, 110 mm.	£3-£5	MPR ☐
485	1966-69	Mini Countryman.	Blue, 2 Red Surfboards/RR/fig. 79 mm.	£35	NC ☐
491	1967-69	Ford Cortina Estate.	Red or Blue, a revised 440. 95 mm.	£25	MPR ☐
600	1984	Ford Escort	Red body, Black seats, OD, 110 mm.		NRP ☐
601	1984	Fiat N.9	Blue body, Black seats, OD, 110 mm.		NRP ☐
602	1984	Mini	Silver body, Brown seats, OD/CTR, 85 mm.		NRP ☐
603	1984	VW Polo	Cream body, Brown seats, CTR/OD, 90 mm.		NRP ☐
604	1984	Renault 5	Dark Blue body, White seats, OD/CTR, 95 mm.		NRP ☐
605	1984	Mini Metro	Red MB, White seats, 90 mm.		NRP ☐
C1009	1984	MG Maestro	Yellow body, White flash 'AA SERVICE'		NRP ☐

Models difficult to catalogue and about which information is required:

i)	OGLE/Reliant Scimitar GTE			NGPP ☐
ii)	Jensen Interceptor			NGPP ☐
iii)	Triumph Herald Coupe			NGPP ☐

Gift Sets

1	1957-62	Carrimore Transporter and 4 Cars.	Contained 4 British Cars plus 1101 in 1957 and 4 U.S. in 1959. 4 various in 1962	£150	NPE ☐
C1	1983	Ford Sierra Set	(299) Blue body with Blue/Cream Caravan	£24	NC ☐
10	1968-69	Camping Gift Set	263 with RR/2 Canoes and 109.	£33	NC ☐
C12	1981-	Glider and TRL Set	345 plus TRL and glider.	£23	NC ☐
13	1969-72	Renault 16 Film Unit	WH/BLK, *Tour De France* cyclist	£33	NC ☐
C13	1981	Tour De France Set	373 plus 3 figs, 4 bikes.	£15	NC ☐
20	1961	Golden Guinea Set	Contains Gold plated 224, 229, 234.	£90	GP ☐
20	1970-72	Transporter and 6 Cars	Contains 1146 plus 6 cars. Price excluding rare 378 variant.	£100	GP ☐
24	1976-	Mercedes and Caravan Set	Contains 285 and 490 with colour change 1980	£23	NC ☐
25	1963-66	BP or Shell Garage Set	Contains Garage, 5 various cars plus figs and ACCS.	£250	NPE ☐
26	1971-75	Beach Buggy Set	381 plus Sailing Boat	£23	MPR ☐
28	1963-66	Transporter and 4 Cars	Contains 1105, 222, 230, 232, 234.	£100	GP ☐
31	1965-68	Buick Boat Set	Contains (245) plus TRL and boat	£40	NC ☐
36	1967-70	Marlin Rambler Set	Contains (263) plus boat	£40	NC ☐
36	1967-70	Oldsmobile Set	Contains (276) plus boat/TRL/3 figs.	£40	NC ☐
37	1979-82	Fiat X19 Set	Fiat X19 plus boat *Carlsberg*.	£20	MPR ☐
38	1977-78	Mini Camping Set	Mini plus 2 figs/tent/barbecue.	£20	MPR ☐
C38	1980-	Jaguar XJS Set	319 plus powerboat or TRL	£20	MPR ☐
48	1966-69	Transporter and 6 Cars	1138 plus 6 various cars	£135	GP ☐
C57		Volvo 740 & Caravan	Red car, White/Red/Blue caravan. Swedish EXPM		NRP ☐
C67/1/ 2/3		Cyclists Sets	Sold in France, 2 cars/2 bikes		NRP ☐

156

Corgi Toys

CARS OF THE 50's SERIES

Ref. No.		Model Type	Model Features and Size	Rarity and Price Grading		
C801	1982	1957 Ford Thunderbird.	White body with Tan hood, PP/SPW/LHD/WWT/OBB/TW/ WS/SS. 132 mm. ARDT.		NRP	☐
C802	1982	1954 Mercedes 300SL.	Burgundy body, OD/SS/DI/PP. 126 mm. P.		NRP	☐
C803	1983	1952 Jaguar XK120 Soft Top Sports	Red body, Black hood, PP/SPKW/OBB/SS/DI/ARDT. 124 mm.		NRP	☐
C803/1	1983	Rally version	Cream body, RN '56' — RARE	£100	GP	☐
	1984	Colour change	White body		NRP	☐
C804	1983	1952 Jaguar XK120. 'Coupes Des Alpes'.	Cream body, Grey/Black tonneau, RN '56' in Blue/Black on BN and doors, CF/PP/BS/WS/OBB/DI/SS/RE/SPKW. 124 mm. ARDT.		NRP	☐
C805	1983	1956 Mercedes 300SC Cabriolet	Black body, Tan hood, PP/SS/WDS/OBB/ARDT.		NRP	☐
	1984	Colour change	Maroon body		NRP	☐
	1986	Colour change	Beige body & hood		NRP	☐
	1987	Colour change	Blue body, Black hood, EXPM		NRP	☐
C806	1983	1956 Mercedes 300SL Open Roadster.	Black body, Grey/Black folded hood, SS/OBB/PP.		NRP	☐
	1986	Colour change	Black/Green body, Beige seats		NRP	☐
	1986	Colour change	Red body, Cream interior, EXPM		NRP	☐
C810	1983	1957 Ford Thunderbird.	White body, ARDT/SPW/LHD/WWT/OBB/TW		NRP	☐
	1984	Colour change	Pink body		NRP	☐
	1987	Colour change	Red body		NRP	☐
C811	1984	1954 Mercedes SL.	All Silver body, ODBN/PP/SS/DI/LHD. 127 mm.		NRP	☐
	1986	Colour change	All Red body		NRP	☐
	1987	Colour change	All Grey body, EXPM		NRP	☐
C812	1985	1953 MG TF	Green body, Tan seats, OBN/PP/RHD/SPW/LGR		NRP	☐
C813	1985	1955 MG TF	Red body, Black hood, OBN/PP/RHD/SPW/LGR		NRP	☐
	1987	Colour change	Cream body, Red mudguards, EXPM		NRP	☐
C814	1985	1952 R.R. Silver Dawn	Red/Black body/TN, Brown S, OBB/PP/WS		NRP	☐
	1986	Colour change	White/Beige body		NRP	☐
	1986	Colour change	Silver/Black body, EXPM		NRP	☐
C815	1985	1954 Bentley 'R' type	Black body, Beige hood, OBB/CTR/ARDT. Also Cream version		NRP	☐
	1986	Colour change	Dark Blue & Light Blue body		NRP	☐
	1986	Colour change	Cream/Brown body, EXPM		NRP	☐
C816	1985	1956 Jaguar XK120	Red body, Black TN, RN '56', ARDT/PP/PCH/OBB		NRP	☐
C819	1985	1949 Jaguar XK120	White body, Black Hood, RN '7', ARDT/PP/PCH/OBB		NRP	☐
C825	1985	1957 Chevrolet Bel Air	Red body, White roof & flash, WWT		NRP	☐
	1987	Colour change	Black body, White RF & flash, EXPM		NRP	☐
C869	1986	MG TF Racing Car	Royal Blue, Black ARB, TN, SPW, Beige seats, RN '113', ARDT/CTR		NRP	☐
C870	1986	Jaguar XK120	Green body, RN '6', Yellow seats, EXPM		NRP	☐

Gift Sets

Ref. No.	Model Type	Model Features and Size	Rarity and Price Grading		
C51	'100 Years of the Car' set	Contains 3 Mercedes — C805 White, C806 Black, C811 Red — Originally a German EXPS	£12-£15	MPR	☐
	'The Jaguar Collection Set'	Contains C804 Cream, C816 Red, C318 Mobil Green/White. Available 'UNIPART' stores	£12-£15	MPR	☐

Auction Price Results
Lacy Scott's Bury St Edmunds Sale 27.2.88
209 Citroen Le Dandy (mint, boxed) £50
207 Standard Vanguard (mint, boxed) £28
302 Hillman Hunter (mint, boxed) £34
Phillips New Bond St, London Sale 24.10.87
Gift Set 48 realised £130

Racing, Rally and Speed Cars

Ref. No.		Model Type	Model Features and Size	Rarity and Price Grading	
C100	1985	'PORSCHE' 956	Yellow/Black body, RN '7', 'CASTROL', 115 mm.	NRP	
C100/2	1986	Design change	Yellow body, RN '7', 'TAKA-Q'	NRP	
C100/3	1988	Design change	All Black body, RC '1', 'BLAUPUNKT'	NRP	
C101	1985	Porsche 956	Red/White body, RN '14', CANON	NRP	
C102	1985	Opel Manta 400	Red body, 'SHELL', RN '43', 105 mm.	NRP	
	1988	Design change	Black body, 'SHELL', RN '18'	NRP	
C10	1985	Design change	Yellow body, 'BRITISH TELECOM', RN '12'	NRP	
C103	1985	Opel Manta 400	White body, 'CASTROL' RN '15'	NRP	
C104	1985	Toyota Corolla 1600	White/Red body, Yellow RN '16' 'LAING'	NRP	
	1986	Design change	White/Red body, RN '2', 'TOTAL'	NRP	
C105	1985	Toyota Corolla 1600	Red body, Yellow design, RN '8', 'DUNLOP'	NRP	
	1986	Design change	Red body, Yellow design, RN '5', 'TOTAL'	NRP	
C106	1985	Saab 9000 Turbo	White body, Red/Yellow design, RN '3'	NRP	
C106/1	1987	Design change	Red body, White design, 'FLY VIRGIN'	NRP	
C106/3	1988	Design change	Black body, RN '7', 'MOBIL'	NRP	
C107	1985	Saab 9000	Red body, Yellow design, RN '41', 'BRITAX'	NRP	
C108	1985	Chevrolet Z28	Red body, Yellow design, RN '52', 'WEBER', 115 mm.	NRP	
C109	1985	Chevrolet Z28	White body, BL/Red bands, Red RN '84', 115 mm.	NRP	
C110	1985	BMW 635	White body, UJ flag, RN '6'	NRP	
C110/1	1986	Design change	Red body, RN '25', 'FERODO'	NRP	
C110/2	1987	Design change	White body, RN '2', 'MOTUL'	NRP	
C110/3	1988	Design change	White body, RN '46', 'WARSTEINER'	NRP	
C111	1985	BMW 635	White/Blue body, RN '18', 'BRITAX'	NRP	
	1986	Design change	White body, RN '8', 'FIRELLI'	NRP	
C113	1987	Saab 9000	All red body, C7PM (Swedish)	NRP	
C139/2	1987	Porsche 911	Orange body, RN '24', 'JAGERMEISTER'	NRP	
C139/4	1988	Design change	Red/Blue body, RN '91', 'DENVER'	NRP	
150	1957-61	Vanwell Racing Car.	Green or Red body, RN '25' No SS/WS/No D. 91 mm.	£38	NC
150S	1961-65	Vanwell Racing Car.	Green or Red body, with suspension	£38	NC
150	1972-74	Surtees TS9 Formula 1.	Blue body, RN '16' BL/WH/ DH. 116 mm.	£15	MPR
151	1958-60	Lotus XI Racing Car.	White body, RN '3' WS/No D/No SS. 83 mm.	£38	NC
151S	1961-63	Lotus XI Racing Car.	Blue body, RN '3' WS/D/SS. 83 mm.	£38	NC
C151	1974-76	'YARDLEY' Mclaren M19A.	White body, RN '55', Red/White DH. 112 mm.	£38	MPR
152	1958-61	BRM Racing Car.	Green body, RN '3' No SS/WS. 91 mm.	£38	NC
152S	1961-65	BRM Racing Car.	Green body, RN '3' SS/WS. 91 mm.	£33	NC
C152	1974-76	Ferrari 312B2	Red body, RN '5' Blue/White DH. 104 mm.	£75	MPR
153	1960-62	Bluebird Record Car.	Blue body, GB/US flags on nose, MW. 127 mm.	£45	NC
153A	1961-65	Bluebird Record Car.	Blue body, GB/US flags on nose, PW. 127 mm.	£40	NC
153	1963-65	Team Surtees TS9B.	Red/Black/White body, RN '26' WS. 112 mm.	£10-£15	MPR
154	1963-72	Ferrari Formula 1.	Red/Silver body, RN '36' D/WS. 91 mm.	£10-£15	MPR
C154	1974-78	'JOHN PLAYER SPECIAL' Lotus.	Black/Gold body, RN '1', Firestone. 130 mm.	£10-£15	MPR
C154	1979-82	'TEXACO' Special Lotus.	Black/Gold body, RN '1', Goodyear. 130 mm.	£7-£9	MPR
155	1965-68	Lotus Climax Racing Car.	Green Yellow body, RN '4' RCD/DS/RUM/SS/EX/PP. 90 mm.	£10-£15	MPR
C155	1974-76	'SHADOW' F1 Racing Car.	Black body, RN '17' D/WS. 90 mm.	£8-£11	MPR
156	1967-69	Cooper Maserati Racing Car.	Blue body, RN '7' White D/WS. 90 mm.	£16	NC
C156	1974-76	Graham Hill's Shadow.	White/Red body, RN '12' RCD, Embassy Racing. 132 mm.	£8-£12	MPR
158	1969-72	Lotus Climax Racing Car.	Red/White body, RN '8' RCD/WS/SS. 90 mm.	£8-£12	MPR
C158	1975-77	Elf Tyrrell Ford F1.	Blue body, RN '1', Elf, RCD. 110 mm.	£7-£10	MPR
159	1969-72	Cooper Maserati.	Yellow/White body, RN '3' RCD/DCST. 90 mm.	£7-£10	MPR
C159	1974-76	Indianapolis Racing Car.	Red body, RN '20', Racing Driver. 130 mm.	£7-£10	MPR
C160	1976-78	Hesketh 308 F1.	WH/Red/Blue, RN '24', Blue DH. 130 mm.	£7-£10	MPR
161	1971-73	Santa Pod 'COMMUTER' Dragster.	Red/Silver body, RN '2' VJ/SS/PP/SPKW/WZW. 123 mm.	£8-£11	MPR
161	1977	'ELF-TYRRELL — Project 34	Blue/White body, RN '3' AF/RCD, Good Year. 113 mm.	£8-£11	MPR
162	1971-72	'QUARTERMASTER' Dragster.	Green and White body, AF/RCD/PW. 146 mm.	£8-£11	MPR
C163	1971-76	Santa Pod 'GLO-WORM' Dragster.	White/Blue body, LOB/VADS/RCD/PW. 113 mm.	£6-£9	MPR
164	1972-75	Ison Bros 'WILD HONEY' Dragster.	Yellow/Red body, Jaguar, WZW. 171 mm.	£8-£11	MPR
165	1974-76	Adams Brothers Dragster.	Orange/Yellow body, 4E/32EX/RCD/WZW. 113 mm.	£8-£11	MPR
166	1971-74	Ford Mustang 'ORGAN GRINDER'.	Yellow/Green body, RN '39' TW/RCD. 102 mm.	£8-£11	MPR
C167	1973-74	U.S.A. Racing Buggy.	White/Red body, RN '7' RCD/PS/SPW/U.S. flag. 95 mm.	£8-£11	MPR
C169	1974-76	Starfighter Jet Dragster.	Blue/Silver/Red body, Firestone. 155 mm.	£8-£11	MPR
C170	1974-76	John Woolfe's 208 Dragster.	Blue/Yellow body, Radio Luxembourg, RCD. 146 mm.	£8-£11	MPR
190	1974-76	'JOHN PLAYER SPECIAL' Lotus.	Black/Gold body, RN '1', Texaco, AF/RCD/TOW. 270 mm.	£24	NC
191	1974-77	'TEXACO MARLBORO' Mclaren.	White/Red body, RN '5', VADS/AF/TOW. 245 mm.	£18	NC
C201	1979-82	Mini 1000 'TEAM CORGI'.	Metallic Silver body, RN '8', VADS. 85 mm.	£8-£12	MPR
227	1962-63	Mini Cooper Rally.	Blue/White body, OC, RN '3', 2 flags. 73 mm.	£32	NC
256	1971-74	VW Safari Rally.	Red body, RN '18', STC/ODBN/rhino. 91 mm.	£33	NC
271/1	—	Aston Martin	Silver body. See Novelty section		
C281	1982-	'DATAPOST' Metro.	Blue/White body, RN '77', VADS/ODHB. 94 mm.	£4-£6	MPR
282	1971-74	Mini Cooper Rally.	White/Black body, RN '177', WZW/ODBN/SL. 73 mm.	£20	NC
C291	1982	M-Benz 'EURO RALLY' 240.	Cream/Black body, SPW/RR/HG/SP/ODBT. 127 mm.	£4-£7	MPR
C299	1987	Sierra Rally	Black body, RN '7', Red 'TEXACO'	NRP	
C300	1979-82	Ferrari 'DAYTONA'.	Green with MLCD flash, RN '5', OD. 120 mm.	£4-£7	MPR
C301	1979-82	Lotus Elite Racing Car.	Yellow/Red body, Ferodo. 120 mm.	£4-£7	MPR

158

Ref. No.		Model Type	Model Features and Size	Rarity and Price Grading	
302	1964-70	Hillman Hunter Rally.	Blue/Black, GJ/TOW/HG/2DSPW/VADS/TB/K. 104 mm.	£33	NC ☐
C302	1979-82	VW Polo.	Met Brown/Red, RN '4', VADS/OHB. 97 mm.	£4-£7	MPR ☐
303	1970-72	Roger Clarks Capri.	White, RN '73', OD/WZW/VADS. 102 mm.	£16	NC ☐
C303	1980-	Porsche 924 Racer.	Yellow/Black, RN '2', *Firelli*, ODHB. 118 mm.	£5-£8	MPR ☐
304S	1961-66	M-Benz 300SL Hard Top.	Yellow/Red or Silver/Red, RN '3', SPKW. 95 mm.	£34	NC ☐
305	1972-73	Mini Marcos GT850.	White/Red body, Blue/White stripes, RN '7'. 86 mm.	£14	NC ☐
C306	1980-	Fiat X19 Racer.	Blue with Red/Yellow bands, RN '3'. 110 mm.	£5-£8	MPR ☐
307	1981-	Renault Turbo.	Yellow/Red body, RN '8', *Cibie*, ODHB/VADS. 100 mm.	£5-£8	MPR ☐
C308	1972-76	Mini Cooper S.	Yellow body, RN '177', 2RE/RR/2SPW. 73 mm.	£20	NC ☐
C308	1982-	BMW M1.	Yellow body, RN '25', *Goodyear*, OHB/DE. 129 mm.	£5-£8	MPR ☐
309	1962-65	Aston Martin DB4.	Green/White body, RN '1', SS/SL/OBN/DE/SPKW. 95 mm.	£33	NC ☐
C309	1982-	VW 'TURBO'.	White/Brown body, RN '14', VADS/OHB. 97 mm.	£5-£8	MPR ☐
C310	1982-	'PORSCHE' 924 Turbo.	Black/Gold, ODHB, *Goodyear*. 124 mm.	£5-£8	MPR ☐
312	1964-68	'E' Type Jaguar.	Chrome/Gold, RN '2', RCD/DI/SS/SPKW. 95 mm.	£38	NC ☐
C312	1983-	Ford Capri 'S'.	White body, RN '6', VADS/HPS/ODB/OHB. 97 mm.	£5-£8	MPR ☐
314	1965-71	Ferrari Berlinetta 250LM.	Red, RN '4', RE/DE/SS. 95 mm.	£25	NC ☐
315	1964-66	Simca 1000.	Chrome/Black, RN '8', SS/WDS. 90 mm.	£20	NC ☐
316	1971-73	Ford GT70.	Met Green body, RN '3', VADS/REC/WZW/SS. 92 mm.	£9-£12	MPR ☐
317	1964	MTC 1964 Mini Cooper S.	Red/White body, RE '1964', RN '37', SL/SS. 73 mm.	£38	NC ☐
318	1965	MTC 1965 Mini Cooper S.	Red/White body RE '1965', RN '37', SL/SS. 73 mm.	£38	NC ☐
C318	1983-	'MOTUL' Jaguar XJS.	Black/Red/White body, RN '4', *Jaguar*. 118 mm.	£5-£8	MPR ☐
C318	1985	Design change	British Racing Green, White band, RN '12'		NRP ☐
319	1967-68	Lotus Elan Hard Top.	Blue/White or Green/White body, RN '6', LOB. 90 mm.	£22	NC ☐
C319	1974-75	Lamborghini Miura.	Silver/Purple/Yellow body, RN '7', WZW/OD/OEC. 95 mm.	£16	NC ☐
321	1965-67	MTC Mini Cooper S.	Red/White body, RN '52', SL/SS/WDS/SW. 73 mm.	£39	NC ☐
322	1965-66	Monte-Carlo Rover 2000.	Plum/White body, RN '136', RE/SS/WDS. 95 mm.	£40	NC ☐
		Design change	White/Black body	£45	NC ☐
323	1965-66	MC Citroen DS19.	Blue/White body, RN '75' RE/SS/SW/WDS. 97 mm.	£45	NC ☐
C323	1974-78	Ferrari Daytona 365 GTB/4.	White/Red/Blue body, RN '81', OD/TG. 122 mm.	£7-£10	MPR ☐
324	1974	Ferrari Daytona Le Mans.	Yellow, RN '33', RE/VADS, *A. Bamford*. 122 mm.	£20	NC ☐
325	1966-69	Ford Mustang.	White or Silver with Red stripes, RN '6'. 95 mm.	£22	NC ☐
328	1966-67	Monte-Carlo Hillman Imp.	Blue/White body, RN '107', RE/SL/SS. 83 mm.	£24	NC ☐
329	1973-76	Ford Mustang.	Green/White body, RN '69', OD/SS. 113 mm.	£9-£12	MPR ☐
330	1967-69	Porsche Carrera 6.	Red/White body, RN '60', RE/RD/RW/SS. 97 mm.	£16	NC ☐
331	1974-76	Ford 'TEXACO' Capri GT.	White/Black body, RN '5'. 102 mm.	£10-£13	MPR ☐
333	1966	Mini Cooper S.	Red/White body, RN '21', *RAC*, decals. 73 mm.	£40	NC ☐
337	1967-69	Chevrolet Stock Car.	Yellow body, PP/SS/WDS, RN '2'. 95 mm.	£15	NC ☐
339	1967-72	MTC 1967 Mini Cooper S.	Red/White body, RN '177', RR/2SPW/PP. 73 mm.	£40	NC ☐
340	1967-68	MTC Sunbeam Imp.	Blue/White body, RN '77', RE '1967', SL/SS. 83 mm.	£28	NC ☐
C340	1981	Rover 'TRIPLEX'.	White/Red/Blue, ODHB/HPS, RN '1'. 140 mm.	£5-£8	MPR ☐
C341	1981-	Chevrolet Caprice.	Red/White/Blue body, ODBN, RN '43', *STP*, 150 mm.	£5-£8	MPR ☐
344	1969-73	Ferrari Dino Sports.	Yellow or Red body, RN '23', AF/WZW. 104 mm.	£22	NC ☐
345	1968-69	MGB GT.	Yellow/Black body, RN '11', OC/OD/SL/TS. 90 mm.	£40	NC ☐
C350	1985	Toyota Celica Supra	Red/White body, RN '14', 'HUGHES', RCT. 112 mm.		NRP ☐
C351	1985	Ford Sierra Pace car	White body, Green/Y TPD, Red/Blue SL, flags		NRP ☐
C353	1987	BMW 325i Rally	White body, Green logo 'CASTROL'		NRP ☐
354	1986	BMW 325	White body, RN '33', 'FAVRAUD' logo		NRP ☐
370	1982	Ford Cobra Mustang.	Yellow/Black, *Mustang*, OBNHB/SR. 135 mm.	£5-£8	MPR ☐
371	1970-73	Porsche Carrera 6.	White/Red, RN '60', TTEC/WZW. 97 mm.	£16	NC ☐
376	1970-72	Corvette Stock Car.	Silver, RN '13', *Go-Go-Go*, WZW. 95 mm.	£16	NC ☐
C380	1983-	BASF BMW M1.	Red/White body, RN '80', AF/OEC/PP. 129 mm.	£6-£9	MPR ☐
C381	1983-	'ELF' Renault Turbo.	Red/White/Blue, RN '5', ODHB/VADS, *Facom*. 100 mm.	£6-£9	MPR ☐
385	1970-76	Porsche 917.	Blue or Red body, RN '3', WZW/OBT/TW. 108 mm.	£8-£11	MPR ☐
386	1987	Mercedes 2.3/16	White body, Black RN '17', 'SERVIS'		NRP ☐
386/4	1988	Design change	SAPM, RN '17', 'BURLINGTON AIR EXPRESS'		NRP ☐
394	1973-76	Datsun 240Z	Red, RN '11', *East African Safari*. 97 mm.	£7-£10	MPR ☐
396	1974-76	Datsun 240Z	Red/White body, RN '46', SPKW/OD. 97 mm.	£7-£10	MPR ☐
397	1974-78	Porsche-Audi 917-10	White or Orange, RN '6', *Corgi*, RCD. 120 mm.	£7-£10	MPR ☐
399	1985	Peugeot 205	Silver body, MLCD TPD, RN '205'		NRP ☐
399/5	1988	Peugeot 205 T16	Yellow body, RN '2', 'VATANEN'		NRP ☐
402	1985	BMW MI	Red/White body, RN '101', 'CASTROL'		NRP ☐
403	1985	Ford Escort	White body, MCCD TPD, RN '84', 'TOTAL'		NRP ☐
404	1985	Rover 3500	Red body, RN '13', 'DAILY MIRROR'		NRP ☐
	1986	Design change	Red body, RN '1', 'TEXACO'		NRP ☐
420	1984	'BMW MI'	Blue/White, RN '11', 'LIGIER'S'		NRP ☐
	1985	Colour change	White body, 'ESSO', RN '17'		NRP ☐
422	1984	'RENAULT 5' TBA	Blue body, RN '25', 'BOSCH' & 'ELF'		NRP ☐
	1985	Colour change	Dark blue body, MLCD TPD, RN '18'		NRP ☐
423	1984	'BROOKLYN' Ford Escort	Blue/White, RN '69' 'SHELL', Red seats		NRP ☐
424	1984	'Ford Mustang'	Black body, Yellow Red TPD, RN '77', 'ESSO'		NRP ☐
426	1984	'HEPOLITE' Rover	Yellow/Red, 'FERODO', RN '4'		NRP ☐
	1988	Design change	Yellow/Red body, 'DAILY EXPRESS', AD		NRP ☐
435/2	1987	Volvo 760 Turbo	White body, Blue/Yellow TPD, 'GILLANDERS'		NRP ☐
C447	1983-	4×4 'RENEGADE' Jeep	Blue/White body, RN '8', SW/SPW/ARB. 100 mm.		NRP ☐
C440	1988	'PORSCHE 944' Rally	White body, Red design		NRP ☐
C448	1984	4×4 'RENEGADE' Jeep	Yellow/Red body, RN '8', HDT/SPW		NRP ☐
C567	1984	Range Rover	White body, 'PARIS MATCH' HDT, 'VSD'		NRP ☐

Racing, Rally and Speed Cars continued
Gift Sets

Ref. No.		Model Type	Model Features and Size	Rarity and Price Grading	
5	1959-63	Racing Car Set	Contains 150, 151 and 152.	£100	GP
6	1968-69	Racing Car Set	Contains 156 and Trailer.	£28	MPR
12	1968-72	Grand Prix Racing Set	Contains 155, 156, Tender/TRL/EQ.	£80	NPE
15	1961-65	Silverstone Set	Contains 150, 151, 152, 215, 304, 309, 417 plus 3 Buildings	£250	NPE
16	1961-66	Ecurie Ecosse TPTR	Contains 1126, 150, 151A, 152S.	£100	GP
17	1963-67	Ferrari and Land Rover Set	Contains 438, 154 and TRL.	£35	MPR
25	1969-71	Racing Car and Tender Set	Contains 159 plus VW Tender.	£35	MPR
C26	1981-	F1 Racing Car Set	Contains C26 plus F1 Racer on TRL.	£10-£15	MPR
29	1975-76	Ferrari Racing Set	Contains 323 and 150.	£15-£20	MPR
C29	1982-	Lotus Racing Set	Black/Gold C301, C154 on TRL.	£10-£15	MPR
32	1976	Lotus Racing Team Set	Green/Yellow 318 and 319, 490 and TRL.	£55	NC
38	1965-67	Monte Carlo Rally Set	Contains 321, 322, 323.	£130	NPE
45	1966	All Winners Set	Exported to France only.		
46	1966-69	All Winners Set	264 or 310, 261, 310, 314, 324, 325.	£130	NPE
C48/1	1986	Racing Set	C100/2 plus 576/2		

Major Packs

Ref. No.	Model Type	Model Features and Size	Rarity and Price Grading	
1126	Ecurie Ecosse TPTR	Dark or Light Blue, SS/OD/SW. 197 mm.	£70	GP

Auction Price Results
Lacy Scott's, Bury St Edmunds sale 27.2.88
1126 realised £70, 345 MGB GT £38

Corgi Classics — Cars

Original Issues — a factory fire ending production in 1969

Ref. No.		Model Type	Model Features and Size	Rarity and Price Grading	
9001	1964-69	1927 3 Litre Bentley. Le Mans Winner.	Dark Green body, RN '3', DTH/SPKW/SPW/RCD/ HBR/SDB/DCH/WS/SW/AR. 102 mm.	£28	NC
9002	1964-68	1927 3 Litre Bentley.	Red body, CD/No RN, then as 9001. 102 mm.	£32	NC
9004	1967-69	The 'WORLD OF WOOSTER' Bentley.	Model 9001 again in Green or Red. Jeeves and Wooster figures. 102 mm.	£65	GP
9011	1964-68	1915 Model T Ford.	Black, SPKW/BRR/SPW/CL/FHD/WS/D and PS. 86 mm.	£32	NC
9012	1965-68	1915 Model T Ford.	Yellow body, SAPM 9011. 86 mm.	£32	NC
9013	1964-69	1915 Model T Ford.	Blue/Black body, LHD/DTH/SPW/D cranks. 83 mm.	£35	NC
9014	—	1915 'LYONS TEA' Van.	In 67/68 Cat but not issued.		NPP
9021	1964-69	1910 38 h.p. Daimler.	Red body, SPKW/FHD/SPW/DCH/AR/D and 3 PS. 108 mm.	£43	NC
9022	—	1910 38 h.p. Daimler.	In 1966 Cat but not issued.		NPP
9031	1965-68	1910 Renault 12/16.	Lavender/Black body, CL/SPKW/LHD. 102 mm.	£32	NC
9032	1965-69	1910 Renault 12/16.	Primrose/Black body, CL/SPKW/LHD. 102 mm.	£32	NC
9041	1966-70	1912 Rolls Royce Silver Ghost.	Silver/Black body, SPKW/CL/SPW/SW/AR. 118 mm.	£32	NC

Note. The boxed models should contain a picture of the model. All card box with picture of model on front

Models re-introduced in 1985 when original tools were discovered. There should be no confusion between the two issues of these models for the re-introductions have 'SPECIAL EDITION' on the base plate and are packed in Grey/Red boxes with no picture of model. Also the model numbers are different, 13,500 of each colour were issued.

C860 (9041)	1985	1912 Rolls Royce Silver Ghost	Available in Silver, Black and Ruby Red designs	£7-£9	MPR
C861 (9002)	1985	1927 Bentley 3 litre (open top)	Available in British Racing Green, Black or Ruby Red designs	£7-£9	MPR
C862 (9031)	1985	1910 Renault 12/16	Available in Yellow, Pale Blue or Brown designs	£7-£9	MPR
C863 (9012)	1985	1915 Model 'Ford' T	Available in Black, Red or Blue designs	£7-£9	MPR

160

Small Commercial Vehicles and Vans
Single Models

Ref. No.		Model Type	Model Features and Size	Rarity and Price Grading		
403	1956-61	Bedford 15 Cwt Van	Blue/Silver body *Daily Express* 83 mm	£65	GV	☐
403	1956-59	Bedford 15 Cwt Van	Red/Silver body *K.L.G. Plugs*, FWM. 83mm.	£75	GP	☐
404	1956-62	Bedford Dormobile	Green, Maroon, Yel or Blue body. 83 mm	£35	NC	☐
404M	1956-59	Bedford Dormobile	Red or Blue body FWM. 83 mm	£45	NC	☐
C405	1982	Ford Transit Milk Float	Blue/White body, *Lotta Bottle* OD. 143mm.	£8-£11	MPR	☐
407	1957-61	Smiths Karrier Bantam Mobile Grocery Shop	Red & White body. *Home Services Hygenic Mobile Shop*. 95 mm	£45	NC	☐
408	1957-62	Bedford 15 cwt (Automobile Association)	Yellow/Black body, *Road Service* on roof and sides with *AA* emblems. 83mm.	£55	NC	☐
411	1958-62	Karrier Bantam Van 'LUCOZADE'	Yellow/Grey body, *Lucozade Replaces Loss Energy* OD. 102 mm.	60	NC	☐
413	1957-62	Karrier Bantam Mobile Butchers Shop	White/Blue body, *Home Services Hygenic Mobile Shop* Meaty Decals. 93 mm.	£50	NC	☐
421	1960-62	Bedford 12 Cwt Van 'EVENING STANDARD'	Black/Sil/Red body, Newsboards on doors *Evening Standard*. 83 mm.	£75	GP	☐
422	1960-62	Bedford 12 Cwt Van 'CORGI TOYS'	Blue/Yellow body, Corgi Livery *Corgi Toys* and Corgi dog decal. 83 mm.	£80	GP	☐
C423	1978	'ROUGH RIDER' Chevvy Van	Yellow body, *Rough Rider* MC decal. 122 mm.	£9-£12	MPR	☐
C424	1977-79	Security Van	Black/Yel/White body, *Security* WDS with grille. 100 mm.	£6-£9	MPR	☐
426	1962-64	Karrier Bantam Van Circus Booking Office	Red/Blue body, circus and office staff (2) decals, *Booking Office*. 91 mm.	£90	GP	☐
C426	1978-81	Chevrolet Booking Office Van	Yel/Red/Blue body, 2 loudspeakers, *Pinder-Jean Richard*	£9-£12	MPR	☐
428	1963-66	Karrier Bantam Van	Blue/White body, DCH salesman swivels. *Mr Softee Ice Cream* Vans. 91 mm	£55	NC	☐
C431	1978-80	'VANATIC' Chevvy Van	White, body, RF. WDS, *Vanatic* TW. 122 mm.	£8-£11	MPR	☐
C433	1978	'VAN-ISHING POINT' Chevvy Van	Gold body, In the 1978 Cat but not issued. 122 mm.		NPP	☐
433	1962-64	Volkswagen Delivery Van	Red/White body, *VW* on R/S/SW/IS. 91 mm.	£35	NC	☐
435	1962-63	Karrier Bantam Dairy Produce Van	Blue/White/Yellow body, DCH/OD *Drive Safely on Milk*	£45	NC	☐
C437	1978-82	'COCA COLA' Chevvy Van	Red/White body, *Enjoy Coca-Cola*. 122 mm.	£8-£11	MPR	☐
441	1963-67	Volkswagen Van 'TOBLERONE'	Blue body, Trans-o-lite headlights, *Chocolate Toblerone*. 91 mm.	£48	NC	☐
443	1963-65	Plymouth Suburban U.S. Mail Car	Blue/White official postal livery *Address Your Mail Carefully*. 104 mm.	£45	NC	☐
447	1964-67	Ford Thames 'WALLS ICE CREAM'	Blue/Cream body, Salesman and boy, OH. 90 mm.	£45	NC	☐
450	1964-67	Austin Mini Van	Green body ODB/OW/IS. 79 mm.	£45	MPR	☐
452	1956-58	Commer Dropside Lorry	Red/Fawn/Silver, TBD drops. 120 mm.	£45	MPR	☐
453	1956-60	Commer Refrigerated Van 'WALLS ICE CREAM'	Cab dark Blue, Box body Cream. *More Than a Treat a Food*	£55	GP	☐
454	1957-62	Commer Platform Lorry	Yel/Grey or Blue/Grey. 120 mm.	£35	MPR	☐
455	1957-61	Karrier Bantam 2 tonner	Blue Cab, Red platform. 102 mm	£40	MPR	☐
456	1960-63	E.R.F 449 Dropside Lorry	Yellow Cab. 120 mm.	£40	NC	☐
457	1957-62	E.R.F. 449 Platform Lorry	Two Tone Blue body. 120 mm. Also Blue/Yellow body.	£40	NC	☐
459	1958-60	E.R.F. 449 Van 'MOORHOUSE'	Yel/Red, *Moorhouses Lemon Cheese* and *Moorhouses Jam*. 117 mm.	£100	GP	☐
462	1970	Commer 'CO-OP' Van	White/Blue body, *Co-op*, PRM. 90 mm.	£49	NC	☐
462	1971	Commer "HAMMONDS" Van	Green/Blue/White body, *Hammond*. PRM. 90 mm.	£55	NC	☐
471	1965-66	Karrier Bantam Van.	Blue/White body, *Joe's Diner*, OH. 95 mm.	£33	NC	☐
474	1965-67	Musical 'WALLS' Ice Cream Van	447 again, with chimes/no figs. 90 mm.	£38	NC	☐
479	1968-71	Commer Mobile Camera Van	Dark Blue White body, Camera/Operator on roof, *Samuelson Film Company Ltd.* 90 mm.	£31	NC	☐
484	1967-71	Dodge Livestock Transporter	Beige/Green body, *Kew Fargo*, 5 figs. 140 mm.	£19	NC	☐

Ford Escort 55 Vans,

Type 1: Black plastic rear bumper, pre 1986

Type 2: Metal rear bumper and fitted to models from mid 1986

Assume models to be Type 1 unless shown differently.

The models feature a metal body with a plastic chassis and wheels. They have a chrome trim, amber side and tail lights, plus an opening rear door. 120 mm.

C496/1	1983	'ROYAL MAIL'	Red body, Gold design. Types 1/2		NRP	☐
C496/2	1986	'POLICE'	White body, Red stripe. Type 2		NRP	☐
C496/3	1983	'BRITISH GAS'	Blue/White body. Types 1/2		NRP	☐
C496/9	1983	'BRITISH TELECOM'	Yellow body, Black ladder. Types 1/2		NRP	☐
C496/15	1988	'HOOVER'	White/Dark Blue body, Red design (2)		NRP	☐
C497	1983	'RADIO RENTALS'	White body, Green/White design		NRP	☐
C503	1984	'DUNLOP'	White body, Yellow/Red/Back TPD, DEL 85		NRP	☐
503	1984	'TELEVERKET'	Orange/Black body, Swedish EXPM		NRP	☐
504	1984	'JOHN LEWIS'	Green with White/Lime Green logo (2500)		NRP	☐
512	1984	'BOLTON EVENING NEWS'	Yellow basic colour, Black/White TPD		NRP	☐
514	198	'CHUBB'	Cambridge Blue, White logo, 500		NGPP	☐
514	1984	'DIGBYS TOYSTORE'	Oxford Blue, Gold TPD /logo (LE 1000)	£9	NC	☐

161

Ford Escort 55 Vans continued

514	1984	'DIGBYS TOYSTORE'	Cambridge Blue, Gold logo (LE 504)	£7	NC	☐
515	1984	'NAT. EXHIBITION CENTRE'	Red/White/Blue body and TPD		NRP	☐
C532	1985	'RAC SERVICES'	White body, Blue/Red stripe, SL/(1 & 2) TB fitted for Gift Set models and 'SERVICE' added		NRP	☐
C534	1985	'PIZZA SERVICE'	White with Red LWB, Red/Black logo		NRP	☐
C537	1985	'AA SERVICES'	Yellow body, White stripe, RLB/(1 & 2), TB fitted for Gift Set models		NRP	☐
	1985	'WAITROSE'	White body, Black/Orange logo (LE 1000)		NGPP	☐
C543	1985	TELEVERKET'	TT Blue body, Red 'TELE' logo		NRP	☐
C549	1985	'HOTPOINT'	Beige and Green body (STRC) DEL 86		NRP	☐
C557	1985	'FIRE SALVAGE'	Yellow body, Black logo		NRP	☐
C559	1985	'JAGO AUTOMOTIVE'	Silver body, Red TPD (LE 1000)		NGPP	☐
C566	1985	'WILTSHIRE FIRES'	Red body, Gold logo, PLD on RF	£14	NC	☐
C562	1985	'GAMLEYS'	Red/White body, Blue TPD (LE 2500)		NRP	☐
C563	1985	'McVITIES'	Blue body, Red/Yellow TPD (LE 2500)		NRP	☐
C496	1985	'MANCHESTER EVENING NEWS'	Yellow and Black body, (LE2644)		NRP	☐
C564	1986	'TELEVERKET'	White body, Blue/Orange TPD, Swedish EXPM (2)		NRP	☐
C577	1985	'PLESSEY'	White/Blue body, Black TPD (LE 25000)		NRP	☐
C578	1985	'BEATTIES'	Black with Yellow labels (LE 2500)		NRP	☐
C626	1986	'CHUBB FIRE'	Blue body, 'FIRE COVER, (LE 5000) (2)		NRP	☐
C632	1986	'KAYS'	White body, Mail order only (2)		NGPP	☐
C496	1987	'BRITISH AIRWAYS'	Black/Silver body, Red flash (2)		NRP	☐
C946	1988	'B.B.C'	Mauve body, Black/White design (2)		NRP	☐

UNCLASSIFIED

    i)   White body, no TPD, issued 1983-84 during receivership
    ii)   Red body, no TPD, issued 1987. Labelled by 'GAMLEYS' — code 2
    iii)   White body — labelled by 'GAMLEYS' — code 2, issued 1983/4

Mercedes 207D Vans, 110 mm,

C516	1985	'BMX SERVICE'	White body, Yellow band, rider design	NRP	☐
C535	1985	'ATHLON'	Colours unknown	NRP	☐
539	1985	'GROUP 4'	White body, Yellow band, 'SECURITY SERVICES'	NRP	☐
548	1985	'SECURITAS'	Blue body, Black/Gold/Red TPD, 6500 ERPM	NRP	☐
564	1985	Swiss 'PTT'	Yellow/White body, Red/Black lines	NRP	☐
568	1986	'B. F. GOODRICH'	Black body, Red/White/Blue design, RR	NRP	☐
576	1986	'PEPSI'	White/Blue body, Red RF — same design colours	NRP	☐
576/2	1986	'PORSCHE RACING'	White body, Red/Blue design, RR, spares	NRP	☐
576	1986	'PARCELINE'	Black/Green body, White logo	NRP	☐
576	1987	'LEKER OG HOBBY'	White body, Red design	NRP	☐
576/9	1987	'OVERNITE TNT'	White UPB, Orange LWB, Black/Red TPD	NRP	☐
588	1987	'CURTIS HOLT'	White (2500), PRO-NGA	NGPP	☐
		'GROUP 4'	White body, 'SECURITY SERVICES' (STRC)	NRP	☐
630	1986	'KAYS'	Produced for 'KAYS' MOM	NGPP	☐
631	1986	'BLUE ARROW'	Produced for 'KAYS' MOM	NGPP	☐

Ford Transit Vans, redesigned issues 1987

656/1	1988	'RAC RESCUE SERVICES'	White body, Blue/Red design	NRP	☐
656/2	1987	'DATAPOST'	Red body, Gold logo 'ROYAL MAIL'	NRP	☐
656/5	1987	'AA SERVICE'	Yellow/White body, Black logo	NRP	☐
656/7	1987	Danish Post Van	Yellow body, Red/Black design	NRP	☐
656/12	1987	'KTAS'	Orange body, Black logo, Danish EXPM	NRP	☐
656/16	1988	'BUNDESPOST'	Yellow body, German EXPM	NRP	☐

Gift Sets

Ref. No.		Model Type	Model Features and Size	Rarity and Price Grading	
11	1960-64	E.R.F. Dropside and TRL	456 and 101 with cement and planks.	£45	GP ☐
21	1962-66	E.R.F. Dropside and TRL	456 and 101 plus milk churns and SAA.	£56	GP ☐
24	1963-68	Commer ¾ ton Vehicle Constructor Set	2 cab and chassis units plus 4 interchangeable bodies, TOL.	£35	NC ☐
1151	1970	Scammell AV 'Co-op' Set	Contains 1147, 466 & 432 in an all Blue/White livery. PRM (Brown box)	£150	GP ☐
C28	1987	Post Set	Contains FTV 656/2, Red Sierra RN '63'	£6-£9	MPR ☐
C43	1985	'TOYMASTER' Transport Set	Contains C496 'ROYAL MAIL', C515 'BMX', plus Volvo 'TOYMASTER' truck	£6-£9	MPR ☐
C62	1986	Swiss Services Set	C554 'PTT', Box Van 'DOMICILE', VW Polo 'PTT'. EXPS	£6-£9	MPR ☐

Auction Price Results
Lacy Scott's Bury St Edmunds, Suffolk, sale 12.12.87
421 realised £44, 428 realised £35, 422 realised £68, 441 realised £30
Gift Set 24 realised £35

Large Commercial Trucks and Tankers
Major Packs and Large Size Models

NB: Excludes models issued as 'Corgi Classics'

Ref. No.	Model Type	Model Features and Size		Rarity and Price Grading	

The model listings are based on an alphabetical sequence linked to commercial vehicle types:—

i)	Bedford Trucks and Tankers
ii)	Berliet Trucks
iii)	Ford Trucks and Box Vans
iv)	Mack Trucks
v)	Mercedes Benz Trucks and Box Vans
vi)	Scammell Trucks and Tankers
vii)	Scania Trucks and Box Vans
viii)	Seddon Atkinson Trucks
ix)	Volvo Trucks

i) Bedford Trucks

Ref. No.	Year	Model Type	Model Features and Size	Price	Grading
1100	1958-63	Bedford Carrimore Low Loader. 'S' Type.	Red/Blue body, OC/AV/DDTG/WO. 220 mm. Yellow cab, Blue loader	£70 £70	NC ☐ NC ☐
1101	1957-62	Bedford Carrimore Car Transporter. 'S' Type	Red cab, TT Blue TPTR, *Corgi Car* Blue cab, Yellow transporter	£50 £50	NC ☐ NC ☐
1104	1958-62	Bedford Carrimore Machinery Low Loader. 'S' Type.	Red/Grey body, AV/DDR/WO/DRAXW. 220 mm. Blue cab with Grey body	£50 £50	NC ☐ NC ☐
1104	1974-77	Bedford TK Horse Transporter	Green/Orange body, *Newmarket*, 4 horses, boy, 3DDR, AV. 256 mm.	£40	NC ☐
1110	1959-65	Bedford 'MOBIL' Tanker. 'S' Type	Red/White body, *Mobil Gas*, AV/DDC. 191 mm.	£95	GP ☐
1129	1962-65	Bedford 'MILK' Tanker. 'S' Type	Blue/White body, AV/DDC. 191 mm	£95	GP ☐
1131	1963-66	Bedford Carrimore 'TK' Machinery Low Loader	Blue/Yel body, AV/2SPW/RVM/SS/DRAXW/DDR/DDC. 241 mm.	£55	NC ☐
1132	1963-65	Bedford Carrimore 'TK' Low Loader	Yel/Red body, AV/2SPW/RVM/SS/DDR/DDC. 241 mm.	£55	NC ☐
1138	1966-69	Bedford Carrimore Car Transporter	Red/Blue body, *Corgi Cars*, AV/CTS/TCB/DDC. 273 mm.	£37	NC ☐
1140	1966-67	Bedford TK Petrol Tanker	Red/Sil/White body, *Mobil Gas*, AV/DDC/RVM. 191 mm.	£95	GP ☐
1141	1966-67	Bedford TK Milk Tanker	Blue/White body, *Milk*, AV/DDC/KVM. 191 mm.	£95	GP ☐

NB: A Bedford Tanker with a 'SHELL' livery was made for the Dutch market. The model is rare and no other details are available at present.   NGPP

ii) Berliet Commercial Trucks

Ref. No.	Year	Model Type	Model Features and Size	Price	Grading
C1105	1977-81	Racehorse Transporter	Brown/White body, 4 horses, AV, 3DDR. 280 mm. *National Racing Stables*, HL/EXP	£20	NC ☐
C1107	1979-	'UNITED STATES LINES'	Blue/White body. 290 mm. 2 Grey CNT, JW/ERP	£16	NC ☐

Large Commercial Trucks and Tankers continued

iii) Ford Commercial Trucks

The models feature a tilt cab which uncouples from the trailer section.

1108	1982	'MICHELIN' CNTT	Blue/White body, 243 mm, tilt cab (2 CNT)	£18	NC	☐
1109	1979	'MICHELIN' CNTT	Blue/Black body, 243 mm, tilt cab (2 CNT)	£18	NC	☐
1137	1966-69	'EXPRESS SERVICES'.	Blue/Sil/Red body, tilt cab, 235 mm. (H series cab)	£28	NC	☐
1138	1966	'CORGI CARS TPTR'	Orange/Silver cab, TT Blue transporter	£32	NC	☐
1157	1976-81	Ford 'ESSO' Tanker.	White/Red body, AV, tilt cab. 270 mm.	£9-£12	MPR	☐
1158	1976	Ford 'EXXON' Tanker	White/Black body, tilt cab. 270 mm.	£18	NC	☐
1159	1976-79	Ford Car Transporter	Green/White body, AV, tilt cab. 360 mm.	£18	NC	☐
1160	1976-76	Ford 'GULF' Tanker	White/Orange body, AV, tilt cab. 270 mm.	£18	NC	☐
1161	1979-80	Ford 'ARAL' Tanker	Blue/White/Black body, AV, tilt cab. 270 mm.	£23	NC	☐
1169	1982	Ford 'GUINNESS' TNK	Cream/Brown/Black body, AV, tilt cab. 270 mm.	£8-£11	MPR	☐
1170	1982	Ford Car Transporter	Red/White/Yel body, AV, tilt cab. 360 mm.	£8-£11	MPR	☐
1191	1985	'FORD QUALITY'	White cab/CH/TPD, 2 Blue containers	£4-£6	MPR	☐
	1985	'BALLANTINES FINEST SCOTCH'	Container holds 6 miniatures! Available duty free shops (20,000)		NGPP	☐
	1985	'KAYS' CNTT	Red/White body, Cerise/Black TPD, MOM (4000)		NGPP	☐

Ford Cargo Box Vans

The models feature 6 wheels, wing mirrors, four headlights plus an authentic radiator design.

1190	1985	'THORNTONS'	Blue/White body, Red logo	NRP	☐
1190	1985	'EVER READY'	Red body, Black CH	NRP	☐
1192	1985	'LUCAS'	Green body, Black CH, White TPD	NRP	☐
1228	1986	'THE NEW LEWIS'S'	White body (2500)	NRP	☐
1249	1986	'WHITES BAZAAR'	Blue body, Red/White TPD, (NGA)	NRP	☐

iv) Mack Commercial Trucks

1100	1971-73	'TRANS CONTINENTAL'	White cab, Brown/Yellow TRC box, SLD/IOW/EXP/TV/JW. 257 mm.	£28	NC	☐
1106	1971-77	'A.C.L.' CNTT	Yel/Black/White body, 2 Red CNT, White logo, IOW/EXP/TU/JW. 290 mm.	£28	NC	☐
1152	1971-75	Mack 'ESSO' Tanker	White/Red/Blue body, AV/TU/DDC/JW/SDH. Gloster Saro Petrol Tanker, 278 mm	£25	NC	☐

v) Mercedes Benz Articulated Container Trucks and Tankers.

The trucks feature 8 wheels, uncoupling trailer, cab streamliner and an authentic radiator design.

1109	1984	'SEALINK'	Blue cab/TRD, 2 White CNT. 220 mm	NRP	☐
1129	1983	'CORGI'	MLCD body, 207 mm	NRP	☐
1129	1984	'ASG'	'TRANSPORT-SPEDITION' EXPM, 220 mm	NRP	☐
1130	1983	'CORGI CHEMCO' TNK	Yellow/Black/Silver body, 110 mm	NRP	☐
1131	1983	'CHRISTIAN SALVESON'	White/Black/Blue body (Fridge Van). 207 mm	NRP	☐
1139	1984	'HALLS BACON'	White/Blue body, MOM (Fridge Van). 220 mm	NGPP	☐
1141	1984	'SHELL' Tanker	Red/Yellow cab, Yellow/Black tank. 170 mm	NRP	☐
1144	1983	'ROYAL MAIL'	Red body, Gold TPD, EIIR Crest. 207 mm	NRP	☐
1145	1984	'YORKIE'	Red/Yellow cab, Blue TRL. 220 mm.	NRP	☐
	1984	'IDM'	*International Distributors Meet* (NGA). 220 mm	NRP	☐
	1984	'HOMESPEED'	'HOME DELIVERIES FROM PICKFORDS' 220 mm	NRP	☐
1146	1983	'DUNLOP'	Black/White/Red/Yellow body, 207 mm.	NRP	☐
1166	1984	'ARLA'	Red TPD on White TRG, EXPM. 207 mm	NGPP	☐
1166	1984	'GUINNESS' Tanker	Black/Cream, MB/CH/FCP. 170 mm	NRP	☐
1167	1984	'DUCKHAMS' Tanker	Yellow/Blue body, 170 mm	NRP	☐
1167	1984	'7 UP' Tanker	Green/White body. 170 mm	NRP	☐
1175	1983	'ZANUSSI'	Black/Yellow. White/Black logo. 207 mm	NRP	☐
1175	1984	'RALEIGH'	TT Blue and Yellow, MB, 207 mm	NRP	☐
1176	1983	'WEETABIX'	Yellow/Red body, Blue logo. 207 mm	NRP	☐
1178	1983	'MAYNARDS'	Red/White/Green body. 207 mm	NRP	☐

Model redesigned in 1985 and features a new style cab and is longer overall at 235 mm.

1112	1985	'MICHELIN'	Yellow body, Blue CH/TPD. 235 mm	NRP	☐
1129	1985	'ASG'	Yellow body, Blue CH/TPD. 235 mm	NRP	☐

Mercedes Benz Box Vans feature 6 wheels and authentic radiator design

1192	1986	'PEPSI'	White body, Red/Blue TPD. 235 mm	NRP	☐
	1985	'HOMESPEED'	'DELIVERIES BY PICKFORDS' (NGA) 235 mm	NRP	☐
1203	1986	'HERNGLAS'	TT Blue MB, EXPM (6500). 235 mm	NRP	☐

Large Commercial Trucks and Tankers continued

vi) Scammell Commercial Trucks

SCAMMELL HANDYMAN ARTICULATED TRUCKS (1146 & 1147, 1151)
Model features 8 wheels, an uncoupling trailer, a jockey wheel and an authentic radiator.

1146	1970-73	Tri-Deck Car Transporter	White/Yel/Blue body, AV/3CTS/DDC. 290 mm.	£55	GP	☐
1147	1970-72	'FERRYMASTERS'	Yel/White body, *International Hauliers*, AV/DDC. 235 mm.	£45	GP	☐
1151	1970	Co-operative Society PRM	Blue/White body plus 462 & 466 PRM. 235 mm	£125	GP	☐

The Scammell model was updated in 1984 and featured a new cab with a cab streamliner, 8 wheels, uncoupling trailer, jockey wheel and an authentic radiator and large front bumper. 220 mm.

1176	1984	'WEETABIX'	Yellow body, Red design		NRP	☐
1177	1984	'NORMANS'	Yellow body, Red TPD/logo		NRP	☐
1177	1984	'RALEIGH'	TT BLue & Yellow body		NRP	☐
1180	1984	Container Truck	White cab/TRL, Red CS/SPN (ASIC). Model may not have been issued		NGPP	☐
1186	1984	'McVITIES'	Blue body, Red/Yellow TPD		NRP	☐
1188	1984	'ROYAL MAIL'	Red/Black body, Gold design		NRP	☐
1189	1985	'DUCKHAMS' Tanker	Blue/Yellow MB, Black FCP area		NRP	☐

Scammell Articulated Trucks redesigned in 1986 and features a sleeping compartment, big horns on cab roof, exhaust pipes, 10 wheels and an authentic radiator. All models are container trucks unless otherwise described.　NRP £4-£6

1220	1986	Flat Bed Crate Truck	Red cab & TRL, Black CH, 4 Beige 'EXPORT' crates (STRL)	NRP	☐
1246/7	1986	'YORKIE'	Beige cab, Blue TRL & Box	NRP	☐
1246	1987	'DR PEPPER'	Red cab, White SLC/TRL. Iced drinks MLCD TPD	NRP	☐
1246	1987	'COCA COLA' Race Team TPTR	Red/White cab, Red TRL, CNT, DDR, with Grey CNT 'RACING TEAM' & car, becomes J3700	NRP	☐
1246	1987	'COCA COLA'	Red cab, Red/White TRL, Black CH	NRP	☐
1246	1987	'HERSHEYS MILK COCHOLATE'	Chocolate Brown body, White CH/logo, Choc Bar MLCD TPD	NRP	☐
1246	1987	'FRANCOIS AVRIL'	Red/White cab/TRL/CNT, Black logo, French EXPM	NRP	☐
1247	1987	'GOODRICH'	Black body, Red/White/Blue TPD	NRP	☐

vii) Scania Trucks

All models are Box Vans unless otherwise specified and feature a cab streamliner, 6 wheels and an authentic radiator design.

1123	1984	'KOHLER' Silo Truck	Red MB & Silos, White CS/FCP. 145 mm	NRP	☐
1132	1984	'SWEDISH POST'	Yellow body, EXPM	NRP	☐
1132	1984	'DANZAS'	Yellow/Black body, 138 mm.	NRP	☐
1133	1983	Giant Tipper	Green/Silver body, 145 mm.	NRP	☐
1146	1983	'CORGI'	White/Blue/Black body, 138 mm.	NRP	☐
1147	1983	'RYDER TRUCK RENTALS'	Yellow/Black body, 138 mm.	NRP	☐
1148	1983	'SECURICOR PARCELS'	Blue/White body, 138 mm.	NRP	☐
1149	1983-	'BRS TRUCK RENTALS'	White/Red/Blue body, 138 mm.	NRP	☐
1150	1983	'BRITISH SUGAR' Silo	Blue/White body, *Silver Spoon*, 145 mm.	NRP	☐
1151	1983	'SPILLERS' Silo Truck	Orange/White body, *Graded Grains*, 145 mm.	NRP	☐
1182	1984	'HONDA'	Red body, White CH/CS/TPD. 140 mm	NRP	☐
1182	1985	'SUZUKI'	Blue cab/CH, Yellow box, Red TPD. 140 mm	NRP	☐
1183	1984	'ADIDAS'	White cab/CH, Blue box, White TPD. 140 mm	NRP	☐
1183	1985	'GLASSENHETER'	Red/White body, EXPM. 140 mm	NRP	☐
1183	1985	'BROSSARD'	Orange body, EXPM. 140 mm	NRP	☐
1238	1987	'McCAIN OVEN CHIPS'	Red cab, Yellow cab RF & CNT. Black/White design	NRP	☐
1238/2	1987	'CADBURYS FLAKE'	Yellow/White cab, Yellow CNT, Purple logo	NRP	☐
1238/3	1988	'SECURICOR EXPRESS'	Blue body, Black CH, White logo, Y/Red TPD	NRP	☐
1251	1987	'B.O.C.' Tanker	All white body, Blue/Red/Y/Grey TPD	NRP	☐
1251/2	1988	'ROLO' Tanker	Red cab/CH/FCP. Red/White logo/TPD	NRP	☐
1264/2	1988	'ELF' Tanker	White cab & tank, CTR/FCP, Orange/Green TPD	NRP	☐

viii) Seddon Atkinson Trucks

The models feature 8 wheels, a sleeping compartment, horns, an uncoupling trailer plus an authentic radiator design. Models are container trucks unless specified otherwise.

1238	1987	'McCAIN OVEN CHIPS'	Red cab, Yellow cab, RF & CNT. Black/White design.	NRP	☐
1238/2	1987	'CADBURYS FLAKE'	Yellow/White cab, Yellow CNT, Purple logo	NRP	☐
1238/3	1988	'SECURICOR EXPRESS'	Blue body, Black CH, White logo. Y/Red TPD.	NRP	☐
1251	1987	'B.O.C.' Tanker	All White body, Blue/Red/Y/Grey TPD.	NRP	☐
1251/2	1988	'ROLO' Tanker	Red cab/CH/FCP, Red/White logo/TPD.	NRP	☐
1264/2	1988	'ELF' Tanker	White cab & tank, CTR/FCP Orange/Green TPD.	NRP	☐
1238/4	1988	'RADIO ROADSHOW'	White body, Red/Blue design	NRP	☐

ix) Volvo Trucks and Tankers

The models listed feature 8 wheels, an uncoupling trailer, chrome trim and an authentic radiator design. Containers have opening rear doors and are plastic. Label designs. Models issued C1221 onwards have improved SLC/HNS/EXP. Most models are container trucks (CNTT) and feature the Volvo Globetrotter (GBT) 205 mm and Volvo F12 Trucks 190 mm.   NRP £3-£5

1193	1984	Volvo GBT Car TPTR	Red body/CH, White upper deck, DDR/RSJ	NRP	☐
1194	1985	Volvo F12 Truck	All Red body, 'LEE COOPER' 190 mm	NRP	☐
1196	1985	Volvo F12 Truck	White body, Black CH, 'HOTPOINT' 190 mm	NRP	☐
1197	1985	Volvo F12 Truck	Yellow cab, Blue TRL. 'AS' 190 mm	NRP	☐
	1985	'TOYMASTERS' GBT	Available in Toymasters Toyshops	NRP	☐
1206	1985	'HILLARDS LOW PRICES'	Red/White body, Black/White TPD GBT (2500)	NGPP	☐
1207	1985	'BRITISH HOME STORES'	Blue & White body with Blue/Silver PCD with 'BHS' on front, GBT	NGPP	☐
	1986	PCD change	'WHEEL' PCD without 'BHS'	NRP	☐
1211	1986	'RILEYS CRISPS' GBT	Red cab, Orange box TRL, MOM	NRP	☐
1212	1986	'TNT OVERNITE' GBT	Red/Orange/White body (NGA) GBT	NGPP	☐
1221	1986	Volvo GBT with Flat Bed TRL	Red/Yellow cab, Red TRL, 2 Beige 'EXPORT' crates plus PLL Drums/Sacks (STRL)	NRP	☐
1222	1986	Volvo GBT Car TPTR	Red cab & LWD, Blue VPD, DDR	NRP	☐
1224	1986	'CADBURYS FLAKE'	Cream cab & TRL/BOX with Blue TPD, GBT	NRP	☐
1225	1987	'BILSPEDITION' SPH	Swedish EXPM	NRP	☐
1227	1986	'BEEFEATER' GBT	White body, 'by LETSUREKING LTD' (2000)	NGPP	☐
1231	1986	'McCAIN OVEN CHIPS' GBT	Red/Yellow body, Black/White TPD/logo, GBT	NRP	☐
1231/2	1986	'WIMPY' GBT	Red and White cab/TRL/CH/BOX/TPD	NRP	☐
1231	1987	'WOOLWORTHS' GBT	Pale Green/Black MB, Red/Black logo	NRP	☐
1231	1987	'TESCO' GBT	White/Red MB & TPD/logo & horns	NRP	☐
		Variation	With cab aerofoil and no horns	NGPP	☐
1231	1987	'B.H.S.' GBT	Blue cab, White TRL, Red/Blue TPD	NRP	☐
1231	1987	'COCAL COLA' GBT	Red cab & TRL. Labels same as 'B.P.' PRO — AVLB B.H.S.	NRP	☐
1231	1987	'MMM MARABOU' GBT	All Black plus sweeties. Swedish EXPM	NRP	☐
1231	1987	'GATEWAY' GBT	Yellow/Green cab/CNT, White logo	NRP	☐
1231	1988	'FRIZZY PAZZY' GBT	Red body, Yellow chassis EXPM GBT	NRP	☐
1231	1988	'MARS' GBT	Black body, Yellow/Red TPD/logo	NRP	☐
1232	1986	'BOSCH PLATINUM' GBT	White cab, Blue CH, Black CNT	NRP	☐
1233	1987	'CADBURY'S CHOCOLATE' GBT	White body, Purple choc bar TPD/logo	NRP	☐
1243	1986	'KAYS' GBT	Produced for 'KAYS' MOM	NGPP	☐
1245	1986	'FUJI FILM' GBT	Red cab, green CNT, Red TPD	NRP	☐
1246	1986	'CARTERS LEMONADE'	White/Orange MB (NGA), GBT	NRP	☐
1246	1987	'GAMINO' GBT	Yellow cab/CNT, White RF/TRL, Red TPD. EXPM	NRP	☐
1250	1987	'TEXACO' Tanker	Red/Silver cab, Red/Black/Grey tank, EM/SDH	NRP	☐
1250	1987	'NOROL' Tanker	White body, Black CH, EM/SDH	NRP	☐
1250	1987	'NORSK OLJE' Tanker	All White body, Red/Blue design. Norway EXPM	NRP	☐
1250/3	1987	'POLO' Tanker	Green/White/Black body & TPD/logo	NRP	☐
1265/1	1987	'TEXACO' Tanker	Red/Silver cab, Red/Black tank '1270'	NRP	☐

Gift Sets

1151	1970	Scammell AV 'Co-op' Set	Contains 1147, 466 & 432 in an all Blue/White livery. PRM (Brown box)	£150	GP ☐

Agricultural Models
Single Models

Ref. No.		Model Type	Model Features and Size	Rarity and Price Grading		
50	1959-66	Massey Ferguson '65' Tractor.	Red/Beige body. 79 mm.	£30	NC	☐
C50	1974-77	Massey Ferguson '50B' Tractor.	Yellow/Black/Red body, WDS. 138 mm.	£10-£15	MPR	☐
51	1959-69	Massey Ferguson Tipper Trailer.	Red/Brown body. 102 mm.	£10-£15	MPR	☐
53	1960-66	Massey Ferguson Tractor with Shovel.	Red/Brown tractor, Grey/Blue shovel. 124 mm.	£38	NC	☐
54	1974	Massey Ferguson Tractor with Shovel.	Yellow/Red or White/Red body. 150 mm.	£6-£9	MPR	☐
54	1958-62	Fordson Half Track Tractor.	Blue/Brown/Silver body, rubber tracks. 91 mm.	£95	GP	☐
55	1961-63	Fordson Major Tractor.	Blue/Grey/Red body. 83 mm.	£38	NC	☐
55	1977	David Brown Tractor.	Black/Red/White body. SW. 105 mm.	£8-£11	MPR	☐
56	1961-63	Four Furrow Plough.	Red/Brown/Yellow body. 90 mm.	£8-£11	MPR	☐
56	1977	Farm Tipper Trailer.	Red/Yel or Red/Wh body, DDTBD. 130 mm.	£3-£5	MPR	☐
57	1963-65	Massey Ferguson Tractor with stock.	Red/Silver/Green body, D/SW. 127 mm.	£38	NC	☐
58	1965-72	Beast Carrier.	Red, Cream and Blue body, 4 calves. 112 mm.	£5-£7	MPR	☐
60	1964-66	Fordson Power Major Tractor.	Blue body, Plough lifts. 83 mm.	£35	MPR	☐
61	1964-70	Four Furrow Plough.	Blue/Silver body. 90 mm.	£3-£5	MPR	☐
62	1965-70	Ford Tipper Trailer.	Red/Yellow body. 144 mm.	£8-£11	MPR	☐
64	1965-69	Conveyor on Jeep.	Red body, Yellow/White, CVB, farmland. 197 mm.	£20	NC	☐
66	1966-72	Massey Ferguson '165' Tractor.	Red/Blue/White body, engine sound. 76 mm.	£38	NC	☐
67	1967-72	Ford Super Major Tractor.	Blue/White/Silver body, Ford 5000. 90 mm.	£35	NC	☐
69	1967-70	Massey Ferguson '165' Tractor and Shovel.	Red/Blue body, Silver Shovel, fig. 127 mm.	£35	NC	☐
71	1967-72	Fordson Disc Harrow.	Yellow/Red/Silver body. 90 mm.	£3-£5	MPR	☐
72	1971-73	Ford '5000' Tractor and Towbar.	Model 67, frame/bucket/pipes. 90 mm.	£35	NC	☐
73	1970-72	Massey Ferguson Tractor and Saw.	Model 66 plus Yellow rotating saw. 90 mm.	£35	NC	☐
74	1969-72	Ford '5000' Tractor and Scoop.	Model 67 plus Yellow/Silver Scoop. 90 mm.	£35	NC	☐
100	1957-61	Dropside Trailer.	Yellow/Red/Grey body. 108 mm.	£7-£9	MPR	☐
101	1958-61	Platform Trailer.	Yellow/Grey body.	£7-£9	MPR	☐
102	1957-65	Rice's Pony Trailer.	Red body, Brown pony, 2DDR. AVI Brown. 86 mm.	£8-£11	MPR	☐

Major Packs and Large Size Models

1	1968-72	Tractor and Beast Carrier Set.	Tractor (67) and Beast Carrier (58).	£45	NC	☐
2	1958-66	Land Rover and Pony Trailer Set.	Land Rover (438), Pony Trailer (102).	£25	NC	☐
4	1974-75	Country Farm Set.	Contains 50, 62, and EQ.	£35	NC	☐
5	1968-72	Agricultural Set.	Contains 484, 438, 71, 69, 62, D/EQ.	£55	NC	☐
7	1959-63	Tractor and Trailer Set.	Contains 50 and 51.	£38	NC	☐
8	1959-61	Combine, Tractor and Trailer Set.	Contains 1111, 50, 51.	£70	NC	☐
9	1968-72	Trailer, Tractor and Shovel Set.	Contains 66, 69 and 62.	£45	NC	☐
13	1964-67	Fordson Tractor and Plough Set.	Contains 60 and 61.	£38	NC	☐
15	1968-76	Land Rover and Horse Box.	Contains 438, Brown, pre 70, Met Blue post, 112, mare and foal. 197 mm.	£10-£15	MPR	☐
18	1961-63	Ford Tractor and Plough Set.	Contains 55 and 56.	£43	NC	☐
22	1963-66	Agricultural Set.	Contains 1111, 50, 438, 100, 55, 61, skip and milk churns.	£135	GP	☐
29	1963-64	Massey Ferguson Tractor and Trailer.	Contains 50, 51, Driver.	£43	NC	☐
C29	1981	'CORGI' Ponyclub.	Contains 441 and accessories.	£10-£16	MPR	☐
32	1965-68	Tractor, Shovel and Trailer Set.	Contains 54, 62.	£43	NC	☐
33	1965-68	Tractor and Beast Carrier.	Contains 55, 58.	£43	NC	☐
34	1977-79	Tractor and Tipping Trailer.	Contains 55, 56 (Trailer).	£12-£17	MPR	☐
C42	1979-80	Agricultural Set.	Contains C34, C43, Silo/Elevator.	£26	NC	☐
C43	1979-80	Silo and Conveyor Set.	Silo and Elevator, Corgi Harvesting Company Ltd.	£18	NC	☐
47	1966-69	Ford Tractor and Conveyor Set.	Model 67, TRL with CVB/D/fig/ACCS.	£48	NC	☐
C47	1978-80	Pony Club Set.	BR/WH, LR, BR/TRL/girl/HS.	£10-£15	MPR	☐

Gift Sets

1111	1959-62	Massey Ferguson Combine Harvester.	Red/Yellow body, metal tines. 172 mm.	£45	GP	☐
1111	1968-72	Massey Ferguson Combine Harvester.	Same as 1111 with plastic tines. 172 mm.	£35	MPR	☐
C1112	1977-78	David Brown Combine Harvester.	Contains C55 plus Red/Wh/Blk CHVR. 220 mm.	£13-£18	MPR	☐
1129	1969-72	Rice Beaufort Double Horse Box	Blue body, White roof. 2HS.	£13-£18	MPR	☐

Ambulance, Fire, Police and Rescue Vehicles

Ref. No.		Model Type	Model Features and Size	Rarity and Price Grading		
209	1958-61	Riley Police Car	Black & Silver body, *Police* Bell. 97mm.	£40	GP	
213	1959-61	Jaguar Fire Service Car	Red body, *Fire* EM/A/bell. 95 mm.	£40	GP	
213S	1961-62	Jaguar Fire Service Car	Red body, *Fire* EM/SS/A/bell. 95 mm.	£40	GP	
223	1959-61	Chevrolet State Police Car	Black/Yel/White body, *State Patrol* A. 108 mm.	£30	GP	
237	1962-66	Oldsmobile Sheriffs Car	White/Black body *County Sheriff* SL/SS. 108 mm.	£30	NC	
299	1985	Sierra 'POLIS' Car.	Blue/Yel/Black body, SL, Swedish EXPM		NRP	
299/7	1986	Colour change	White body version		NRP	
C317	1986	Peugeot 'POLITI'	Black/White body, SL, Norway EXPM		NRP	
C326	1980-81	Chevrolet Caprice Police Car	Black/White body, *Police.* ODB/SS. 150 mm.	£18	NC	
C332	1980-81	Opel Doctors Car	White/Red body, *Notartz* OD. 142 mm.	£18	NC	
C339	1980	Rover Police Car.	White and Red body, EM, *Police.* 140 mm.	£5-£7	MPR	
353	1987	BMW 'NOTARZT'	Red/White body, 2 Blue SL, German EXPM		NRP	
357	1987	Sierra 'BRANDCHEFF'	Red body, DBG, FLL plus 2 RSL		NRP	
C358/1	1987	Ford Sierra 'POLICE'	White body, Yellow/Black stripe, FLLB		NRP	
358	1987	Sierra 'POLITI'	White body, Red/Blue TPD, FLLB, EXPM		NRP	
358	1987	'POLICE' Sierra	White body, Red TPD, SL, Dutch EXPM		NRP	
358	1988	Sierra 'LEGE'	White/Red body, 2 SL/EM, Norway EXPM		NRP	
361	1987	Volvo 'POLIS'	White body, Black/Yel TPD, Swedish EXPM		NRP	
373	1970-76	VW 1200 Police Car.	Black/White/Blue body, *Police.* 91 mm.	£13-£18	MPR	
373	1987	Peugeot 'POLITI'	Black/White body, 2 SL, RSL, Norway EXPM		NRP	
386	1987	Mercedes 'POLIZEI'	Green/White body, 2 Blue SL, German EXPM		NRP	
402	1974-77	Ford Cortina Police Car.	White/Red body, *Police,* SL/OD. 102 mm.	£14	NC	
405	1956-60	Bedford Fire Tender.	Green body, Sil Ladder, A.F.S. in Yel. 83 mm.	£65	GP	
405M	1956-59	Bedford Fire Tender.	Red body, Sil Ladder, *Fire Dept,* in Yel. 83 mm.	£70	GP	
C405	1978-80	Chevrolet Ambulance.	White/Orange, OD/STR/AM/SL. 119 mm.	£8-£12	MPR	
C406	1980-81	Mercedes Ambulance.	White/Red body, OD/STR/2AM/SL. 150 mm.	£8-£12	MPR	
406	1987	M'BENZ BONNA Ambulance	'FALCK' livery, Danish EXPM		NRP	
406	1988	French issue	White body, Blue 'AMBULANCE', 2 SL, ARDT		NRP	
406	1987	Bonna Ambulance	White/Red body, 2 Blue FLC, 'SDL 951', EXPM		NRP	
412	1957-60	Bedford 15 CWT Ambulance.	Cream body, *Ambulance.* 83 mm.	£45	GP	
C412	1976-78	Mercedes Police Car.	Black/White body, *Polizei,* OD/SL. 108 mm.	£8-£11	MPR	
414	1976-77	Jaguar XJ12C.	White/Blue body, *Coastguard,* OL.	£8-£11	MPR	
416	1958-62	R.A.C. Land Rover.	Blue body, *Radio Rescue,* A/No SS. 95 mm.	£35	NC	
416	1962-64	R.A.C. Land Rover.	Blue body, *Radio Rescue,* A/SS. 95 mm.	£35	NC	
C416	1977-79	Buick Police Car.	Met Blue body, *Police,* 2PM. 150 mm.	£8-£11	MPR	
419	1960-63	Ford Zephyr Motorway.	White/Blue body, *Police.* 97 mm.	£35	NC	
421	1977-79	'FOREST WARDEN'S FIRE' Land Rover.	Red/White body, SPW/RR/SL/OD. 135 mm.	£14	NC	
422	1977-80	Riot Police Wagon.	Red/White body, *6 Riot Police.*	£14	NC	
423	1960-62	Bedford Fire Tender.	Red body, Blk/LD, *Fire Dept.* 82 mm.	£65	NC	
C428	1978-79	Renault Police Car.	Black/White body, *Police,* ODHB/SL/A. 97 mm.	£8-£11	MPR	
C429	1978-80	Police Jaguar XJ12C.	White/Red/Blue body, *Police,* ODB/SL/A. 127 mm.	£8-£11	MPR	
C430	1978-80	Porsche 924 Police Car.	Black/White body, *Police,* ODHB/SL/A. 118 mm.	£8-£11	MPR	
437	1962-68	Superior Cadillac.	Blue/White body, plain or battery versions. 114 mm.	£28	NC	
438	1987	Rover Sterling 800	White body, Red stripe, 'POLICE', FLLB		NRP	
439	1963-65	Chevrolet Fire Chiefs Car.	Red/White body, *Fire Chief,* SL/A/2FM. 108 mm.	£35	NC	
454	1984	'POLIZEI' Sierra	Green/White body, Swiss EXPM	£5-£8	MPR	
456	1986	'POLIZEI' Sierra	Green/White body, German EXPM	£5-£8	MPR	
448	1964-69	Police Mini Van.	Blue body, *Police,* dog and PM/SL/OD. 79 mm.	£38	NC	
461	1971-79	Range Rover Police Vehicle. German issue	White/Red/Blue body, PM/FB/9BLS/3WNS. 108 mm.	£12	NC	
463	1964-66	Commer 'AMBULANCE'.	Cream body, Blue TW/SL. 90 mm.	£33	NC	
464	1963-68	Commer 15 cwt Police Van. German issue	Blue body, *County Police* or *Police,* BOFL. 90 mm. Green body, 'POLIZEI'	£33 £100	NC NPE	
481	1965-69	Chevrolet Police Car.	White/Blk body, *Police Patrol,* SL/2PM/A. 108 mm.	£33	NC	
482	1966-69	Chevrolet Fire Chief.	White/Red body, *Fire Chief,* PP/Badge. 108 mm.	£38	NC	
482	1974-77	Range Rover Ambulance.	White/Red/Blue body, *Ambulance,* SL/STR/2PM.	£9-£12	MPR	
C484	1978-80	AMC Pacer 'RESCUE'.	White/Orange/Black body, RN '35', OHB/SL. 118 mm.	£18	NC	
C489	1980	VW Polo 'POLICE' Car.	White/Green body, *Polizei,* ODHB/SL. 97 mm.	£8-£11	MPR	
492	1966-69	Volkswagen Police Car.	Green/White body, *Polizei,* SVRMSL. 91 mm.	£20	NC	
506	1968-71	Sunbeam Imp Panda Car.	Blue/White body, *Police,* TS/SL/FS. 83 mm.	£20	NC	
509	1970-72	Porsche Targa Police Car.	White/Red body, *Polizei,* siren/SL. 95 mm.	£16	NC	
513	1970-72	Citroen ID19 'ALPINE RESCUE'.	White/Red body, Roof Rack/fig/dog/sled/skis/poles. 108 mm.	£38	NC	
541	1986	Sierra 'POLICE'	Black/White body, Norway/Denmark EXPM		NRP	
541/2	1988	Sierra 'NOTRUF'	Red body, 2 Blue SL/RSL. German EXPM		NRP	
541	1986	Sierra 'POLICE' Car	Black/White body, Denmark/Norway EXPM		NRP	
542	1987	Bonna 'AMBULANCE'	Red/White body, 2 FLL, Norway EXPM		NRP	
576	1988	Mercedes 207D Van	Red body, White 'POMPIERS'. French EXPM		NRP	
597	1986	Sierra 'POLICE' Car	White body, Yellow/Black TPD, 2 SL, EM		NRP	
598	1986	Range Rover 'POLICE'	White body, Yellow/Black TPD, 2 SL, EM		NRP	
619	1988	Land Rover	Red/White body, 'SAPEUR POMPIERS' EXPM		NRP	
621	1986	'POLICE' Escort Van	White body, Red/Black side flash, Blue logo		NRP	
656	1987	Ford TSV	White/Red body, FLLB, Red Cross 'AMBULANCE'		NRP	
656	1987	Ford TSV 'POLICE'	Black body, White TPD/logo. Finnish EXPM		NRP	
656	1987	Ford TSV 'FALCK'	White body, 2 Red stripes, FLLB EXPM		NRP	
656	1987	Ford TSV	White/Red, 'AMBULANSE', FLLB. Norway EXPM		NRP	
700	1974-79	Motorway Ambulance	White/Red body, *Accident,* Red Cross. 98 mm.	£7-£9	MPR	
703	1976-78	Hi-Speed Fire Engine.	Red body, Yellow ladder, SL. 115 mm.	£7-£9	MPR	
921	1975-81	Hughes OH-6A HLC.	White/Red, *Police, Rescue,* SL. 143 mm.	£4-£7	MPR	

924	1977-81	Air Sea Rescue HLC.	Orange/Yellow/Black body, *Rescue*, 150 mm.	£4-£6	MPR ☐
927	1978-79	Surf Rescue HLC.	Blue/White body, *Surf Rescue*. 156 mm.	£4-£6	MPR ☐

Major Packs and Large Size Models

Ref. No.		Model Type	Model Features and Size	Rarity and Price Grading	
C1001	1981-	HCB Angus Firestreak.	Red/White/Silver, *Rescue*, 2FM/LD/EQ. 165 mm.	£33	NC ☐
1103	1976-81	'PATHFINDER AIRPORT CRASH TRUCK'.	Red/Silver, *Airport Fire Brigade*, OWP. 240 mm. 1st issue has working siren.Orange red decal 2nd does not. Brick Red decal	£33	NC ☐
1120	1984	Dennis Fire Engine.	Red body, TUT/EBMS/LD/RST/2SL. Plastic Yellow ladder, crest design	£6-£8	MPR ☐
1126	1977-81	'SIMON SNORKEL' Fire Engine.	Red/White/Yellow, TUT/EBMS/LD/RSJ/2SL/6FM. 265 mm. (Dennis)	£11-£14	MPR ☐
1127	1964-74	'SIMON SNORKEL' Fire Engine.	Red/Yellow/Silver, TUT/EBMS/RSJ/6FM/2SL. 252 mm. (Bedford TK)	£25	NC ☐
C1143	1969	'AMERICAN LA FRANCE' Fire Engine.	Red/White/Yellow, TUT/RCTLD/4ELD/5FM. 285 mm. Early Box Type only	£33 £38	NC ☐ NC ☐
1185	1985	Mack Fire Engine	Red body, 4 SL/CTR, 'HAMMOND FIRE DEPT'	£5-£7	MPR ☐

Auction Price Result
Lacy Scott auction 27.2.88
1103 realised £36

Gift Sets

Ref. No.		Model Type	Model Features and Size	Rarity and Price Grading	
18	1976-77	Emergency Gift Set.	Contains 402, 482, C921.	£22	NC ☐
C19	1979-82	Emergency Gift Set.	Contains C339 and C921.	£22	NC ☐
C20	1978-80	Emergency Gift Set.	Contains C429, C482, C921.	£22	NC ☐
C35	1978-79	'CHOPPER SQUAD' Surf Boat.	Contains 927, 419, TRL, Rescue Boat.	£22	NC ☐
C44	1978-80	Metropolitan Police Land Rover and Horsebox.	Contains LR, HSB, HP, HS and PM.	£22	NC ☐
C45	1978-80	Royal Canadian Mounted Police Land Rover and Horsebox.	Contains LR, HSB, HP, HS and PM.	£22	NC ☐

Export Sets — Emergency Services

NRP — £6-£9 unless shown differently

Ref. No.	Model Type	Model Features and Size	Rarity and Price Grading	
C54	Swiss Rega Set	Bonna Ambulance and Helicopter		NRP ☐
C55	Norway Emergency Gift Set	Police Car, Breakdown Truck, Ford Transit Ambulance		NRP ☐
C56	Swedish Set	Sierra 'POLIS', Bonna Ambulance		NRP ☐
C57	Swedish Set	Contains Volvo and Caravan	£12-£15	MPR ☐
C61	Swiss Fire Set	1120 Dennis FE, Sierra 'POLITZEI', Escort Van 'NOTRUF'	£12-£15	MPR ☐
C63	French Set	Bonna AMB, Peugeot 505, Renault 5 'POLICE'		NRP ☐
C65	Norway Set	Ford Transit Ambulance plus Helicopter		NRP ☐
C70	Danish 'FALCK' Set	Bonna Ambulance plus Ford Breakdown		NRP ☐
C1412	Swiss Police Set	Range Rover and Helicopter 'POLITZEI'		NRP ☐
C72	Norway Set	Contains C542 plus Helicopter 'LN OSH'		NRP ☐

HOW TO OBTAIN EXPORT MODELS

Collectors should contact Susan Pownall of the Corgi Collectors Club (address given on the Corgi Collector page) who will supply full details of the dealers in the UK stocking the models. Please enclose a stamped addressed envelope.

Taxis

Ref. No.		Model Type	Model Features and Size	Rarity and Price Grading	
221	1960-63	Chevrolet Impala Cas	Yellow, *Taxi* LHD/A *Yellow Taxis*. 108 mm.	£32	GP ☐
c327	1980	Chevrolet Caprice Taxi	Yellow, *Think TWA*, fare on door. 90 mm.	£12	NC ☐
388	1987	Mercedes 190 Taxi	White body, Yellow Black 'TAXI' EXPM		NRP ☐
c411	1976-80	Mercedes Benz 240D	Orange/Black, *Taxi* on roof. 127 mm. Also Off White.	£7-£10	MPR ☐
418	1971-74	Austin Taxi	Black body, Orange sign, SS (1963). 97 mm.	££25	NC ☐
c425	1978	London Taxi	Black, *Taxi*, whizz wheels. 121 mm.	£5-£9	MPR ☐
425/1	1986	London Taxi	Black body, 'RADIO CAB', Yellow door design		NRP ☐
430	1962-64	Ford Bermuda 'TAXI'	WH/GR/Red DC/LHD/D *Bermuda*. 102 mm.	£38	NC ☐
434	1985	Mercedes 'TAXI'	Yellow body, Red taxi sign, CTR		NRP ☐
480	1965-66	Chevrolet Impala Taxi	Yellow/Red *Taxi* fares on door. 108 mm.	£30	NC ☐
507	1969	Chrysler Bermuda Taxi	Shown in catalogue — not issued.		

Gift Sets

Ref. No.		Model Type	Model Features and Size	Rarity and Price Grading	
11	1971-75	London Gift Set	468 *Outspan*, 418 and 226 Mini	£50	NC ☐
C11	1980	London Gift Set	Contains C469 *B.T.A., C425 and PM*	£20	MPR ☐
35	1965-68	London Gift Set	Contains 648 *Corgi Toys*, 418 Taxi and PM	£75	GP ☐
	1985	Wiltshire Fire Brigade	Details unknown (1000)		NGPP ☐
C1/2	1985	London Scene	469 'LONDON STANDARD', Sierra Police Car and 425/1 Taxi	£10-£15	MPR
C/2	1986	Fire Set	Ford Transit Van 'FIRE', Fire Chief's Red Sierra, 1185/1 Mack Fire Engine	£10-£15	MPR ☐
C/8/2	1986	Police Set	Sierra 'POLICE', Ford Escort 'POLICE' and Ford Transit Breakdown 'POLICE'	£10-£15	MPR ☐
C/19	1986	Emergency Police Set	Ford Transit Van 'POLICE', Ford Sierra 'POLICE'	£6-£9	MPR ☐
C/27	1986	Emergency Set	1185/1 Mack Fire Engine and Red Fire Chief's Sierra	£6-£9	MPR ☐

Corgitronics and Corgimatics

Ref. No.		Model Type	Model Features and Size	Rarity and Price Grading	
C1001	1982	HCB Angus Firestreak.	Red/Yellow/White, *Rescue*, BOMCA/ELS/2FB/OOS. 165 mm.	£20	NC ☐
C1002	1981	Sonic Corgi Truck Set.	Yellow/White/Black/Red, *Shell Super Oil, BP Oil*, Tanker, AV/BOMCA/FW/RV/RCC. 228 mm.	£20	NC ☐
C1002	1981	'YORKIE' Truck Set.	White/Yellow/Blue/Orange, *Milk Chocolate Yorkie*, AV/CS/BOMCA/FW/RV/RCC. 228 mm.	£20	NC ☐
C1003	1981	Ford Road Hog.	Black with Yellow/White twirls, 2A/PDS/BOMCA/two tone horn. 150 mm.	£10	NC ☐
C1004	1981	Beep Beep Bus.	Red body, *BTA Welcome To Britain*, PDS/BOMCA/two tone horn. 123 mm.	£20	NC ☐
	1983	Design change	Red, *Welcome To Hamleys* logo.	£20	NC ☐
C1005	1982	Police Land Rover.	White/Red/Blue, *Police*, PDS/BOMCA/ELS/FB. 132 mm.	£10	NC ☐
C1006	1982	'RADIO WEST' Roadshow.	Yellow, Red and Blue, *Your Local Radio 605*, OOS/BOMCA/AM Radio/3LS/OD. 123 mm.	Not Issued	☐
C1006	1982	'RADIO LUXEMBOURG'.	Red/White body, 'RTL 208', OOS/BOMCA/AM Radio/3LS/OD. 123 mm.	£10	NC ☐
C1007	1982	Road Repair Unit. Land Rover TRL and FIG.	Yellow/Red/Silver, *Roadworks*, SPW/drill/BOMCA/Road Drill Sound/PDS. 264 mm.	£10	NC ☐
C1008	1982	Fire Chief's Car.	Red/White/Yellow/Silver, *Fire Department*, PDS/BOMCA/ELS/FB. 150 mm.	£10	NC ☐
C1009	1983	MG Maestro 1600.	Yellow/Black, PDS/BOMCA/WHL/WRL. 118 mm.	£12	NC ☐
C1024	1983	Beep Beep Bus.	Red, *BTA*, Supplied to Mothercare exclusively.	£20	NC ☐

Military and R.A.F. Models
Single Models

Ref. No.		Model Type	Model Features and Size	Rarity and Price Grading	
350	1958-62	Thunderbird GMS on Loading Trolley.	Red/White Missile, R.A.F. Blue, LTRL. 140 mm.	£38	NC ☐
351	1958-62	R.A.F. Land Rover.	Blue/Silver, R.A.F. roundel, SPW/WDS. 95 mm.	£33	NC ☐
352	1958-62	R.A.F. Vanguard Staff Car.	Blue/Silver, R.A.F. roundel, WDS. 95 mm.	£33	NC ☐
353	1959-61	Decca Radar Scanner.	Blue/Orange, scanner rotates. 83 mm.	£23	MPR ☐
354	1964-66	Commer Military Ambulance.	MG, Red Crosses, S/SW/SS/AD. 90 mm.	£43	GP ☐
355	1964-65	Commer 'MILITARY POLICE' Van.	MG, AD/BOFL/S/SW/SS. 90 mm.	£43	GP ☐
356	1964-66	Commer Personnel Carrier.	MG, AD/S/SW/SS/WHS, US Personnel. 91 mm.	£43	GP ☐
357	1964-66	Land Rover Weapons Carrier.	MG, S/SW/SS/DC/A/Star. 95 mm.	£43	GP ☐
358	1964-68	1961 Oldsmobile Staff Car.	MG, S/SW/SS/AD/3PS/A/Star. 108 mm.	£43	GP ☐
359	1964-66	Commer Army 'FIELD KITCHEN'.	MG, S/SW/SS/DI/OWD, Attendant. 91 mm.	£43	GP ☐
414	1961-64	Bedford Military Ambulance.	Military Green, Red Crosses, WDS. 83 mm.	£43	GP ☐
500	1963-64	US Army Land Rover.	MG, Rare version of 357. 95 mm.	£48	GP ☐
C900	1974-78	German Tiger MK1 Tank.	Brown/Green, FSH (12)/RTR/A, '144'. 103 mm.	£7-£10	MPR ☐
C901	1974-78	Centurion MK Tank.	MGC, FSH(12)/RTR/A/UJ. 121 mm.	£7-£10	MPR ☐
C902	1974-80	American M60 A1 Tank.	MGC, FSH(12)/RTR. 115 mm.	£7-£10	MPR ☐
C903	1974-80	British Chieftain Tank.	MG, FSH(12)/RTR. 125 mm.	£7-£10	MPR ☐
C904	1974-78	German King Tiger Tank.	MGC, FSH(12)/RTR, 'B 34'. 120 mm.	£7-£10	MPR ☐
C905	1975-76	Russian SU100 Tank Destroyer.	Grey, FSH(12), EG/OH/AD/Red Star. 112 mm.	£7-£10	MPR ☐
C906	1975-76	Saladin Armoured Car.	MG, FSH(12), EG. 108 mm.	£7-£10	MPR ☐
C907	1976-80	German Half Track Rocket Launcher.	Steel Blue/Red, FRK(12)/DAT/BC. 167 mm.	£7-£10	MPR ☐
C908	1977-80	French AMX Recovery Tank.	MG, CR/LDB/SL/EQ, 3 figures. 127 mm.	£7-£10	MPR ☐
C909	1977-80	British Tractor, Gun and Trailer.	Sandy, Gun and TRL, DT, FSH(12). 280 mm.	£17	NC ☐
C920	1977-80	Bell Army Helicopter.	MGC, FRK(12), US Army. 130 mm.	£4-£6	MPR ☐
C923	1977-80	Sikorsky Sky Crane, Helicopter.	MG, Red Cross, Army. 160 mm.	£6-£8	MPR ☐

Major and Large Size Models

Ref. No.		Model Type	Model Features and Size	Rarity and Price Grading	
1106	1959-61	Karrier Decca Radar Van.	Cream/Orange, RTT Scanner, A. 134 mm.	£70	NC ☐
1108	1958-61	Bristol Bloodhound, GMS on Launching Ramp.	MG, LRP/LM, Yellow/Red/WH, GMS, R.A.F. MK. 178 mm.	£55	NC ☐
1109	1959-62	Bristol Bloodhound, GMS on Loading Trolley.	MG, LTRL/SPW, Yellow/Red/WH, GMS, R.A.F. MK. 228 mm.	£55	NC ☐
1112	1959-62	Corporal GMS on LRP.	MG, LRP/LM, WH/Red GMS, PH/EDI. 330 mm.	£35	GP ☐
1113	1959-62	Corporal GMS and Erector Vehicle.	MG, V/SPW/BM/LM, GMS/PH/EDI. 292 mm.	£80	GV ☐
1115	1958-62	Bristol Ferranti Bloodhound GMS.	Yellow/Red/White with R.A.F. MK.	£33	NC ☐
1116	1959-62	Bristol Ferranti Bloodhound Launching Ramp.	Military Green, rotates/LM.	£33	NC ☐
1117	1959-62	Bristol Ferranti Bloodhound Loading Trolley.	Military Green, SPW/TB pivots.	£33	NC ☐
1118	1958-62	International 6×6 Army Truck.	Military Green, six wheels, WDS. 140 mm.	£68	NC ☐
1124	1959-62	Corporal GMS, Launching Ramp.	Military Green, LM/AFT.	£33	NC ☐
1133	1965-66	Troop Transporter.	MG, 'US 7811332', 6W/DC. 140 mm.	£65	NC ☐
1134	1965-66	'US ARMY' Fuel Tanker.	MG, US Star, AV/DDC, 'No Smoking'. 191 mm.	£125	GP ☐
1135	1965	'US ARMY' Heavy EQ, TPTR.	MG, US Star, D/AV/DDR/RVM/DRAXW/2SPW. 241 mm.	£85	GP ☐

Gift Sets

Ref. No.		Model Type	Model Features and Size	Rarity and Price Grading	
3	1959-62	LR with Thunderbird GMS Set.	Contains 350 and 351.	£75	NPE ☐
4	1959-62	Bristol Ferranti Bloodhound GMS Set.	Contains 351, 1115, 1116, 1117.	£75	GP ☐
6	1959-62	Guided Missiles Set.	Contains 350, 351, 352, 353, 1106, 1108, 1117.	£175	NPE ☐
9	1959-62	Corporal GMS Set.	Contains 1112, 1113, 1118.	£75	NPE ☐
10	1974-78	Centurion Tank and TPTR Set.	Contains 901 and TPTR/DRAXW/AV.	£30	NC ☐
17	1976-81	Military Set.	Contains 900, 906, 920.	£25	NC ☐

Auction Price Results
Lacey Scott auction 27.2.88
Gift set No. 4 realised £55

Ref. No.		Model Type	Model Features and Size	Rarity and Price Grading	
104	1965-66	Dolphin 20 Cabin Cruiser.	Blue/White boat, Red TRL, helmsman. 136 mm.	£15	NC
C107	1967-70	Batboat on Trailer.	Black/Red body, many decals. 140 mm.	£15	NC
201	1970-72	The Saint's Volvo P1800.	White/Red, Saint design. No D/WZW. 90 mm.	£9-£12	MPR
258	1965-69	The Saint's Volvo P1800.	White/Red, D/SL/SS, Saint design — black, red or blue.	£40	NC
C259	1979-	Penguinmobile.	White, Driver under Red/Yellow parasol. 95 mm.	£4-£6	MPR
C260	1981-	Superman Police Car.	Blue, *City of Metropolis*. 150 mm.	£14	NC
261	1965-68	James Bonds DB5 Aston Martin.	Gold body, RTT gun, ejector seat, bullet shield, D/PS. 97 mm.	£55	NC
C261	1979-82	Spiderbuggy.	Red/Blue body, 2 figures. 150 mm.	£14	NC
C262	1979-82	Captain Marvel's Porsche.	White with flames and stars. D. 120 mm.	£14	NC
C263	1979-82	Captain America's Jetmobile.	Red/White/Blue body with Blue D. 155 mm.	£14	NC
C264	1979-82	Incredible Hulk Van.	Hulk in cage on Mazda pick-up. 120 mm.	£14	NC
C265	1981-82	Supermobile.	Blue/Red/Silver body, pilot/RL. 148 mm.	£14	NC
266	1968-72	Chitty Chitty Bang Bang.	Silver body, Yellow/White RTT, wings, D/3PS, SL/DI/HBR/CL/horn/SPW/SW/WS. 162 mm.	£135	GP
C266	1979-	Spider Bike.	Red/Black MC, Red/Black figure, RL. 115 mm.	£8-£12	MPR
C267	1966	Batmobile.	Black/Red body, RL, Batman/Robin. RT/W2W. 127 mm.	£75	NC
		2nd Issue	Black/Red body	£25	NC
268	1967-70	Green Hornet.	Black body, driver and gunman. RL. 127 mm.	£120	GP
C268	1978-	Batmans Bat Bike.	Black/Red M/C with Batman. RL. 110 mm.	£5	NC
C269	1977-81	James Bond's Lotus Esprit.	White body, hydroplanes. 120 mm.	£15	NC
270	1968-76	J.B's Aston Martin.	Silver body, ejector seat and passenger. 102 mm.	£30	NC
270	1968	J.B's Aston Martin.	Rare early version with spoked wheels.	£40	NC
C271	1978-	J.B's Aston Martin.	Silver body, ejector seat and passenger. 130 mm.	£14	NC
C272	1982-	J.B's Citroen 2CV.	Yellow body, ORF/ODB/LHD. 108 mm.	£4-£6	MPR
277	1968-70	The Monkeemobile.	Red/White body, DE, 4 Monkees. 127 mm.	£48	NC
C278	1981-	Dan Dare Car.	Red/Yellow body, retractable wings. 132 mm.	£10	NC
C290	1976-81	Kojak Buick.	Bronze body, ODB/SL, badge, 2 figures. 150 mm.	£12	NC
C292	1978-81	Starsky and Hutch Ford Torino.	Red/White body, 3 figures. 153 mm. Reissued in 1986 20,000 (EX PM)	£12	NC
C298	1983-	Magnum PI Ferrari.	Red/Tan body, WS/LHD. 115 mm.	£7-£9	MPR
C320	1978-81	The Saints Jaguar XJS.	White body, OD, Saint logo on BN. 128 mm.	£12	NC
336	1967-69	James Bond's Toyota 2000.	White body, D/PS/A, SS/RL in boat. 102 mm.	£75	NC
C342	1980-82	'PROFESSIONALS' Ford Capri.	Silver/Black body, TW/OD, 3 figures. 124 mm.	£15	NC
C348	1980-	Vegas Thunderbird.	Red body with Dan Tanner. 124 mm.	£12	NC
395	1972-73	Fire Bug.	Orange body, Yellow LD, *Firebug*. 83 mm.	£14	NC
426	1962-63	Circus Booking Office.	Red/Blue body, *Booking Office*. 93 mm.	£88	GP
C426	1978-82	Circus Booking Office.	Yellow/Red body, *Jean Richard Pinder*. 122 mm.	£23	NC
C434	1978-82	'CHARLIE'S ANGELS' Van.	Pink body, DI/TW. 122 mm.	£8-£12	MPR
C435	1980-	'SUPERVAN'.	Grey body, OD, laboratory. 122 mm.	£8-£12	MPR
C436	1980-	'SPIDER-VAN'.	Blue body, OD, laboratory. 122 mm.	£8-£12	MPR
436	1963-65	Citroen 'WILDLIFE' Safari ID19.	Yellow body, D/PS/OT/BEM/HRS/DI/SS. 108 mm.	£33	NC
472	1964-66	Land Rover LS Vehicle.	Green/Brown/Yellow body, *Vote For Corgi*. 91 mm.	£38	NC
475	1964 only	Citroen Safari Olympic Winter Sports	White/Yellow, *1964*, HRS/OT/BEM/RR/Skier/Skis. 108 mm.	£40	NC
475	1965-66	Citroen Safari.	White/Yellow body, *Corgi Ski Club*, HRS/OT/BEM/RR/Skier/Skis. 108 mm.	£33	NC
486	1967-69	'KENNEL CLUB TRUCK.'	Red/White body, trainer and 4 dogs. 108 mm.	£28	NC
487	1966-69	'CHIPPERFIELDS PARADE VEHICLE'.	Red body, animal figures, *Circus Is Here*. 91 mm.	£65	NC
C495	1984	'CORGI' 4×4 OBT	Blue body, White RF, Black TR, HDT/ARB		NRP
497	1966-69	Man from U.N.C.L.E.	Blue body, 2PS plus *Waverley* ring. 108 mm.	£75	NC
		Variant	White body — rare	£150	GP
499	1968-69	Citroen 1968 'GRENOBLE' Olympics.	White/Blue/Red, 2 figures, HRS/OT/BEM/RR/Sled/Skis. 108 mm.	£33	NC
503	1966-72	Giraffe TPTR.	Red/Blue body, 2 giraffes, *Chipperfields Circus*. 97 mm.	£55	NC
510	1970-72	Citroen DS19 Team Managers Car.	Red, *Tour De France*, fig/LSP, *Paramount*, LHD/D/4 wheels/A. 108 mm.	£33	NC
511	1970-72	Circus Poodles Truck. 'CHIPPERFIELDS'.	Red/Blue livery, 6 dogs and trainer, *Performing Poodles*. 108 mm.	£125	GP
513	1970-72	Citroen Safari Alpine Rescue Car.	White/Red/Yellow, *Alpine Rescue*, HRS/OT/RR/dog/sled/male fig. 108 mm.	£33	NC
607	1962-68	Elephant Cage.	Brown/Yellow/Blue body, *Chipperfields Circus*. 76 mm.	£23	NC
C647	1981	Buck Rogers Starfighter.	Yellow/White/Blue, RTT wings, 2 figs. 150 mm.	£14	NC
C648	1980	NASA Space Shuttle.	White body, *U.S.A. Satellite*, OH. 156 mm.	£10	NC
C649	1980	J.B's Space Shuttle.	Same as C648 with *Moonraker*. 156 mm.	£15	NC
801	1969-75	Noddy's Car.	Yellow/Red/Silver, 3 Noddy figures. 95 mm.	£75	GP
802	1970-72	Popeye's Paddle Wagon.	MLCD, Popeye, Olive, Sweet Pea, Bluto, Wimpey, all	£150	GP
803	1969-70	The Beatles Submarine.	Yellow/White, 2 OH, 4 periscopes, 4 Beatles. 133 mm.	£150	GP
805	1970	Hardy Boys Rolls Royce.	Red/Yellow, RR, 5 figures. 118 mm.	£55	NC
806	1970-72	Lunar Bug.	Red/White/Black, WDS/DDR. 127 mm.	£50	NC
807	1972	Magic Roundabout Car.	MLCD, Dougal, Dylan and Brian, all HP. 118 mm.	£75	NC
807	1974	Dougals Car.	MLCD, Brian, Dougal and Dylan. 118 mm.	£45	NC
808	1972	Basil Brush's Car.	Red/Yellow, HP, Basil and laugh tapes. 95 mm.	£45	NC

Novelty, Film and TV Tie-In Models
Single Models cont.

Ref. No.		Model Type	Model Features and Size	Rarity and Price Grading		
809	1974	Dick Dastardly's Car.	MLCD plus Dick and Muttley. 128 mm.	£45	NC	☐
811	1972-73	J B's Moon Buggy.	White/Blue/Yel, with Red gear, U.S. flag. 113 mm.	£100	GP	☐
851	1973-74	Magic Roundabout Train.	MLCD, Dougal, Mr Rusty, Basil, Rosalie and Paul, Loco and 2 carriages. 311 mm.	£90	GP	☐
852	1973-74	Musical Carousel.	MLCD, Dylan plus the children. 200 mm.	£90	GP	☐
853	1973-74	Magic Playground.	Contains 851, 852, 860/1/2, 868 and kids. 820 mm.	£295	NPE	☐
859	1973-74	Mr McHenrys Trike.	MLCD, Mr McHenry and Zebedee. 117 mm.	£38	GP	☐
		Models 860-868	860 Dougal, 861 Florence, 862 Zebedee, 863 Mr Rusty			
		Individual Magic Roundabout	864 Brian Snail, 865 Basil, 866 Ermintrude the Cow			
		Figures.	868 Dylan the Rabbit.	£10	NC	☐
C926	1976	Stromberg Helicopter	Black/Yellow body (J. Bond)	£5-£7	MPR	☐
C925	1981	Batcopter.	Black/Red body, *Batman* winch. 143 mm.	£5-£7	MPR	☐
C928	1981	Spidercopter.	Blue/Red body, RTT tongue. 142 mm.	£5-£7	MPR	☐
C929	1981	'DAILY PLANET' Jetcopter.	Red/White body, RL. 156 mm.	£5-£7	MPR	☐
C930	1980	Drax Helicopter.	White/Yel, *Drax Airlines,* RL. 156 mm.	£5-£7	MPR	☐

Major Packs

Ref. No.		Model Type	Model Features and Size	Rarity and Price Grading		
1119	1960-62	H.D.L. Hovercraft.	Green, Blue and White body, *SR-N1.* 120 mm.	£30	NC	☐
1121	1960-68	Circus Crane Truck.	Red/Grey/Yellow, *Chip Circus* in Blue H. 200 mm.	£45	NC	☐
1123	1961-63	'CHIP' Circus Cage.	Red and Blue body, 2AN/TB/H. 127 mm.	£30	NC	☐
1130	1962-72	Circus Horse TPTR.	Red and Blue body, CHS/AV/DDR, *Chipperfields Circus.* 260 mm.	£75	NC	☐
1139	1969-72	Scammell Handyman Circus Transporter.	Red and Blue body, 3 cages, 4 animals, *Chip Circus Menagerie.* 232 mm.	£75	GP	☐
1144	1970-72	Circus Crane and Cage.	Red and Blue body, plastic cage with rhino, *Chipperfields.* 200 mm.	£75	NC	☐
C1163	1978-82	Circus Cannon Truck.	Red and Blue body, *Marvo* figure. 130 mm.	£15	NC	☐
C1164	1980-83	Dolphinarium Truck.	Blue body, P tank, girl and dolphin. 290 mm.	£15	NC	☐
2030-2032		Muppets	Kermit, Miss Piggy or animal	£10 each		☐

Gift Sets

Ref. No.		Model Type	Model Features and Size	Rarity and Price Grading		
C3	1981	Batmobile and Batboat.	267 and Batboat.	£30	NC	☐
7	1968-75	'DAKTARI' Gift Set.	Land Rover, tiger, lions, figures.	£75	NC	☐
8	1960-74	'LIONS OF LONGLEAT' Set.	Land Rover, keeper, 3 lions, dens and meals.	£75	NC	☐
12	1961-66	Circus Gift Set.	Contains 1121 and 1123.	£95	NC	☐
14	1969-73	Giant 'DAKTARI' Set.	Contains 484, 503, Land Rover.	£75	NC	☐
19	1962-68	'CHIPPERFIELDS' Circus Cage Set.	Contains 438, 607 and elephant.	£50	NC	☐
21	1969-71	Circus Gift Set, 'CHIPPERFIELDS'.	Contains 1144 and 1139.	£135	NC	☐
C21	1980-82	Superman Set.	Contains 260, 265 and 925.	£30	NC	☐
C22	1980-82	James Bond Set.	Contains 269, 271 and 649.	£40	NC	☐
23	1963-66	Circus Gift Set. 'CHIPPERFIELDS'.	Contains 101, 406, 426, 607, 1121, 2×1123.	£350	GP	☐
C23	1980-82	Spiderman Set.	Contains 261, 266 and 928.	£30	NC	☐
C30	1978-80	Circus Gift Set.	Land Rover and Trailer.	£24	NC	☐
C31	1977-80	Safari LR and TRL.	White with black Zebra stripes.	£25	NC	☐
C36	1977-78	Tarzan Set.	LR, TRL, dinghy and animals.	£30	NC	☐
40	1967-69	The Avengers Set.	Steed's Bentley plus Emma Peel and her Lotus Elan Convertible.	£225	GP	☐
C40	1977-80	Batman's Gift Set.	Contains 107, 267, 925.	£50	NC	☐
C40	1980	Batman's Gift Set.	Contains 2 models	£25	NC	☐
C41	1977-81	Silver Jubilee Set.	State Landau with their Majesties.	£7-£9	MPR	☐
C48	1978-81	Circus Set. 'JEAN RICHARD PINDER'.	Contains C426, C1163, C30, ringmaster, artists, animals.	£80	NC	☐

Novelty, Film & TV Tie-in Models
Auction price results
Christies, 85 Old Brompton Road, London SW7 3LD
Sale dated 28.5.87:
Gift set 23 — £240
Model 803 — £190

Roadmaking Vehicles, Crane and Hoists
Single Models

Ref. No.		Model Type	Model Features and Size	Rarity and Price Grading	
54	1974-	Massey Ferguson TRC/Shovel	Yellow Red or Red White body. 150 mm.	£7-£9	MPR ☐
109	1968-69	'PENNYBURN' Trailer	Blue cabinet, Yellow chassis. 76 mm.	£10	NC ☐
403	1974-79	Thwaites Skip Dumper	Yellow/Green body, DMP tips, Driver. RT/WZW. 83 mm.	£7-£9	MPR ☐
406	1971-75	Mercedes Benz Unimog	Yel/Grn body, DRF/SL/RUM/SS/H. 91 mm.	£9-£12	MPR ☐
409	1971-75	Unimog Dumper	White/Red body, SL/RUM/SS/H. 104 mm	£9-£12	MPR ☐
C409	1981	'ALLIS CHALMERS' Forklift	Yellow body, pallets/load/D. 112 mm.	£7-£9	MPR ☐
458	1958-66	E.R.F. Earth Dumper	Red and Yellow body. E.R.F. Cast in. 95 mm	£28	NC ☐
459	1974-78	Raygu Rascal Roller	Yellow/Green body, *Road Roller*. 125 mm.	£6-£8	MPR ☐
460	1959-63	E.R.F. Cement Tipper	Yellow/Grey body, (Neville) E.R.F. CI. 95 mm.	£28	NC ☐
483	1968-72	Dodge Tipper Truck	Yellow Black body, Kew Fargo. 136 mm	£23	NC ☐
494	1967-72	Bedford Tipper	Red/Yellow body, RVM. 102 mm.	£18	NC ☐

Major Packs

Ref. No.		Model Type	Model Features and Size	Rarity and Price Grading	
C1101	1976-81	Mobile Crane	Yellow/Blue body, *Warner & Swasey*. 150 mm.	£10-£15	MPR ☐
1102	1958-62	EUCLID TC 12 TRC	Green/Silver/Black body, on tracks. 159 mm.	£38	NC ☐
C1102	1976-77	'BERLIET' Bottom Dumper	Yellow and Black body, *Road Construction*. 287 mm.	£20	NC ☐
1103	1960-63	'EUCLID' Crawler TRC	Yellow/Green/White body, No D, on tracks. 111 mm.	£36	NC ☐
1107	1963-66	'EUCLID' with Dozer	Yellow/Green body, Driver, on Tracks. 159 mm.	£36	NC ☐
1110	1976-80	J.C.B. Crawler	Yellow and White body, Driver. 115 mm.	£9-£12	MPR ☐
		Variant	Light Blue/Orange, Powder Blue chassis		NGPP ☐
C1113	1981-	'HYSTER' Handler	Yellow or Black/White MB *US Lines* HST. 212 mm.	£9-£12	MPR ☐
	1987	Design change	SAPM with 'SEALINK' CNT, EXPM		NRP ☐
1122	1984	Mercedes Mixer	Orange body, Black/stripes	£5-£8	MPR ☐
	1985	Colour change	SAPM, White RVD, Black/Yellow design	£4-£7	MPR ☐
1128	1963-76	'PRIESTMAN' cub Shovel	Red/Yellow body, Driver. 165 mm	£19	NC ☐
1128	1984	Mercedes Tipper	Yellow cab, Red tipper, 6 W 'BLOCK' logo		NRP ☐
1128	1985	Mercedes Tipper	Black body, White logo 'TARMAC'.		NRP ☐
1145	1970-76	Unimog Goose Dumper	Yellow/Red body '406'. 171 mm.	£9-£13	MPR ☐
1152	1983-	'BARRATT' Tipper	Green/White body, Tips. 145 mm		NRP ☐
C1153	1983-	'WIMPEY' Tipper Truck.	Green/Silver body. Tips. 145 mm (SCANIA)		NPR ☐
	1984	Colour change	Yellow body		NRP ☐
	1985	'LAING' logo	Yellow body, Black logo, CRT		NRP ☐
1153	1973-74	'PRIESTMAN' Crane	Red/Orange body *Higrab*. 230 mm.	£39	NC ☐
1154	1974-76	PRIESTMAN Crane Truck	Yellow/Red body, Silver boom H. 240 mm	£36	NC ☐
1154	1979	'BLOCK CONSTRUCTION' Crane	Orange/Yellow crane, CH/JIB, White body, Brick PLL		
C1155	1975-79	'SKYSCRAPER' Tower Crane	Yellow/Red body, Black Tracks. 340 mm.	£10-£15	MPR ☐
1156	1977-	Volvo Concrete Mixer	Yellow/Red, *Block Construction*	£10-£15	MPR ☐

Gift Sets

Ref. No.		Model Type	Model Features and Size	Rarity and Price Grading	
2	1971-73	Unimog Dumper and Shovel	Contains 1128 and 1145	£28	NC ☐
C2	1980	Construction Site Set	Contains 440 and 54.	£28	MPR ☐
27	1963-72	Priestman 9ft Set	Contains 1128 and 1131 Bedford TPTR	£70	GV ☐
14	1961-65	Tower Wagon Set	Contains Jeep FC 150, and fig/EQ	£28	NC ☐

Miscellaneous
Jeeps, Land Rovers, Pick-ups, Breakdown Trucks, Caravans, Motor Cycles, Go-Karts and Trailers, Public Service Vehicles

Ref. No.		Model Type	Model Features and Size	Rarity and Price Grading	
C46	1983-	Super Karts.	Blue or Orange, MB, Red/Silver RCD.	£5-£8	MPR ☐
100	1957-61	Dropside Trailer.	All Yellow or Red body, TB. 108 mm.	£5-£8	MPR ☐
101	1958-61	Platform Trailer.	Grey/Yellow body, axle swivels, TB. 108 mm.	£5-£8	MPR ☐
C171	1982-	Street Bike.'	Red, Silver and Black body, MLCD, swirl.	£4-£6	MPR ☐
C172	1982-	'POLICE' Bike.	White, Black and Silver body.	£4-£6	MPR ☐
C173	1982-	Cafe Racer.	Silver and Black, RN '26', *750cc Class.*	£4-£6	MPR ☐
406	1957-63	Land Rover Pick-up.	Yellow/Black body, OC/SPW/TBD. 95 mm.	£33	NC ☐
409	1959-63	Forward Control Jeep.	Blue body, Red R grille, TBD/SWP. 91 mm.	£24	NC ☐

Ref. No.		Model Type	Model Features and Size	Price and Rarity Grading	
C415	1976-78	Mazda Camper PV.	Red body, DDTBD plus White caravan. 140 mm.	£8-£11	MPR ☐
417	1963-65	Land Rover.	Red/Yellow/Silver, SPW/H/WKW, 'BREAKDOWN'.	£23	NC ☐
C419	1978-79	Covered Jeep CJ5.	Green with White plastic top. 100 mm.	£5-£8	MPR ☐
420	1962-66	Ford Thames 'AIRBORNE' Caravan.	TT Green or TT Blue or TT Pink or Blue/Grey body.	£32	NC ☐
C421	1977-79	Land Rover Safari.	Gold/Black body, RR/LD/SPW/SDW(3)/ODB. 114 mm.	£6-£9	MPR ☐
		Variant	With 'FOREST FIRE WARDEN'	£5-£7	MPR ☐
431	1964-66	Volkswagen Pick-up.	Yellow/Red, S/SW/SS/DC. 91 mm.	£28	NC ☐
434	1963-66	Volkswagen Kombi MB.	Two Tone Green, Yellow S/IS. 91 mm.	£26	NC ☐
438	1963-77	Land Rover with SPWB.	Early models — Red or Green body. 95 mm.	£8-£11	MPR ☐
C440	1979-	Mazda Custom Pick-up.	Orange/Yellow/Red, US flag, MLCD. 120 mm.	£6-£9	MPR ☐
C441	1979-82	'GOLDEN EAGLE' Jeep.	Brown/Tan or Gold/Wh, DRF/SPWS. 100 mm.	£6-£9	MPR ☐
C448	1985	4 × 4 'RENEGADE' Jeep.	Red/White body & BM. ARB, 100 mm.	£3-£5	MPR ☐
C457	1981-3	Talbot Matra R.	Red/Black or Green/Black, ODB/OT/TS. 120 mm.	£3-£5	MPR ☐
C457	1984	Rancho	Green body, Brown seats, 120 mm	£3-£5	MPR ☐
465	1963-66	Commer Pick-up Truck.	Red/Orange, S/SW/SS/TOL. 90 mm.	£25	NC ☐
470	1965-72	Forward Control Jeep.	Blue/Grey, OC/DC/SS/LHD. 91 mm.	£18	NC ☐
477	1966-67	Land Rover Breakdown.	Red/Yellow/Silver, SPWS/WKW/H. 114 mm.	£18	NC ☐
478	1965-69	Jeep Tower Wagon.	Green, Yellow and Silver body, figure. 129 mm.	£18	NC ☐
C490	1967-70	Volkswagen Breakdown.	Beige/Red, Tool Box, 2SPW. 102 mm.	£23	NC ☐
C490	1976-79	Touring Caravan.	White and Blue body, OD/TB. 125 mm.	£6-£9	MPR ☐
C493	1976-78	Mazda B 1600 Pick-up.	Blue body, DDTB. 120 mm.	£8-£11	MPR ☐
C495	1983-	4 × 4 Mazda 'OB TRUCK'.	Blue/Black, *Corgi Cruiser*, DDTB. 121 mm.	£5-£8	MPR ☐
	1985	Colour/TPD change	Blue/White body 'SURF RIDER'	£3-£5	MPR ☐
C501	1984	Range Rover	Beige and Dark Brown body	£3-£5	MPR ☐
C501	1985	Range Rover	Blue body, HDT, NSTW	£3-£5	MPR ☐
C619	1986	Range Rover	Beige (dirty) body, Black LD/RR/SPW/LG	£5-£7	MPR ☐
C674/1	1988	'A.A.' Ford Transit Breakdown	Yellow body, White stripe, FLLB, Black rear lifting gear	£2-£4	MPR ☐
C674/2	1988	'R.A.C.' Ford Transit Breakdown	White body, Red/Blue stripe, FLLB, Black rear lifting gear	£2-£4	MPR ☐
681	1971	Stunt Bike	Colours unknown — embossed on rear Black wheel is 'AVON' and 'BRITAINS LTD'		NGPP ☐
702	1975-79	Breakdown Truck.	Red/Black, single BM/H. 100 mm.	£3-£4	MPR ☐

Major Models

Ref. No.		Model Type	Model Features and Size	Rarity and Price Grading	
1106	1984	'CORGI' Loadlugger	Yellow body & CH, Red 'BIG BIN'		NRP ☐
1114	1984	Mercedes Gritter	Yellow/Black body and plough. LD/SL	£6-£9	MPR ☐
	1984	TPD & logo change	SAPM with Red stripes, 'MOTORWAY MAINTENANCE'	£5-£8	MPR ☐
1115	1985	Parisienne Refuse Truck	Green body, LRS, 'PARIS' TPD (EXPM)	£8-£12	MPR ☐
1116	1979	Refuse Collector.	Orange/Silver body, *City Sanitation*. 151 mm.	£6-£9	MPR ☐
1116/2	1988	Design change	Blue cab, White tipper 'BOROUGH COUNCIL'	£3-£5	MPR ☐
1117	1980	Streetsweeper.	Orange/Yellow body, 'FAUN' plus operator.	£6-£9	MPR ☐
	198	Colour change	All Yellow body	£3-£5	MPR ☐
1117/2	1988	Design change	Red cab, White collecting bin, operator	£3-£5	MPR ☐
1140	1982	Ford Transit Wrecker.	White/Red, *24 Hour Service*, WO/H. 131 mm.	£6-£9	MPR ☐
		Logo change	With 'RELAY' logo	£5-£7	MPR ☐
1140	1982	Export model	Red/Yellow body, 'ABSCHLEPPDEENST' EXPM	£5-£7	MPR ☐
1140	1987	Export model	Red body, Gold 'FALCK' logo, Danish EXPM	£3-£5	MPR ☐
1140	1987	Export model	Red body, Yellow SPN, FLLB, 'VIKING'	£3-£5	MPR ☐
1142	1967-74	'HOLMES WRECKER' Recovery Vehicle.	Red/White/Blue, TC/2SPW/LD/SL/2WD/2H. 114 mm.	£25	NC ☐
1144	1975-78	Berliet Wrecker Recovery Vehicle.	Red/Grey body, 2 hoists and hooks. 130 mm.	£18	NC ☐
1150	1974-77	Unimog with Snow Plough.	Yellow/Brown body, Sil Blade, 2 flags. 155 mm.	£15	NC ☐

Gift Sets

Ref. No.		Model Type	Model Features and Size	Rarity and Price Grading	
17	1963-67	Land Rover and Ferrari Set.	(438) LR plus (154) Ferrari on TRL.	£30	NC ☐
19	1973-77	'CORGI FLYING CLUB' Set.	Green/Brown LR, Yel/Red AC.	£20	NC ☐
28	1963-66	Mazda Dinghy Set.	Mazda (493) plus dinghy and TRL.	£16	NC ☐
C49	1978-80	'CORGI FLYING CLUB' Set.	Green/White Jeep, Blue/White AC.	£15	NC ☐
64	1965-69	Forward Control Jeep 150 and Conveyor Belt.	Jeep (409), Yellow/Wh CVB.	£28	NC ☐
C/20/2	1986	A.A. Set	Ford Escort, Ford Transit Van & Ford Transit Breakdown	£8-£11	MPR ☐
C/21/2	1986	R.A.C. Set	Range Rover, Ford Escort and Ford Transit Breakdown	£8-£11	MPR ☐

Corgi Classics — Box Vans, Trucks, Tankers, Vans, Buses and Tramlines

This excellent 1/43 scale series was introduced in 1985 and features finely engineered models of classic vehicles. Great care has been taken to ensure that each model is a faithful replica of its original both in terms of its features and authentic liveries.

1 A.E.C. FORWARD CONTROL CABOVERS
- a Box Vans
- b Tankers

2 BEDFORD 'OB' SERIES VEHICLES
- a Box Van
- b Single Decker Coaches
- c Pantechnicons

3 FORD MODEL 'T' VEHICLES
- a Vans
- b Tankers

4 MACK TRUCKS

5 MORRIS 1000 VEHICLES
- a Vans
- b Cars

6 1926 RENAULT TRUCKS
- a Box Vans
- b Canvas backed Trucks
- c Open backed Trucks

7 1929 THORNEYCROFT VEHICLES
- a Box vans
- b Box Vans with Billboards
- c Beer Trucks with Barrels
- d Canvas backed Trucks
- e Double Decker Bus
- f Open backed Trucks
- g Thorneycroft body/Renault bonnet

8 TRAMLINES
- a Single Decker Trams
- b Double Decker Trams

9 GIFT SETS

N.B.: A.E.C. Classic Series Buses listed in the Buses Section.

1 A.E.C. FORWARD CONTROL CABOVERS

a BOX VANS

Ref. No.		Model Type	Model Features and Size	Rarity and Price Grading	
C897/1	1987	'CARTER PATERSON'	Black/Red body 'ATORA FOR XMAS' (STRL)		NRP
C897/2	1987	'JOHN KNIGHT HUSTLER SOAP'	Dark Blue/Cream body, Red/Gold design (STRL)		NRP
897/3	1987	'L.M.S. EXPRESS PARCELS'	Brown/Black body, Red/White 'PUCK' design (STRL)		NRP
897/4	1988	'DUCKHAMS WEARCURE'	Silver/White body, Green/Blue design 'TABLETS' (STRL)		NRP
897/5	1988	'AMPLION RADIO'	Two tone Blue body, Brown radio design (STRL)		NRP
897/6	1988	'WEETABIX'	Dark Yellow/White body, Red cab roof & logo (STRL)		NRP
	1988	'POTTERS ASTHMA CURE'	Two tone Green body, only available as a 'BP' promotional and to Corgi Club members (LE)	£20	NC
897/8	1988	'HIS MASTERS VOICE'	Silver/Dark Green body, Red design plus famous dog (STRL)		NRP

b TANKERS

Ref. No.		Model Type	Model Features and Size	Rarity and Price Grading	
C945/1	1987	'FLOWERS BREWERY'	Cream and Green body and chassis (STRL)		NRP
C945/2	1987	'GAYMERS CIDER'	Dark Blue and Red body and chassis (STRL)		NRP
C945/3	1988	'CARLESS CAPEL'	Dark Green body, Cream tank, Yellow logo (STRL)		NRP
C945/4	1988	'DUCKHAMS OILS'	Blue body, Silver tank, White logo (STRL)		NRP
	1988	'BP PETROLEUM'	Green Red body and tank. Only available as a BP promotional and to Corgi Club members (STRL)	£20	NC
	1988	'SOMERLITE LTD'	Late entry — no details		

2 BEDFORD 'OB' SERIES

a BOX VANS

C822/1	1988	'PERSIL'	Green body, White roof, lady design (STRL)		NRP	☐
	1988	'GILLETTE'	Late entry — no details.		NGPP	☐

b SINGLE DECKER COACHES

C949/1	1987	'NORFOLKS OF NAYLAND'	Green body with Yellow stripe			
		1st type	With a Pale Yellow stripe and small 'IPSWICH' print on the destination blinds (LE)	£16	NC	☐
		2nd type	With Bright Yellow stripe and large 'IPSWICH'		NRP	☐
C949/2	1987	'ROYAL BLUE'	Yellow/Dark Blue body and stripe (STRL)			
		1st type	With Dark Blue skirt between front and rear doors	£20	NC	☐
		2nd type	Without the Dark Blue skirt		NRP	☐
C949/3	1987	'ALEXANDER BLUEBIRD'	Cream body, Yellow roof and bodystripe (STRL)		NRP	☐
C949/4	1987	'GREYCARS'	Grey body, Cream roof, Red bodystripe & MDGDS (STRL)		NRP	☐
C949/5	1987	'CROSVILLE'	Cream body, Green roof and bonnet (STRL)		NRP	☐
C949/6	1987	'SOUTHDOWN'	Two tone Green body and roof, Cream bodystripe (STRL)		NRP	☐
C949/7	1988	'EASTERN COUNTIES'	Cream body, Red roof, bonnet and stripe (STRL)		NRP	☐
	1988	'HIGHLAND'	Brown/Cream body, Kays MOM (LE)		NGPP	☐
	1988	'SOUTH MIDLAND'	Late entry — no details.		NGPP	☐

c PANTECHNICONS

C953/1	1987	'PICKFORDS'	Dark Blue body, White roof, Red wheels (STRL)	£15	NC	☐
C953/2	1987	'WARING & GILLOW'	Green/White/Black body (STRL)		NRP	☐
C953/3	1987	'FRASERS OF IPSWICH'	Dark blue/White body, Grey roof (STRL)		NRP	☐
C953/4	1987	'STEINWAY & SONS'	Two tone Green body, Black roof (STRL)		NRP	☐
C953/5	1988	'GRIFF FENDER'	Blue body, Grey cab & roof, Grey/Black design (STRL)		NRP	☐
C953/6	1988	'DUCKHAMS'	Mid Green body, White roof, 'NOL MOTOR OILS' (STRL)		NRP	☐
	1988	'CAMP HOPSON'	Late entry — no details.		NGPP	☐

3 FORD MODEL 'T' VEHICLES

a VANS

C865	1986	'LYONS TEA'	Blue/White body, Gold design (STRL)	NRP	☐
C865/1	1987	'NEEDLERS'	Brown body, Red chassis and roof (STRL) with Billboards	NRP	☐
C865/2	1987	'DRUMMER DYES'	Yellow body, Red logo, drummer design (STRL) with Billboards	NRP	☐
C865/3	1987	'KALAMAZOO'	Red body, Gold design 'FIRE DEPT' (STRL) with Billboards	NRP	☐
C865/4	1987	'PEPSI COLA'	White body, Blue chassis and roof (STRL) with Billboards	NRP	☐
C873	1986	'ZEBRA GRATE POLISH'	Yellow body, zebra design (LE)	NRP	☐
C874	1987	'CORGI COLLECTOR CLUB 2nd ANNIVERSARY'	Yellow/Blue body (LE)	NGPP	☐
C875	1986	'SCHOKOLADE GOLD'	Maroon/Black body, 'STOLLWERCK' (LE 5000)	NRP	☐
C876	1986	'DICKINS & JONES'	Green/White body, Yellow design (LE 5000)	NRP	☐
C877	1986	'ROYAL MAIL'	Red/Black body, Gold design 'G.R.' (LE)	NRP	☐
C965	1986	'FORDS 75th ANNIVERSARY'	Blue body, White roof. Gold logo 'EXCO' (LE)	NGPP	☐
C966	1986	'FORDS 75th ANNIVERSARY'	Same as previous model with White/Gold logo (LE)	NGPP	☐
			N.B. Issued with numbered certificates	NGPP	☐
	1987	'TWININGS'	Late entry — Issued with certificates	NGPP	☐
	1987	'SWAN VESTAS'	Gift Set issue		
	1987	'THE TIMES'	Gift Set issue		
	1987	'KAY & CO'	Gift Set issue		

b TANKERS

C864	1986	'PRATTS MOTOR SPIRIT'	Green body, Yellow tank, Red logo (STRL)	NRP	☐
C864/1	1987	'STALEY SALES CORP'	Black body, Silver tank, Gold filler caps (STRL)	NRP	☐
C864/2	1987	'RIMER BROS LTD'	Green body, Black tank, Gold filler caps (STRL)	NRP	☐
C864/3	1987	'SAN FRANCISCO'	Red body & tank, Gold trim & logo 'FIRE DEPT' (STRL)	NRP	☐
C864/4	1987	'NATIONAL'	No details available (STRL)	NRP	☐
C872	1986	'DOMINION'	Two tone Blue body, Yellow/Blue design (LE)	NRP	☐
C880	1986	'B.P.'	Green body, Green/Yellow tank, Yellow design (LE)	NRP	☐
C864/6	1988	'OLYMPIC GASOLINE	Dark Green body, Yellow design, Kays MOM (LE)	NGPP	☐

4 MACK TRUCKS

Code	Year	Name	Description	
C906/1	1987	'MACK TRUCKS	Green body and roof rack, Cream roof (STRL)	NRP ☐
C906/2	1987	'SUNSHINE BISCUITS'	Blue/Black body, Yellow/Red design (STRL)	NRP ☐
C906/3	1987	'WHITE ROCK'	Yellow/Black body, Red roof, White design (STRL)	NRP ☐
C906/4	1987	'BUFFOLO FIRE DEPT'	Red body, Black roof rack, 'RESCUE' (STRL)	NRP ☐
C906/5	1987	'PEPSI COLA'	Blue/White body, Red roof 'REFRESHING' (STRL)	NRP ☐
C906/6	1988	'STANLEY TOOLS'	Yellow body, Red roof, Red/White design, RR (STRL)	NRP ☐
C906/7	1988	'PEERLESS LIGHT'	Cream body, Maroon bonnet & roof, Red/Blue design (STRL)	NRP ☐
C906/9	1988	'CARNATION'	Red/White body, White billboard & design	NRP ☐
C906/10	1988	'GULDENS MUSTARD'	Yellow bonnet/roof, Red billboards/chassis, White side (STRL)	NRP ☐
	1988	'BOVRIL'	Late entry — no details.	NGPP ☐

5 MORRIS 1000 VEHICLES

a VANS

Code	Year	Name	Description	
C957/1	1987	'ROYAL MAIL'	Red body, Gold design 'E II R' with crown (STRL). Metal or plastic base	NRP ☐
C957/2	1987	'GAS'	Green body, Red design (STRL)	NRP ☐
C957/3	1987/88	'CORGI COLLECTOR CLUB — 3rd ANNIVERSARY'	Yellow/Blue body (LE)	NGPP ☐
C957/4	1988	'CASTROL'	Green body, White side panel with Red logo (STRL)	NRP ☐
C958	1987	'POST OFFICE TELEPHONES'	Green body, Gold/Red crown, White logo (STRL) Metal or plastic base.	NRP ☐
C959	1987	'SMITHS CRISPS'	Dark Blue/White body, Red/Blue design (STRL)	NRP ☐
C959/6	1988	'FOYLES FOR BOOKS'	Red body, White blade/panel, 'Join the Book Club' (DTRL)	NRP ☐
		'MAC FISHERIES'	Late entry — no details.	NGPP ☐

N.B. The first C957 and C958 models to be issued had plastic baseplates. They were made in Portugal and this is clearly shown on the first type of box. These models are worth more than the later die-cast types at £12 NC.

b CARS

Code	Year	Name	Description	
C702/1	1988	'BRITISH SCHOOL OF MOTORING'	Black body, Red learner signs front and rear (STRL)	NRP ☐
C703/1	1988	'POLICE'	Blue/White body, Dark Blue 'Police' signs on roof and Beige side panels (STRL)	NRP ☐

6 1926 RENAULT

a BOX VANS

Code	Year	Name	Description	
C917	1986	'COURVOISIER'	Green body, Gold/Red design 'NAPOLEON' (STRL)	NRP ☐
C824/3	1988	'THE LIPTON'	Dark Blue body, Brown roof, Red/Blue/White design, EXPM (STRL)	NRP ☐
		'MARCEL-GARDET'	Late entry — no details.	NGPP ☐
		'ROYAL MAIL'	For details see under 7g.	

b CANVAS BACKED TRUCK

Code	Year	Name	Description	
C922	1986	'GALERIES LAFAYETTE'	White body, Green design (STRL)	NRP ☐
C925	1986	'GERVAIS DANONE'	Blue body, Yellow design (Export Special)	NGPP ☐

c OPEN BACKED TRUCKS

Code	Year	Name	Description	
C823/1	1985	'JULES COLARD'	Blue body, Gold/White design (STRL)	NRP ☐
C824/1	1988	'HERLOIN'	Grey/Blue body, Red/White striped side panel (EXPORT)	NRP ☐

7 1929 THORNEYCROFT VEHICLES

a BOX VANS

Code	Year	Name	Description		
C821	1985	'CASTROL MOTOR OILS'	Green body, Red/Gold design (STRL)		NRP ☐
C821/1	1988	'BUHRMANN'	Green body, Gold logo (Dutch Export)		NGPP ☐
C828	1985	'GAMLEYS TOYS'	Blue body, Red/Silver design (LE 2500)		NGPP ☐
C830	1985	'W & R JACOB'	Rust body, White roof, Gold design (LE 2500)		NGPP ☐
C831	1985	'HUNTLEY & PALMERS'	Blue body, Gold/White design (LE 2500)		NGPP ☐
C832	1985	'CORGI COLLECTOR CLUB — 1st ANNIVERSARY 1985'	Green body, 2000 to Club members, 500 to trade		NGPP ☐
C833	1985	'MACFARLANE LANG'	Green body, Gold/Green design (STRL)		NRP ☐
C834	1985	'LYONS SWISS ROLLS' (with certificates)	Dark Blue body, Gold design (Mail order LE 2500). NB: 27.2.88 Model sold for £35 at Lacey Scott auction	£30	GP ☐
C839		'NURDIN & PEACOCK'	Blue body, Silver/White design (LE 5000) (with certificates)	£20	NC ☐
C840	1985	'ALLENBURYS'	Red/White body, Red/White design (LE 2500)		NGPP ☐
C841	1985	'PEEK FREANS'	Green/Cream body, 'BISCUITS' logo (LE 2500)		NGPP ☐
C842	1985	'CARTER PATERSON'	Green/Red body, Red design 'EXPRESS' (LE 2500)		NGPP ☐
C843	1985	'EDDERSHAWS'	Brown body, Gold design, 'HOUSE' (LE 2500)		NGPP ☐
C845	1985	'DUCKHAMS OIL'	Silver body, Blue/Red design 'PERFECTION' (SS)		NGPP ☐
C846	1985	'IND COOPE'	Green body, Black/Gold design 'BREWERS' (LE 3500)		NGPP ☐
C847	1985	'KEILLERS'	Cream body, 'DUNDEE' logo (LE 2500)		NGPP ☐

C848	1985	'NEWS OF THE WORLD'	Black body, Silver/White design (LE 5000)		NRP ☐
C849	1987	'GOODYEAR'	Blue body, Brown cab, 'WINGFOOT EXPRESS', US EXPM (LE)	£30	NC ☐
C853	1985	'M. A. RAPPORT'	Maroon/Cream body, 'CARDIFF' logo (LE 2500)	NGPP	☐
C854	1985	'LINCOLNSHIRE AMBULANCE'	White body with Service badge (LE 5000)		NRP ☐
C855	1985	'LINCOLNSHIRE FIRE'	Red body with brigade badge (LE 5000)		NRP ☐
C856	1985	'LINCOLNSHIRE POLICE'	Black body with police badge (LE 5000)		NRP ☐
C907	1986	'HP SAUCE'	Red body, White roof, Gold design (LE2500)		NGPP ☐
C910	1986	'SMALL & PARKES'	Black body, White roof and design (LE 5000)		NRP ☐
C911	1986	'PERSIL'	Green/Red body, German lettering (Export model)		NGPP ☐
C913	1986	'DEWARS WHISKY'	Red/White body, Red roof and design (STRL)		NRP ☐
C914	1986	'LIPTONS TEA'	Dark Blue body, Gold/Red design (STRL)		NRP ☐
C915	1986	'OXO'	Red body, White design 'MEAT/DRINK' (STRL)		NRP ☐
C923	1986	'RED CROSS AMBULANCE'	Olive Green body, 4 Red crosses (STRL)		NRP ☐
C924	1986	'SAFEWAY'	Red/Black body, brass radiator (LE)		NRP ☐
C926	1986	'DOUBLE DIAMOND'	Black body, Gold design, 'BURTON ALES' (LE 5000)		NRP ☐
C931	1986	'STEPNEY TYRES'	Red body, Gold logo, bulldog design (LE)		NRP ☐
C932	1986	'PURITAN SOAP'	Yellow/Black body, lady design (LE)		NRP ☐
C933	1986	'BUY PUNCH'	Red/Black body, '3rd' design (LE)		NRP ☐
C968	1986	'RADIO STEINER'	Dark Blue body, 'BERN' logo (Swiss Export, 1500 UK) (SPB)	£35	GP ☐
	1986	'SAFETY FIRST'	Late entry — no details.		NGPP ☐

b BOX VANS WITH BILLBOARDS

C859	1986	'THORLEYS CATTLEFOOD'	Yellow/Red body (STRL)		NRP ☐
C859/1	1987	'SCOTTS EMPIRE BREAD'	Blue/Red body, Yellow design (STRL)		NRP ☐
C859/2	1987	'CHIVER'S JAMS'	Green/Cream body, Blue/Gold design (STRL)		NRP ☐
C859/3	1987	'ARNOTTS BISCUITS'	Red body, Yellow design, Australian Export model (LE) 7500 (5000 with certificates)		NGPP ☐
C859/4	1987	'GOODYEAR'	'GOODYEAR' model but has no billboards so see 849		
C859/5	1987	'GRATTANS 75th'	Green body. Mail Order Gift Set (LE) (5000)		NGPP ☐
C859/6	1987	'KAYS'	As part of C68 Mail Order Gift Set (LE)		NGPP ☐
C859/8	1988	'VOLVULUTUM'	Two tone Green body, Brown bonnet, Yellow logo (STRL)		NRP ☐
C860/1/2/3			Details given in the 'CLASSIC CARS' section		
C929	1986	'GAMLEYS'	Green/Black body, Red design (LE)	£15	NC ☐
C933	1986	'BUY PUNCH'	Red/Black body, '3rd' design (LE)		NGPP ☐

c BEER TRUCKS WITH BARREL LOAD

C867	1986	'THOMAS WETHERED'	Green/Red body, 'THE BREWERY MARLOW' (STRL)		NRP ☐
C867/1	1987	'CHARLES WELLS'	Brown/Cream body, Red/Gold design. 'BEDFORD' (STRL)		NRP ☐
C867/2	1987	'TOOHEYS PILSENER'	Red/White body, 'BREWERY SYDNEY' (STRL)		NRP ☐
		Colour change	Blue/White body, same logo (STRL)		NRP ☐
C867/3	1987	'SWAN LAGER'	Black/Red body (STRL)		MPR ☐
C882	1986	'ST WINEFRED'S'	Red body, Mail order model (LE)	£7-£9	
CV883/ C928	1988	'TAUNTON CIDER'	Green body, Red/Yellow design (LE)	£7-£9	MPR ☐
	1988	'HEIDELBERGER'	Green body, Dutch Export model (LE)		NGPP ☐
	1988	'CARLSBERG'	Late entry — no details.		NGPP ☐

d CANVAS BACKED TRUCKS

C827	1985	'G.W.R.'	Brown body, Cream canvas, 'EXPRESS CARTERS' (LE 5000)	£15	NC ☐
C836	1985	'L.M.S.'	Maroon body, Cream canvas 'EXPRESS PARCELS' (LE 2500)	£20	GP ☐
C837	1985	'SOUTHERN RAILWAY'	Olive Green body, Cream canvas 'EXPRESS BARCELS' (LE2500)	£20	GP ☐
C838	1985	'L.N.W.R.'	Blue body, Cream canvas 'EXPRESS PARCELS' (LE 2500)	£20	GP ☐
			N.B. C827, C836/7/8 issued with numbered certificates.		
		'FIELD AMBULANCE'	Late entry — no details.		NGPP ☐

e DOUBLE DECKER BUS

1st type with four supporting top rail struts
2nd type with eight supporting top rail struts

C858	1986	'SANDEMANS'	Red body, Black/Green design 'GENERAL' (STRL) (1st type)		NGPP ☐
			2nd type		NRP ☐
C858/1	1987	'NATIONAL MOTOR MUSEUM'	Red body and design, 'BEAULIEU' (STRL) (2nd Type)		NRP ☐
C858/2	1987	'CHARLIE CHAPLIN'	Yellow/Red body, 'DOUGLAS TRAMWAYS' (STRL) (2nd Type)		NRP ☐
C858/3	1987	'PALM TOFFEE'	Green body, Yellow/Brown design, (2nd Type)		NRP ☐

C858/4	1987	'IDRIS SODA WATER'	Black/Yellow body, 'VANGUARD'		NRP ☐
C858/5	1987	'THE TIMES'	Red body, Gold design		NRP ☐
C858/6	1987	'L. & N.W.R.'	Dark Green body, Brown bonnet, Yellow/White design (STRL)		NRP ☐
C858/7	1988	'OAKEY'S KNIFE POLISH'	Red/White body, Blue/Yellow design (STRL)		NRP ☐
	1988	'SCHWEPPES'	Red body, Yellow side panel. Only available as a 'BP' promotional model or to Corgi Club members	£20	NC ☐
C884	1986	'BEER IS BEST'	Red body, White panel, 'GENERAL' (LE) (1st Type)		NRP ☐
C885	1986	'THOMAS TILLING'	Yellow body and logo on Black panel (LE) (1st Type)		NRP ☐
			2nd type		NGPP ☐
C888	1986	'GRANTS MORELLO CHERRY BRANDY'	Red body. Mail order only (LE) (1st type)		NGPP ☐
C975	1986	'ALLENBURYS PASTILLES'	Orange body, Rust bonnet (LE)		NRP ☐
	1988	Military Issue	Dark Green body, '2nd DIVISION' & '66', Kays MOM Set		NGPP ☐
	1988	'BAXTERS THE BUTCHERS'	Red/White body, Blue/Yellow design, Kays MOM Set		NGPP ☐

f OPEN BACKED TRUCKS

C820/1	1985	'EAST ANGLIAN FRUIT COMPANY'	Brown body, Black bonnet (STRL)		NRP ☐

g THORNEYCROFT BODY AND RENAULT BONNET

C902	1985	'ROYAL MAIL'	Red/Blue/Gold body 'G.R.'. (LE 2500) with certificates	£35	NC ☐

8 TRAMLINES

a SINGLE DECKER TRAMS

C990/1	1988	'SOUTHAMPTON CORPORATION'	Red/White body (STRL)		NRP ☐
C990/2	1988	'SHEFFIELD CORPORATION'	Dark Blue/White body (STRL)		NRP ☐

b DOUBLE DECKER TRAMS

OPEN TOP TRAMS

C991/1	1988	'L.C.C.'	Red/White/Black body (STRL)		NRP ☐
C991/2	1988	'BLACKPOOL CORPORATION'	Green/White body, Yellow/Blue design (STRL)		NRP ☐

CLOSED TOP TRAMS

C992/1	1988	'LEEDS CITY TRANSPORT'	Red/White body, Black/White design 'MATHERS BLACK BEER' (STRL)		NRP ☐
C992/2	1988	'GLASGOW CORPORATION'	Yellow/White body, Black logo (STRL)		NRP ☐
C992/4		'L.C.C.'	Red/White/Black body (LE). GUS MOM		NGPP ☐

9 GIFT SETS

C49	1986	Transport of the 30s Set	'TIMES' Set Contains 'TIMES' Thorneycroft Bus plus 'TIMES' Model 'T' Van (STRL)	£16-£19	MPR ☐
C50	1987	Transport of the 30s Set	'LONDON MARKETS' Contains 3 Model 'T' Ford Vans, 'SMITHFIELD', 'COVENT GARDEN' and 'BILLINGSGATE' (STRL)	£16-£19	MPR ☐
C68	1987	Transport of the 30s Set	'KAYS' (MAIL ORDER) Contains Thorneycroft Box Van and Model 'T' Ford (LE)	£30	NC ☐
C69	1987	Transport of the 30s Set	'BRYANT & MAYS' MAIL ORDER Contains Thorneycroft Box Van and Model 'T' Ford (LE)	£30	NC ☐
C88	1988	Military Gift Set	Contains Dark Green Thorneycroft Bus '2nd DIVISION', plus Model 'T' Ford Van with Red cross and 'ORDER OF ST JOHN' design. Kays MOM	£35	NRP ☐
C89	1988	60 Years of Transport	Contains Red/White Thorneycroft Bus 'BAXTERS', plus Brown/Cream 'OB' Series Coach 'HIGHLAND' and Green/White Tram 'FORD FOR VALUE', Kays MOM	£70	NRP ☐
C90	1988	Model 'T' Ford Utility Set	Contains Brown/White 'ROYAL LAUNDRY' plus White/Black 'SUNLIGHT', Kays MOM	£30	NRP ☐

Buses, Minibuses and Coaches

1. **ROUTEMASTER DOUBLE DECKER BUSES**
   a) Identification
   b) General issue and limited issue models sold through normal outlets
   c) Difficult to catalogue Routemasters
   d) Customer exclusive models
   e) Electronic issues
   N.B.: Only models thought to have been 100% produced by Corgi have been included in the listings.

2. **A.E.C. REGENT DOUBLE DECKER BUSES (CORGI CLASSICS)**

3. **METROBUS MK 2 DOUBLE DECKER BUSES**

4. **PLAXTON PARAMOUNT COACHES**

5. **CORGI COACHES — MISCELLANEOUS**

N.B. For Thorneycroft Double Decker Buses see CORGI CLASSICS

1. **ROUTEMASTER DOUBLE DECKER BUSES**

1a. Identification

1ST CASTING 1864-1975 — MODEL No. 468 ONLY — CLOSED TOP MODEL

Length 114 mm, die-cast body comprised of two separate castings which make up the lower and upper decks. The castings are separated by a white plastic joint. The baseplate is die-cast and painted grey and stamped 'CORGI TOYS', 'LONDON TRANSPORT', 'ROUTEMASTER', 'MADE IN ENGLAND' plus the Patent No. 904525. The early issues had uncast smooth metal wheels with rubber tyres. These lasted until 1973 when cast metal wheels were introduced with plastic tyres and in 1974/75 Whizzwheels were seen. The early issues had jewelled headlights which were replaced in 1973 by the cast-in type painted silver. The decals were of the transfer printed variety and there is a board at the front only. The model has spring suspension, windows, a metal platform handrail and a driver and clippie. The interior seats are white or cream.

2ND CASTING – 1975 ONWARDS — CLOSED TOP AND OPEN TOP MODELS

MODEL Nos:— C460, C463, C464, C467, C469, C470, C471, C473, C475, C476, C477, C479, C480, 1004 and all the numbers allocated to the 'Specials'.
Length 123 mm, die-cast body comprised of two separate castings which make up the lower and upper decks. The castings are separated by a cream plastic joint for normal issues and very often by a coloured joint for 'Specials'. Until Model No. 480 was issued as an AEC Renown in 1983 the plastic baseplates were stamped 'CORGI', 'LONDON TRANSPORT', 'ROUTEMASTER' and 'MADE IN ENGLAND'. However 'LONDON TRANSPORT' and 'ROUTEMASTER' were removed from this time onwards. The logos were firstly stick-on labels and followed by tampo printing in the mid-eighties. The seats were normally white or cream but other colours are used for the 'Specials' e.g. red in the 'BRITISH DIE-CAST MODEL TOYS CATALOGUE' Special. The model has silver painted cast-in headlights, spring suspension, windows, a metal platform handrail but apart from the very early issues does not have a driver or clippie. The wheels are of the whizzwheel type. The early issues were of a close fitting type e.g. 'BTA', 'SWAN & EDGAR', 'DISNEYLAND'. However by the time the model was issued they had become protruding. The wheel hubs are either chrome (earlier models) or painted and the tyres are plastic.

1st CASTING 114 mm 1964-1975

468	1964-66	'NATURALLY CORGI TOYS'	Red body, Route 'LONDON BRIDGE', fleet name 'LONDON TRANSPORT', 'CORGI CLASSICS' side decal	£45	NC	☐
468	1964	'NATURALLY CORGI TOYS'	Green, Cream and Brown body, fleetname 'NEW SOUTH WALES', 'CORGI CLASSICS' decal. Australian issue	£250	NPE	☐
468	1967-75	'OUTSPAN ORANGES'	Red body, Route '10', fleetname 'LONDON TRANSPORT'. Uncast, cast or whizzwheels	£30	NC	☐
468	1968	'GAMAGES'	Red body, Route '10', fleetname 'LONDON TRANSPORT'	£75	GP	☐
468	1969	'CHURCH'S SHOES'	Red body, Route '10', fleetname 'LONDON TRANSPORT'. Union Jack flag decals on sides	£75	GP	☐
468	1970	'VISIT MADAME TUSSAUDS'	Red body, Route '10', fleetname 'LONDON TRANSPORT'	£60	GP	☐
468	1975	'VISIT THE DESIGN CENTRE'	Red BODY, Route '10', fleetname 'LONDON TRANSPORT'	£50	GP	☐

2nd CASTING 123 mm 1975 onwards — Listed in Numerical Order

C460	1984	'BOLTON EVENING NEWS'	Maroon body, Route '197 LEE LANE', 5000 issued. 'YOUR COMPLETE EVENING', 'BOLTON TRANSPORT' Fleet	£6-£9	MPR	☐
C463	1984	'BRITISH MEAT'S GOT THE LOT'	Red/White body, Route '279', 'LT' Fleet, Cream interior, 2500 issued	£6-£9	MPR	☐
C464	1984	'THE BRITISH MOTOR SHOW'	Blue/Red body, Route 'NEC', Cream seats, 'JOHN MENZIES' Fleetname, 5000 issued	£6-£9	MPR	☐
C467	1977	'SELFRIDGES'	Red body, Route '12', fleetname 'LONDON TRANSPORT'	£18	NC	☐
C469	1975-76	'BTA WELCOME TO BRITAIN'	Red body, Route '11', fleetname 'LONDON TRANSPORT', plus driver and clippie	£18	NC	☐
C469	1976	'VISIT THE DESIGN CENTRE'	Red body, Route '11', fleetname 'LONDON TRANSPORT', plus driver and clippie. Black or red lettering	£200	GP	☐
C469	1977	'CADBURYS' DOUBLE DECKER	All Orange body. Direct offer pack cased PRO	£10	NC	☐
C469	1979	'SELFRIDGES'	Red body, Route '12', fleetname 'LONDON TRANSPORT'	£15	NC	☐
C469	1979	'LEEDS PERM' BUILDING SOCIETY	Dark Green and Yellow body, Route '22'. 'GEORGE SHILLIBEER 1829 — LONDON TRANSPORT 1979'	£16	NC	☐
C469	1979	'SWAN & EDGAR'	Red body, Route '11', fleetname 'LONDON TRANSPORT'	£50	GP	☐
C469	1979	'HAMLEYS'	Red body, Route '11', fleetname 'LONDON TRANSPORT'. Manufacturing problems so few issued.	£20	NC	☐
C469	1978-80	'BTA'	Red body, Routes '11' '7' '12', fleetname 'LT'	£12	NC	☐
C469	1982	'BLACKPOOL ILLUMINATIONS'	All Cream body with Green labels, Route '21', 'BLACKPOOL TRANSPORT'	£35	NC	☐
C469	1983	'GAMLEYS'	Red body, 'TOYSHOP OF THE SOUTH', White seats	£9-£13	MPR	☐
C469	1983	'EAGLE STAR'	White/Black body, Route '1 THREADNEEDLE STREET'	£6-£9	MRP	☐
C469	1983	'REDGATES'	Cream and Brown body, Route '25', Red interior	£45	NC	☐
C469	1983	'LONDON TRANSPORT GOLDEN JUBILEE'	Red, White and Silver body, Route '21', Black seats, interior, '1933-1983' decal. 1000 issued	£45	NC	☐
C469	1983	'DIECAST AND TINPLATE'	Black body, Route 'JOHN GAY UPCHURCH' (500)	£10	NC	☐
C469	1983	'BLACKPOOL PLEASURE BEACH'	Cream body, Green roof, Blue labels 'BRITAIN'S No 1 TOURIST ATTRACTION', 'BLACKPOOL TRANSPORT 23'.	£45	NC	☐
C469	1983	'BLACKPOOL PLEASURE BEACH'	Open Top version	£45	NC	☐
C469	1983	'NORBROOK MOTORS'	Dark Blue body, Route '57', White interior	£20	NC	☐
C469	1983		Red body version	£30	NC	☐
C469	1983	'JOLLY GIANT'	Yellow/Green body, Route '459', White interior	£10	NC	☐
C469	1983		Red version	£15	NC	☐
C469	1983	'GLOUCESTER TRAIN AND TOY SALE'	Black body, Yellow labels/Red lettering, Route '25'	£10	NC	☐
C469	1983	'ARMY AND NAVY'	Red body, Route '24', 'LONDON TRANSPORT' fleetname	£4-£6	MPR	☐
C469	1983	'MANCHESTER UNITED'	Open Top version with Red body. Route '83'	£4-£6	MPR	☐
C469	1983	'LLANDRINDROD FESTIVAL'	Green and White body, Blue labels. Route '14'	£10-£14	NC	☐
C469	1983	'DION DION DION'	Dark Blue body, Orange lettering 'SAVES YOU MORE'. South African export model	£15	NC	☐
C469			'SAVES YOU MONEY' incorrect label version	£20	NC	☐
C469	1983	'TROWBRIDGE TOYS AND MODELS'	Two tone Blue body, Route '5'	£7-£11	MPR	☐
C469	1983	'THORNTONS'	Brown/Cream body, Route '14'	£5-£7	MPR	☐
C469	1983	'MANCHESTER LIONS CLUB'	Cream body, Route '105BN MANCHESTER', Red seats, Cream labels with purple lettering	£25	NC	☐
C469	1983	'MANCHESTER EVENING NEWS'	Open Top bus, Yellow body, Route '164'	£5-£7	MPR	☐
C469	1983	'ROUND LONDON'	Open Top bus, Red or Orange body	£5-£7	MPR	☐
C469	1983	'BTA WELCOME'	Open Top bus, Red body, Route '14'	£5-£7	MPR	☐
C469	1983	'BRITISH TOY'	Red body, Route '14', White seats	£5-£7	MPR	☐
C469	1984	'JOHN WEBB'	Red/Green body, Route 'JOHN WEBB'	£10	NC	☐
C469	1984	'TWININGS'	Blue/Black body, Route '11'	£4-£6	MPR	☐
C469	1984	'STRETTON SPRING WATER'	White/Yellow body, Route '2'	£4-£6	MPR	☐
C469	1984	'READING EXPRESS'	Maroon body, 'GOLDLINE', Route '11' (700)	£10	NC	☐
C469	1984	'LIVERPOOL GARDEN FESTIVAL'	Green body, route '46 PENNY LANE', 'MERSEYSIDE TRANSPORT' fleet, 5000 issued	£4-£6	MPR	☐
C469	1984	'HAMLEYS'	Red body, Route '6', 'LT' fleet, White seats	£4-£6	MPR	☐
C469	1984	'THE NEW CORGI COMPANY'	Red body, Route '29th MARCH 1984', White seats, 'SOUTH WALES /DE CYMRU' fleetname, 2000 issued	£25	MPR	☐
C469	1984	'GEMINI DIECAST'	Red body, Green roof, Route '24', 'LONDON COUNTRY' fleetname, 1000 issued	£6-£9	MPR	☐
C469	1984	'BTA'	Red body, Route '24'. 'LT' fleet, White seats	£4-£6	MPR	☐
C469	1984	'MIDLAND BUS MUSEUM'	Blue/Cream body, Route '750 WYTHALL', 1000 issued, 'BaMMOT' fleetname, 'BIRMINGHAM'S MUSEUM OF TPT'	£5-£9	MPR	☐
C469	1985	'GREAT WESTERN RAILWAY'	Brown/Cream body, Route '150 PADDINGTON', White seats, 'GREAT WESTERN' fleet, 1000	£7-£11	MPR	☐
C469	1985	'ESSEX ORGAN STUDIOS'	Blue body, Route '18 FOULNESS', White seats, 'SOUTHEND TRANSPORT' fleetname, 500	£13	NC	☐
C469	1985	'FAREWELL TO ROE'	Red body, Route '24', 'WEST RIDING' fleetname	£5-£7	MPR	☐
C469	1985	'HAMLEYS'	Red body, Route '6', new 'five man' logo, 'LT'	£5-£7	MPR	☐
C469	1985	'HAMLEYS'	Open Top bus, Cream/Green body, Route 'BATH', 'FINEST TOYSHOP IN THE WORLD' decal	£5-£7	MPR	☐
C469	1985	'UNDERWOODS'	Red body, Route '19 PICCADILLY', White seats	£4-£6	MPR	☐
C469	1985	'JUST A SECOND'	Green body, Route '1 NEWPORT', 'SOUTHERN VECTIS' (1500)	£4-£6	MPR	☐

Routemaster Bus 2nd Casting cont.

C469	1985	'COWES STAMP & MODEL SHOP'	Green body, Route '1A COWES', 'SOUTHERN VECTIS' fleetname, White seats, 500 issued	£15	NC	☐
C469	1985	'OLD SMUGGLER'	Brown/White/Maroon body, Route 'FINEST SCOTCH', 'WHISKY' fleetname, White seats, 1000	£10	NC	☐
C469	1985	'B.T.A.'	Open Top Bus. Route '24' (10000)	£4-£6	MPR	☐
C469	1985	'HARLANDS LABELS'	Red body, Route 'LAND OF GREEN GINGER'	£4-£6	MPR	☐
C469	1985	'FARNHAM MALTINGS'	Red body, Route '268', 'ALDER VALLEY' (500)	£20	NC	☐
C469	1986	'LONDON STANDARD'	Red body, 'GREAT NEWSPAPER' STRL		NRP	☐
C469	1988	'LONDON STANDARD'	Same as 1986 issue with 'eyebrows' on DBD		NRP	☐
C470	1977	'DISNEYLAND'	Yellow Open Top with cartoon characters	£16	NC	☐
C471	1977	'SEE MORE LONDON'	All Silver body, Route '25', 'THE QUEENS SILVER JUBILEE LONDON CELEBRATIONS 1977' lower body decal	£16	NC	☐
C471	1977	'WOOLWORTHS'	All Silver body, Route '25', 'WOOLWORTH WELCOME THE WORLD' and 'QUEENS SILVER JUBILEE', 1977 decals	£20	NC	☐
C473	1985	'GAMLEYS'	Red body, Route '16', 'LONDON TRANSPORT' fleet (2500)	£4-£6	MPR	☐
C475	1983	'TAKE OFF FROM BRISTOL'	Blue body, Route 'BRISTOL', White interior	£4-£6	MPR	☐
C476	1983	'BRITISH TELECOM'	Yellow body, Routes '14' or '406'	£4-£6	MPR	☐
C477	1983	'THE BUZBY BUS'	Pale to Dark Blue shades on body, Blue seats	£4-£6	MPR	☐
C478	1983	'SUNDECKER'	Open Top bus, White/Orange body, Route 'MARRAKESH'	£4-£6	MPR	☐
C479	1983	'LONDON CRUSADER'	Green and White body, Routes '14' or '406'	£4-£6	MPR	☐
C480	1983	'WHITE LABEL WHISKY'	Blue body with Yellow and White bands, White seats. The AEC Renown model without 'ROUTEMASTER' on base	£4-£6	MPR	☐
C481	1984	'BEA'	Blue and White body, Black band, Route 'BEA'	£4-£6	MPR	☐
C482	1984	'SCHILLIBEER OMNIBUS'	Specifications as for the earlier 469 (1979) issue, but with the 'ADDIS' decal replacing the 'LEEDS'	£5-£7	MPR	☐
C483	1984	'HMV SHOP'	Red and Yellow body, Route 'FARE 30p KNIGHTSBRIDGE'	£4-£6	MPR	☐
C485	1984	'ISLE OF WIGHT COUNTY PRESS'	Light Blue body, Dark Blue labels with Yellow letters. Route '1 NEWPORT', decals 'CENTENARY 1988-1984' plus couple reading a newspaper and as emblem (1500)	£7-£10	MPR	☐
	Design change		Couple replaced by 'SOUTHERN VECTIS' (1000)	£9-£13	MPR	☐
C485	1984	'ML ELECTRICS'	Light Blue body, 'SOUTHERN VECTIS' (1500)	£4-£6	MPR	☐
C486	1984	'THE CULTURE BUS'	Yellow body, Route 'CULTURE BUS', fleetname	£4-£6	MPR	☐
			Open Top version, 500 issued	£15	NC	☐
C488	1984	'THE NEW CORGI COMPANY'	Green body, Route '29 MARCH 1984', fleetname 'SOUTH WALES/DE CYMRU', white seats (7800)	£4-£6	MPR	☐
C488	1984	'BEATTIES'	Red body, Routes '24' & '25', White seats	£4-£6	MPR	☐
C492	1984	'GLOBAL SALES'	Yellow body, 'H A RAPPORT & Co Ltd' (2500)	£4-£6	MPR	☐
C521	1984	'HAIG WHISKY'	Yellow body, Route '16' (3000)	£4-£6	MPR	☐
C523	1984	'BRITISH DIE-CAST MODEL TOYS CATALOGUE'	Red body, White roof, Red seats, Black labels. Route 'No 1 EDITION 1934-1984 1ST FIFTY YEARS'. Fleetname 'SWAPMEET TOYS & MODELS LTD'. Numbered certificate with each model. Decals read 'YOU CAN'T AFFORD TO BE WITHOUT A BRITISH DIE-CAST MODEL TOYS CATALOGUE'			
			All White letters on side labels. 800 issued	£10	NC	☐
			Gold and White letters on side labels. 300 issued	£20	GP	☐
C524	1984	'STEVENSONS'	Yellow, Black and White body. 2500 issued	£5-£10	MPR	☐
C527	1984	'TIMBERCRAFT CABINETS'	Green, Orange and Black body. 1000 issued	£20	NC	☐
C529	1984	'1985 CALENDAR BUS'	Black and Orange body, Route 'G WARD', (2000)	£4-£6	MPR	☐
C530	1984	'YORKSHIRE POST'	Two tone Green body, Route '41', (4000)	£4-£6	MPR	☐
C558	1985	'RADIO VICTORY'	Open Top Bus with Red, White and Blue body (2500)	£4-£6	MPR	☐
C566	1985	'GELCO EXPRESS'	Blue and White body with Blue and Green decor	£8-£12	MPR	☐
C567	1985	'LINCOLN CITY'	White and Green body with Black decor (2500)	£4-£6	MPR	☐
C567	1985	'SEE MORE LONDON'	White body, tourist ADS	£4-£6	MPR	☐
C570	1985	'BUS COLLECTORS SOCIETY'	Blue and Navy body with Red and Black decor. Open Top Bus, Route '96 LUTON', 2500	£5-£7	MPR	☐
C571	1985	'THE TIMES'	Maroon body (2500)	£4-£6	MPR	☐
C572	1985	'THE TIMES'	Blue body with thin labels	£12	NC	☐
			Blue body with wide labels	£4-£6	MPR	☐
C574	1985	'BLACKPOOL CENTENARY'	Red and White body, 2500, 'TRAMWAY CENTENARY'	£4-£6	MPR	☐
C580	1985	'GUIDE DOGS'	All Blue body, Route '2', 'BARCLAYS'	£5-£10	MPR	☐
C583	1985	'MANCHESTER EVENING NEWS'	Yellow and Black body. Route '4' (2500)	£4-£6	MPR	☐
C589	1985	'AUTOSPARES'	Red body (2500)	£4-£6	MPR	☐
C590	1985	'MEDIC ALERT SAVES LIVES'	Open Top Bus, Mauve and Yellow body, 'SPONSORED BY LIONS CLUBS', Lions emblem for fleetname	£4-£6	MPR	☐
C591	1985	'MEDIC ALERT'	Closed Top version of C590	£4-£6	MPR	☐
	1985	'ROLAND FRIDAY KEYBOARDS'	Red body (no details)		NGPP	☐
C596	1986	'HARRODS'	Red body, Route '30', MARBLE ARCH	£4-£6	MPR	☐
C627	1986	'MODEL MOTORING'	Brown/White body, 'EDINBURGH CORPORATION', 'MODELS — 87 BROUGHTON ST, EDINBURGH' logo (LE)	£6-£9	MPR	☐
C628	1986	'POLCO PLUS'	Red body, 'ROTARY INTERNATIONAL' (LE)	£4-£6	MPR	☐
C633	1986	'HOSPITAL RADIO'	Blue body, Route 'BLACKPOOL 86' EXPM (LE)	£10	NC	☐
C638	1986	'WEETABIX'	All Yellow body, Blue logo (LE)	£4-£6	MPR	☐

1c Routemasters Difficult to Catalogue

Shortly before and after Mettoy ceased trading during the period 1982/3/4 the following models were all given a 469 number and were issued in rapid succession in many different colour variations. The models were issued in normally a closed top version but some will also be found as open tops as well. These were issued (the Open Tops) in either an orange or yellow livery with often a 'BOURNEMOUTH' fleetname. The Route numbers seen were usually 14 or 24. Corgi have referred to this period as the 'oddball patch'.

THE MODELS:— 'OLD HOLBORN', 'OXO', 'AERO', 'TDK', 'LION BAR', 'BARRATT', 'WORLD AIRWAYS', 'PENTEL', 'BUY BEFORE YOU FLY — DUTY FREE'.

THE COLOURS SEEN:— BROWN AND CREAM, BLUE AND CREAM, GREEN, BLUE, GREEN AND YELLOW, BLACK, CREAM, WHITE.

Fleetnames were not used on the majority of these issues with the following exceptions:—

      'TAYSIDE' — 'BARRATT', 'OXO', 'AERO'
      'TRANSCLYDE' — 'WORLD AIRWAYS', 'BUY BEFORE YOU FLY'
      'SOUTH YORKS' — 'TDK', 'WORLD AIRWAYS'
      'LONDON TRANSPORT' — 'LION BAR', 'OXO', 'AERO'

Model No 470 was issued bearing the 'LONDON COUNTRY' fleetname in respect of the following issues:— 'BARRATT', 'PENTEL', 'BUY BEFORE YOU FLY', 'TDK' and no doubt others. It is known that at the time of Mettoy going into receivership batches of labels were sold off to the trade which no doubt accounts for many of the different variations to be found. Therefore with this background it's not possible to provide meaningful price and rarity guidance.

1d Customer Exclusive Models

C468	1965	'RED ROSE COFFEE'	Brown body, 1st casting. Australian promotion. Doubtful if even issued	NGPP	☐
C469	1977	'METTOY SALES CONFERENCE'	Red body	NGPP	☐
C469	1977	'M.G.M.W. DINNER'	Red body	NGPP	☐
C469	1977	'QUALITOYS VISIT'	Red body	NGPP	☐
C469	1977	'VEDES VISIT TO SWANSEA'	Red body	NGPP	☐
C469	1977	'MARKS & SPENCER VISIT SWANSEA'	Red body	NGPP	☐
C469	1977	'HAROLD LYCHES VISIT'	Red body	NGPP	☐
C469	1977	'METTOY WELCOMES SWISS BUYERS TO SWANSEA'	Red body	NGPP	☐
C469	1978	'FINNISH VISIT TO SWANSEA'	Red body	NGPP	☐
C469	1978	'M.G.M.W. DINNER'	Red body	NGPP	☐
C469	1983	'OCTOPUSSY'	Red body	NGPP	☐
C469	1983	'MARRIOT HOTELS'	Red body, 'GROSVENOR HOUSE'	NGPP	☐
C469	1984	'CHARLIE'S ANGELS	Red body, 200 issued to TV-AM (Open Top model)	NGPP	☐
C469	1984	'CORGI COLLECTORS VISIT'	Red body, Route 'SWANSEA JUNE 1984', fleetname 'SOUTH WALES/DE CYMRU. 12 issued. See Catalogue photo.	NGPP	☐

N.B.: JOHN RAMSAY the Catalogue compiler was an invited guest at this first ever two-day collectors' meeting with the Company Management. At the end of the visit those attending received the special issue model to mark the occasion.

C469	1984	'REDDITCH'	Red body, Route '14', fleetname 'MIDLAND RED', 'SUCCESS IN THE HEART OF ENGLAND' decal	NGPP	☐
C469	1984	'SKYRIDER BUS COLLECTORS SOCIETY'	White body with Red and Blue decor, Route '72', fleetname 'SOUTH WALES'	NGPP	☐
C469	1985	'WHATMAN PAPER'	Red body, fleetname 'LONDON TRANSPORT'. Initial order for 240 models for special promotion	NGPP	☐
C469	1985	'COLT 45 SALES CONFERENCE'	Red or Two tone Blue body. Route '45', fleetname 'LONDON TRANSPORT'	NGPP	☐
C469	1985	'INTERNATIONAL DISTRIBUTORS' MEETING SKYRIDER'	No details	NGPP	☐
C461	1986	'MANNHEIM VISIT 1986'	Red, Yellow panel, Blue logo	NGPP	☐

N.B.: There is little real opportunity of collectors obtaining these models as very few were issued — usually 50 or less.

1e Electronic Issues

1004	1981	'CORGITRONICS FIRST IN ELECTRONIC DIE-CAST'	Red body, Route '11', White seats. Fleetname 'LONDON TRANSPORT'	£12	NC ☐

Other issues will be found combining the 'BTA', 'HAMLEYS', 'OXO', etc labels with the above main 'CORGITRONICS' logo. Route Nos '11', '6' or '14'. Details are given in the 'NOVELTY' toys chapter.

Buses, Minibuses, Coaches cont.

2. A.E.C. Regent Double Decker Bus (Classic Series)

Models issued from 1986 onwards. Compared to the Routemaster the model has a changed lower deck plus an A.E.C. radiator design whilst retaining the Routemaster upper deck. Labels will be found on the early issues with Tampo print designs being used in part from 599/2.

C593	1988	'GLASGOW CORPORATION'	Brown/Green body with Red mudguards. 'CROWN WALLPAPERS'		NRP ☐
C599	1987	'TRUSTEE SAVINGS BANK	Dark Blue and Cream body. 'NOTTINGHAM CITY'		NRP ☐
C599/1	1986	'WISK'	Red body, Yellow side panels. 'LONDON TRANSPORT'		NRP ☐
C599/2	1987	'WOODHAM SCOOTERS'	Dark Blue and Cream body. 'EASTBOURNE'		NRP ☐
C599/3	1987	'HUNTLEY & PALMERS'	Brown body, White windows, 'LEICESTER CITY'		NRP ☐
	Various		SAPM without White windows	£20	NC ☐
C634	1986	'MAPLES'	Red body and new bolt head type wheels. 'LONDON TRANSPORT'		NRP ☐
C643	1986	'NEWCASTLE ALE'	Yellow/White body. 'NEWCASTLE TRANSPORT'		NRP ☐
		'PREMIUM BONDS'	Late entry — 'RHONDA'.		NRP ☐

3. Metrobus Mk 2 Double Decker Bus

C675/1	1988	'WEST MIDLANDS TIMESAVER'	Silver body, Purple logo, 'HASBURY'		NRP ☐
C675/2	1988	'READING TRANSPORT GOLDLINE'	Dark Brown and White body, Gold logo		NRP ☐
C675/3	1988	'WEST MIDLANDS TRAVEL'	Purple/Cream body, Yellow on White design		NRP ☐

4. Plaxton Paramount Coaches

C769	1985	'NATIONAL EXPRESS'	Red, White, Black and Blue body, clear windows, 4 wheels with chrome hubs, 'RAPIDE' decal. (STRL)		NRP ☐
C770	1985	'HOLIDAY TOURS'	Red, White and Yellow body, clear windows. (STRL)		NRP ☐
C771	1985	'AIR FRANCE'	Red, Blue, White body, clear windows. (STRL)		NRP ☐
	1985	'SAS'	White MB, Blue SLW, Black logo		NRP ☐
C773	1985	'GREEN LINE'	White and Green body, clear windows. LE		NRP ☐
C774	1985	'RAILAIR LINK'	White body with Yellow/Black decor		
		'ALDER VALLEY'	'READING — HEATHROW' decal, DBD (10000)		NRP ☐
C775	1985	'CITY LINK'	White with Blue/Yellow decor, 'OXFORD' (2500)		NRP ☐
C776	1985	'SKILLS SCENICRUISERS'	Blue/Orange with Yellow decor (2500)		NRP ☐
C777	1985	'TAYLORS TRAVEL'	White body, with Yellow, Red and Black decor (2500)		NRP ☐
C791	1985	SWISS 'PTT'	Yellow, White, Red and Black body (EXPM)	£6-£9	MPR ☐
C792		'GATWICK FLIGHTLINE'	Pale green, Dark Green and (STRL)		NRP ☐
C1223	1986	'PHILIPS'	All Blue body, White logo (EXPM) (LE)		NRP ☐
C769	1987	'CLUB CANTABRICA	Dark Blue body, Red flash and logo, CHT		NRP ☐
C769/4	1987	'S.A.S.'	White body, Black logo, 'FLYBUSSEN' (EXPM)		NRP ☐
C769/5	1988	'GLOBAL'	White body, Red/Purple/Yellow design		NRP ☐

10. Ford Transit Minibus

C676/1	1988	'SCOTTISH MIDLAND BLUEBIRD'	Purple/White body and logo		NRP ☐
C676/2	1988	'SOUTH WALES TRANSPORT'	Two tone Green body, Red logo		NRP ☐
C676/3	1988	'BADGERLINE'	White body with Green/Yellow stripe design		NRP ☐

5. Corgi Coaches

1120	1961-62	'MIDLAND RED COACH'	Red body and Black roof, uncast smooth metal wheels, Yellow interior, 'BIRMINGHAM — LONDON MOTORWAY EXPRESS' decal in Gold with Silver trim (STRL)	£55	GP ☐
C1168	1983	'GREYHOUND'	Red, White and Blue body, tinted windows (STRL). 'GREYHOUND' and 'AMERICRUISER' decals, 6 wheels	£9-£13	MPR ☐
C1168	1983	'MOTORWAY EXPRESS'	White body, Brown/Yellow/Red labels, clear windows, six wheels (LE)	£7-£10	MPR ☐
C1168	1983	'EURO EXPRESS'	White main body, Red/B'ue on sides, clear windows, six wheels with Red hubs (LE)	£7-£10	MPR ☐
C1168	1983	'ROVER BUS'	Blue body, clear windows, six wheels, 'TO THE CHESHAM TOY AND MODEL FAIR' (LE)	£5-£7	MPR ☐
			All Cream version	£10	NC ☐

BUDGIE TOYS — 'They speak for themselves'

Budgie Toys were made in England from 1959-1966 approx. and were largely developed by Morris & Stone from their earlier 'Morestone' product range.

In 1961/62 the company was taken over by the S. Guitermann Group who produced models until 1966 when production ceased through financial difficulties. Modern Products who had previously supplied parts to Guitermanns took over and sold the products through a new company called Budgie Model (Continuation) Ltd. Eventually they sold out to Starcourt Ltd who will be most remembered for the models they produced for H. Seener

Ltd eg F×4 Taxi & Scammell Scarab Models.

In 1986 Dave Gilbert of D.G. Models bought the 'BUDGIE' dies from Starcourt Ltd and intends to gradually reissue most of the range using modern techniques and tampo point designs.

The Budgie slogan 'they speak for themselves' aptly sums up the interesting range of models issued — many of them quite unique eg 256 'ESSO' Aircraft Refuelling Tanker 'Pluto'. Budgie Toys produced two main series — MAJOR MODELS and the 'MINIATURE SERIES' and the listings follow.

BUDGIE TOYS — MAJOR MODELS

Ref. No.	Model Type	Model Features and Size	Rarity and Price Grading	
Models produced circa 1958-1966 with some models being reissued in the 1980's				
100	Hansom Cab	Gold plated body and horse	£8-£12	MPR ☐
101	Austin FX4 Taxi	Maroon or Black body, NP-'MDL101S'	£8-£12	MPR ☐
	Promotional	Grey body, NP-'MAY 59', 'London Vintage Taxi', (1000)	£8-£12	MPR ☐
102	R.R. Silver Cloud	Metallic Brown body, NP-'RR 1959'	£8-£12	MPR ☐
202	Refrigeration Truck	Red cab, Silver TRL, 'COAST TO COAST', 1.76	£16-£22	MPR ☐
204	Volkswagen Pick up	Blue body, White tilt, 'EXPRESS DELIVERY', 1.40	£16-£22	MPR ☐
	Recent Reissues	Light Blue body, Cream tilt, 'BUDGIE SERVICE (500)	£9-£12	MPR ☐
		Red body, White tilt, Red 'COCA-COLA' (500)	£9-£12	MPR ☐
		Red/Brown body, Cream tilt, no logo (1000)	£9-£12	MPR ☐
		Yellow body and tilt, 'KODAK' in Red/Black (500)	£9-£12	MPR ☐
		Red body and tank with 'ESSO' (500)	£9-£12	MPR ☐
206	Leyland Hippo Truck	Green cab/CH, Fawn truck body, 'COAL AND COKE' cast in 1.76	£16-£22	MPR ☐
208	R.A.F. Personnel Carrier	Airforce Blue body, with R.A.F. roundels. Length 4½ ins. 1.76	£16-£22	MPR ☐
210	Army Personnel Carrier	Military Green body	£15-£20	MPR ☐
212	U.S. Army Personnel C	Brown body with star on bonnet	£15-£20	MPR ☐
214	Thorneycroft Crane	Red body, Blue crane with Yellow generator	£16-£22	MPR ☐
216	Renault Long Wheelbase	Yellow cab, Red body & canopy, 'FRESH FRUIT DAILY'	£16-£22	MPR ☐
218	Seddon 'A.A.' Jumbo Traffic Control Unit	Yellow tractor unit and articulated caravan with Black side flash and A.A. decals.	£75	GP ☐
220	Leyland Hippo Cattle Truck	Orange cab, Fawn Luton style box, drop down ramp	£16-£22	MPR ☐
222	U.S. Artic Tank TPTR	Army Green, White star on bonnet, Centurion tank load, AV	£35	NC ☐
224	0-6-0 Tank Locomotive	Red body, 'BRITISH RAILWAYS' & 7118 cast in.	£12-£16	MPR ☐
		Later issues in other colours with labels	£9-£12	MPR ☐
226	Foden Dump Truck	Orange or Grey six wheel half cab with tipper	£16-£22	MPR ☐
228	Commer Van	Yellow/Red body, plus 12 crates, 'COCA-COLA' on doors	£55	GP ☐
230	Seddon Timber TPTR	Orange cab, Yellow logo TRL, 'B.R.S.' on doors, AV.	£30-£35	MPR ☐
232	Seddon Cable Drum TPTR	Red cab, Yellow LLD, 3 'STANDARD' cable drums, AV.	£55	GP ☐
234	Tractor Transporter	Orange cab, Fawn trailer, caterpillar tractor load, AV.	£45	GV ☐
236	Routemaster Bus	Red body, 'ESSO GOLDEN' or 'ESSO UNIFLO' logos.	£15-£20	MPR ☐
		Red body, 'GO ESSO BUY ESSO DRIVE ESSO' logo.	£15-£20	MPR ☐
		Red or Green body 'UNIFLO SAE W/50 MOTOR OIL'	£15-£20	MPR ☐
	Recent reissues	Packed in 'Made for 'H. SEENER LTD' boxes.	£10-£15	MPR ☐
238	Scammel Scarab 'BRITISH RAILWAYS'	Maroon and Cream body, 'CADBURYS CHOCOLATE', cab separates by twisting 90° — later reissues are push in.	£55	NC ☐
238	'RAIL FREIGHT'	All Yellow body, 'CADBURYS CHOCOLATE'.	£45	NC ☐
	Recent reissues	With 'ROYAL NAVY' etc. logo — push in connectors.	£10-£15	☐
242	Euclid Tipper Truck	Red/Orange body, 'EUCLID' cast on doors.	£14-£19	MPR ☐
244	Austin Breakdown Truck	Blue body, Yellow jib 'BUDGIE SERVICE'.	£20-£25	MPR ☐
246	Wolseley 'POLICE' Car	Black body, 2 sirens, aerial and bell.	£35	NC ☐
	Recent reissue	Blue body.	£10-£15	MPR ☐
248 & 250	No models issued.			
252	Austin Container Truck	Maroon/Cream cab, Maroon TRL, 'BRITISH RAILWAYS', AV.	£25	NC ☐
	Variant	Red cab and trailer 'DOOR TO DOOR' logo.	£25	NC ☐
254	A.E.C. Fire Escape	Red body, Silver ladder revolves and extends	£35	NC ☐
256	'ESSO' 'Pluto' Tanker	Red body, 'ESSO AVIATION PRODUCTS', Foden AV.	£75	GP ☐
258	Daimler 'AMBULANCE'	Cream body, 'EMERGENCY', Opening rear doors.	£25	NC ☐
260	Ruston Excavator	Red/Yellow body, Green chassis and jib.	£14-£19	MPR ☐
262	Racing Solo Motorcyclist	No details available.		NGPP ☐
264	Racing sidecar outfit	Rider and passenger with helmets and goggles.		NGPP ☐
266	Delivery sidecar outfit	Motorcycle, rider with 'EXPRESS DELIVERY' logo.		NGPP ☐

No.	Model	Description	Price	Code	
268	'A.A.' Land Rover	Yellow body, Black hard top, SPWB, 'ROAD SERVICE'.	£30	NC	☐
270	Leyland Hippo Tanker	Red body, 'ESSO PETROLEUM' etc. on White side panel, AV.	£75	GV	☐
272	'SUPERCAR'	Red/Silver body, retractable wings, plus driver.	£125	GP	☐
274	Refuse Truck	Yellow or Blue body with Silver bin.	£16-£22	MPR	☐
276	Bedford Tipper	Red cab/CH, Yellow body, 'HAM RIVER GRIT' on some.	£16-£22	MPR	☐
278	'R.A.C.' Land Rover	Blue body, 'RADIO RAC RESCUE' in White	£30	NC	☐
280	A.E.C. Refuelling Tanker	White cab and tank, Green canopy and chassis, 'AIR BP' logo, longest Budgie model.	£125	GP	☐
282	'EUCLID' 32 yard scraper	Yellow or Light Green body	£15-£20	MPR	☐
284 & 286	No details of any models issued.				
288	8 Wheel Albion Carrier	Red cab & chassis, 3 Yellow sides, 'BULK FLOUR'.	£24	NC	☐
290	Bedford Ice Cream Van	Blue body, 'TONIBELL' & 'SOFT ICE CREAM' logos.	£45	GP	☐
292	Albion Milk Tanker	Blue/White body, 'YOU'LL FEEL A LOT BETTER' logo.	£65	GP	☐
294	Bedford TK Horse Box	Cream cab, Brown huton box, 'EPSOM STABLES' logo.	£16-£22	MPR	☐
296	Motorway, Express Coach, 'MIDLAND RED'	Red body, Black roof, destinations front & sides.	£55	GP	☐
	'BLUE LINE SIGHTSEEING'	Pale Blue body, Cream roof, 'WASHINGTON DC', VSIM.	£250	GP	☐
298	Alvis Salamander Tender	Red body, Silver ladder & bell, 'FIRE SERVICE'.	£35	NC	☐
300	'LEWIN SWEEPMASTER'	Blue/Silver body, 'PUBLIC WORKS DEPT No. 300'.	£35	GP	☐
302	Commer Lift Truck	Blue/Silver body, 'B.O.A.C. CABIN SERVICE'.	£35	GP	☐
304	Bedford TK Glass Truck	White/Green body, 'TOWER GLASS COMPANY' plus 'glass' load.	£35	GP	☐
306	Tractor with Shovel	Orange body with Blue shovel	£16-£20	MPR	☐
308	Seddon Low Loader Alligator LLD	Green/Yellow body, 'PITT TRAILER'	£25	NC	☐
310	Leyland Cement Mixer	Orange cab, Silver drum, 'INVICTA CONSTRUCTION Co'.	£25	NC	☐
312	Bedford long wheelbase	Dark Green cab, Silver body, 'SUPER TIPMASTER'.	£20	NC	☐
314	Tractor with blade	Orange tractor, Blue bulldozer blade.	£20	NC	☐
316	Overhead Tower Wagon	Green half cab and chassis, Silver arm	£20	NC	☐
318	'EUCLID' Mammoth Dumper	Green/Yellow body, Orange/Yellow trailer	£20	NC	☐
320	No model issued.				
322	Scammel Routeman Pneumanjector Bulk TPTR	Blue cab and chassis, White tank, 'THE ATLAS CARRIER Co. FLOUR SUGAR SAND'.	£50	GP	☐
324	Douglas — Duo Tipper	Blue/Silver body, 'VICTORIA BALLAST Co'.	£30	GP	☐
326	Scammel Highwayman TPTR	Yellow cab, Green trailer, White/Red pipes load.	£35	NC	☐
328	Scammel Handyman Truck	Planned but not produced.			
330	Land Rover	Planned but not produced.			
332	Kenning Tow Truck	Planned but not produced.			
334	Gypsy Fire Tender	Planned but not produced.			
452	A.A. Motor Cycle Patrol	Yellow/Black body, A.A. decals, aerial	£25	NC	☐
454	R.A.C. Motor Cycle Patrol	Blue/Black body, R.A.C. decals, aerial.	£25	NC	☐
456	Solo Motor Cyclist issues.				
	TT Rider	Gleam finish 3¼ in.		NGPP	☐
	Dispatch Rider	Gleam finish 3¼ in.		NGPP	☐
	G.P.O. Messenger	Gleam finish 3¼ in.		NGPP	☐
	Police Patrol	Gleam finish 3¼ in.		NGPP	☐
?	Wagon Train	3 Wagons with pairs of horses and an outrider (one of the first TV programme linked models)		NGPP	☐

BUDGIE TOYS — MINIATURE SERIES

These models were issued 1959-66 and are an excellent range for the younger collector as most models may be obtained for a few pounds.

1-4	No models issued.
5	Wolseley six eighty Black police car.
6	No model known.
7	Mercedes Rauns Car — white.
8	Blue Volkswagen Sedan.
9-10	No models issued.
11	Trojan 'ROYAL MAIL' Van.
12	Blue or Tan VW Micro Bus.
13	Black Austin FX3 Taxi.
14	Fawn Packard Convertible.
15	Blue Austin A95 Westminster.
16	Red Austin Healey sports car.
17	No model issued.
18	Red Foden Dump Truck.
19	Yellow or Green Rover 105.
20a)	White Austin A95 Emergency Car.
b)	Pink Plymouth Belvedere.
21a)	Red Tipper Truck.
b)	Gold, Green or Brown Olds Mobile Sedan.
22	Green mobile crane truck.
23	Red/White cement mixer lorry.
24	Refuse truck with Green, Yellow or Orange cab.
25	Brown cattle truck.
26	Green diesel roller.
27	Red Wolseley six-eighty fire chief's car.
28-49	No models issued.
50	Green/White 'BP RACING TANKER'.
51	Yellow/Red 'SHELL' gasoline truck.
52	Red/Yellow 'SHELL BP' tanker.
53	Blue/Yellow 'NATIONAL BENZOLE' tanker.
54	Yellow/Green 'BP' gasoline truck.
55	Red/Blue 'MOBIL' gasoline truck.
56	Green 'HERTZ' truck.
57	Green 'REA EXPRESS PARCELS' delivery van.
58	Brown or Green 'MODERN REMOVALS' van.
59	Red fire engine, Silver ladder.
60	Red or Black Rover 105 squad car.
61	Black or Blue Austin A95 'Q' car.

Miniature Series features to look out for:—

i) Base Plates	a. Silver with axles exposed eg No.5 Police Car. b. Black with axles concealed eg No. 19 Rover 105. c. Black with axles exposed and mounted on pillars eg No. 11 Royal Mail Van. d. The baseplate seats and driver are from one casting eg 16 Austin Healey.
ii) Model number & names	Usually but not always shown.
iii) Wheels	Three types with crimped or riveted axles. Grey metal, Grey plastic or Black plastic.
iv) Packaging	Models sold 1964-66 were in 'bubble' or 'blister packs'. Several of the models listed appeared in the 'ESSO PETROL PUMP SERIES'. Each model was boxed in an imitation Red and White petrol pump — expect these models to cost £15-£20

BUDGIE GIFT SETS

Issued between 1959-66 and it appears that only 'Miniature Series' models were involved. The first sets were numbered GS4, 6, 8, 10 and 12 with the number indicating how many models were in the set. Prices for the sets range from £30-£80 for the biggest. 'THREE IN ONE' Gift sets — never seen apart from a catalogue.

96	Road Construction Set	Contains 18, 23, 28	NGPP ☐
97	Truck Set	Contains 21, 22, 25	NGPP ☐
98	Utility Vehicle Set	Contains 12, 24, 50	NGPP ☐
99	Traffic Set	Contains 8, 15, 27	NGPP ☐
'LARGE' Gift Sets — never seen			
PL6	Six model set	Contains 8, 18, 22, 23, 25, 55	NGPP ☐
PL12	Twelve model set	Contains 8, 12, 15, 18, 21, 22, 23, 24, 25, 26, 27, 55	NGPP ☐

MORRIS & STONE MODELS 'MORESTONE'

Made in England during the 1950's by Morris & Stone (London) Ltd. The amount of information available is limited so the listings are unable to provide details of all the models issued. The compiler would welcome any further information.

"TRUCKS OF THE WORLD INTERNATIONAL" SERIES. Models packed in Pale Blue and White boxes displaying five flags.

Leyland Scammel 17 ton motive unit	Orange cab, Cream artic tank trailer. 'LIQUID IN STOCK' cast into side, 8 wheels.	£35	GP ☐
International A-170 Refrigeration Truck	Two tone Red and Blue tractor unit, Red chassis, Grey metal container box.	£35	GP ☐

'MORESTONE' SERIES

Guy Arab Double Deck Omnibus	Red or Green body, cast in No. '7', no windows, White label 'FINEST PETROL ESSO EXTRA IN THE WORLD' or 'ESSO FOR HAPPY MOTORING' in Blue and Red.	£75	GP ☐
Guy Otter Pantechnican	Dark Blue body, White roof, Silver trim, no windows, unpainted hubs, crimped axles, Black rubber tyres — 'PICKFORDS REMOVERS & STORERS BRANCHES IN ALL LARGE TOWNS' logo in White, ORD.	£75	GP ☐
Foden Petrol Tanker	Red body, White label 'MOTOR OIL ESSO PETROL' logo, 8 wheels. Also issued with no 'ESSO' logo.	£75	GP ☐
Foden Long Distance Wagon	Beige cab, Red flatbed, no windows		NGPP ☐
Foden Dump Truck	Six wheel half cab with tipper, no number plate	£35	GP ☐
Foden 14 ton Chain Lorry	Grey cab & chassis, Yellow flatbed	£45	GP ☐
Daimler Ambulance	White body, no decals, opening rear doors.	£35	GP ☐
Personnel Carrier	Army Green body, removable Brown canopy, 8 wheels.	£35	GP ☐
Albion Milk Wagon	Green cab, Beige truck body.	£75	GP ☐
Caravan	Yellow and Green body, Brown horse	£100	GP ☐
N.B. This model sold at Lacy Scott's March 1988, Bury St Edmunds Auction for £140.			
Stage Coach	No details available.		NGPP ☐
Bedford Dormobile	No details available.		NGPP ☐
Hansom Cab	No details available but no doubt same as Budgie issue.		
A.A. M/Cycle Patrol	Yelllow motorcycle and sidecar, A.A. decals.	£25	GP ☐
R.A.C. M/Cycle Patrol	Blue motorcycle and sidecar, R.A.C. decals.	£25	GP ☐
A.A. Land Rover	Yellow body, Black roof, A.A. decals aerial.	£35	GP ☐

'MODERN PRODUCTS' SERIES

Mobile Police Car	Black body, siren bell and aerial.	£35	GP ☐
Covered Wagon	Metal wagon and canopy with 6 horses.		NGPP ☐
Fire Engine	No details available.		NGPP ☐
'BRITISH RAILWAYS' Loco.	No details available.		NGPP ☐
Aveling Bamford Roller	No details available.		NGPP ☐

N.B. The Compiler would welcome any further information on Morestone Models.

"MORESTONE" SERIES

STAGE COACH   —   HANSOM CAB
A.A. M/CYCLE COMBINATION PATROL
A.A. ROAD SERVICE JEEP
R.A.C. M/CYCLE COMBINATION PATROL
C A R A V A N   —   D U L C I M E R
DOUBLE DECKER OMNIBUS
FODEN LONG DISTANCE WAGON
PETROL TANKER   —   MILK WAGON

★

"MODERN PRODUCTS" SERIES

M O B I L E P O L I C E C A R
FIRE ENGINE   —   COVERED WAGON
(6 Horses)
BRITISH RAILWAYS LOCOMOTIVE
(Fits 'OO' Gauge)
DIESEL ROAD ROLLER—(Aveling Barford)

★

These are some of our exciting scale models which are true to life in every detail and which are now available at your local Toy Shop. Ask to see them and look out for the new models which are being added to the Series at regular intervals

Manufactured in England by
MORRIS & STONE (London) LTD.,
95 Stoke Newington Church Street, London, N.16

Printed in England

Box Insert issued with 'MORESTONE' models

189

Crescent Toys
The Crescent Toy Company Limited

Founded in July, 1922 by Henry G. Eagles and Arthur A. Schneider, in a workshop 30 feet square at the rear of a private house at 67 De Beauvoir Crescent, Kingsland Road, London N.1. They manufactured model Soldiers, Cowboys, Kitchen Sets etc. from lead alloy. These were hollow castings, hand painted, packed 1 dozen in a box and sold to wholesalers at 6/0d per dozen boxes. The small firm prospered and eventually opened up a factory in Tottenham. With World War II came a ban on metal toys and production was changed to munitions. After the war the firm resumed making metal hollow cast toys and in addition marketed the diecast products of a firm called DCMT (Die Casting Machine Tools Ltd). As a consequence early postwar models had DCMT cast into the underside of the body.

In 1949 the firm opened a modern factory on a 4¼ acre site at CWMCARN, a Welsh mining village near Newport, Mon (now Gwent), and two years later transferred all production there, maintaining only an office in London. Furthermore, from this time Crescent Toys produced their own diecast products and DCMT disappeared from the body undersides. Hence, it is possible to find the same models with and without DCMT cast in. Die Casting Machine Tools Ltd went their own way and from 1950 produced models under the name of 'Lone Star'.

Crescent Toys will probably be best remembered certainly by the diecast collectors for their excellent range of military models, their farm equipment models and probably most of all for their superb reproductions of the racing cars of the 1950's. The following post-war model listings have been extracted from a unique collection of original trade catalogues (1947-80) most kindly provided by Mr. J.D. Schneider, the former Managing Director of Crescent Toys Ltd. All of the original research and actual compiling of the lists has been undertaken by Ray Strutt of the "Collector Gazette". Ray being a racing car enthusiast himself, was particularly keen to see that those produced by Crescent Toys were included in the new edition together with the Company's other products.

As Crescent Toys only produced Trade Catalogues very little information has previously been published on the models which Crescent produced. Consequently on behalf of all diecast model collectors, the catalogue compiler would like to express sincere appreciation to Mr. J.D. Schneider and to Ray Strutt for producing such useful information.

It is not possible to quote the likely Crescent model price as a survey has still to be completed. However, they are normally reasonably priced and more information will be given in the next edition.

Racing car collectors will be interested to see the racing car set No. D6300 in the special display box which is a unique picture from an early trade catalogue. If any reader does own such a set the compiler would be delighted to receive details.

It is to be hoped that the provision of these listings will rekindle interest in collecting this most interesting model range.

The Early Post-War Models

Ref. No.	Dates	Model Type	Model Features and Size	Rarity and Price Grading
800	1947-49	Jaguar	Bright colours	
802	1947-49	Locomotive	Assorted colours	
803	1947-48	Locomotive	Silver	
804	1948-49	Police Car	Black	
223	1948	Racing Car		
1221	1949	Fire Engine		
422	1949	Sports Car	Assorted colours	
423	1949	Oil Lorry		
424	1949	Truck Lorry		
425	1949	Saloon Car	Assorted colours	

Crescent Toys cont.

Farm Equipment/Implements

Ref. No.	Dates	Model Type	Model Features and Size	Rarity and Price Grading
1802	1949-60	Tractor and Hayrake		
1803	1967-74	Dexta Tractor and Trailer		
1804	1950-59	Tractor and Disc Harrow		
1805	1950-61	Tractor		
1806	1950-60	Hayrake		
1807	1950...	Disc Harrow		
1808	1950-56	Platform Trailer		
1809	1950-56	Ricklift Trailer		
1809	1962-80	Dexta Tractor		
1810	1950-80	Box Trailer/Farm Trailer (No. 148 1968-74)		
1811	1950-67	Animal Trailer/Cattle Trailer (No. 149 1968-71)		
1811	1975-81	Dexta Tractor & Trailer		
1813	1950	Timber Wagon (Horse Drawn)		
1814	1950-60	Plough Trailer (No.150 1968-71)		
1815	1950...	Hayloader		
1816	1950...	Roller Harrow		
1817	1950-56	Timber Trailer		
1818	1954-60	Tipping Farm Wagon		
1819	1954-55	Large Farm Wagon		

Diecast Action Toys

Ref. No.	Dates	Model Type	Model Features and Size	Rarity and Price Grading
1268	1954-59	Mobile Space Rocket		
1269	1954-59	Mobile Crane		
1272	1954-59	Scammel Scarab and Box Trailer		
1274	1955-59	Scammel Scarab and Low Loader Trailer		
1276	1955-59	Scammel Scarab and Oil Tanker Trailer		
2700	1956-60	Western Stage Coach		
2705	1955	Scammel Set — Mechanical Horse, Box Trailer and Low Loader		

Military Models

Ref. No.	Dates	Model Type	Model Features and Size	Rarity and Price Grading
696	1954-56	British Tank		
698	1954-56	Scout Car		
699	1954-56	Russian Tank		
650	1954-55	A Set of 2 No. 696 — 1 No. 698 — 1 No. 699		
1248	1957	Fiel Gun		
1249	1958-79	18 Pdr. Quick Firing Gun		
1250	1958-80	25 Pdr. Light Artillery Gun		
1251	1958-80	5.5in. Medium Heavy Gun Howitzer		
1260	1976-79	Supply Truck		
1263	1962-80	Saladin Towing Vehicle/Scout Car/Armoured Car		
1264	1975-80	Scorpion Tank		
1265	1977-80	M109 Self Propelled Gun		
1266	1978-79	Recovery Vehicle		
1267	1958-63	'Corporal' Type Rocket and Lorry		
1270	1958-60	Heavy Rescue Crane		
1271	1958-60	Long Range Mobile Gun		
1271	1976-80	Artillery Force		
155	1960-68	'Long Tom' Artillery Gun		
2154	1962-74	Saladin Armoured Patrol (No. 1270. 1975-80)		

Historical Models

Ref. No.		Model Type	Model Features and Size	Rarity and Price Grading
1953	1954-60	Coronation State Coach		
1450	1956-60	Medieval Catapult		
1300	1975-76	Royal State Coach		
1301	1977-79	Royal State Coach (Commemorative Box)		
1302	1977	Royal State Coach and Figures		

Miniature Wild West Transport

Ref. No.	Dates	Model Type	Model Features and Size	Rarity and Price Grading
906	1956	Stage Coach		
907	1956	Covered Wagon		

Grand Prix Racing and Sports Cars

Ref. No.	Dates	Model Type	Model Features and Size	Rarity and Price Grading
1284	1956-60	Mercedes Benz	Silver	
1285	1956-60	B.R.M. Mk.2	Bright Green	
1286	1956-60	Ferrari	Orange Red	
1287	1956-60	Connaught	Dark Green	
1288	1956-60	Cooper Bristol	Light Blue	
1289	1956-60	Gordini	French Blue	
1290	1957-60	Maserati	Cherry Red	
1291	1957-60	Aston Martin DB3S	White/Light Blue Stripes	
1292	1957-60	Jaguar D Type	Dark Green	
1293	1958-60	Vanwall	Dark Green	
6300	1957	Set of Six Grand Prix Racing Cars	(1284, 1285, 1286, 1287, 1288, 1289) in Display Box.	
	1958-60	As above, with 1290 replacing 1284.		

Long Vehicles

Ref. No.	Dates	Model Type	Model Features and Size	Rarity and Price Grading
1350	1975-80	Container Truck		
1351	1957-80	Petrol Tanker		
1352	1975-80	Girder Carrying Truck		
1353	1975-80	Flat Platform Truck		

Trukkers

Ref. No.	Dates	Model Type	Model Features and Size	Rarity and Price Grading
1360	1976-81	Cement Mixer		
1361	1976-81	Covered Truck		
1362	1976-81	Tipper Truck		
1363	1976-81	Recovery Vehicle		
1364	1978-81	Super Karrier		

CRESCENT TOYS
The Racing Car Specialists

EXACT REPLICAS, TRUE TO SCALE

FAITHFUL IN DETAIL

Models available

1284 MERCEDES BENZ (Germany)
2.5 LITRE GRAND PRIX (ILLUSTRATED)

1285 B.R.M. MK.2 (Britain)
GRAND PRIX MODEL

1286 FERRARI (Italy)
2.5 LITRE GRAND PRIX MODEL

1287 CONNAUGHT (Britain)
2 LITRE GRAND PRIX MODEL

1288 COOPER BRISTOL (Britain)
2 LITRE GRAND PRIX MODEL

1289 GORDINI (France)
2.5 LITRE GRAND PRIX MODEL

1290 MASERATI (Italy)
2.5 LITRE GRAND PRIX MODEL

1291 ASTON MARTIN D.B.3.S. (Britain)
2.9 LITRE SPORTS

1292 JAGUAR D TYPE (Britain)
3.5 LITRE SPORTS

(Winner 1st 4 places 1957 Le Mans 24hrs. Senior Class)

1284 MERCEDES BENZ
2.5 LITRE GRAND PRIX MODEL

THE CRESCENT TOY CO. LTD., CWMCARN, MONMOUTHSHIRE

Copy of 6300 Box Insert

Crescent Toys cont.

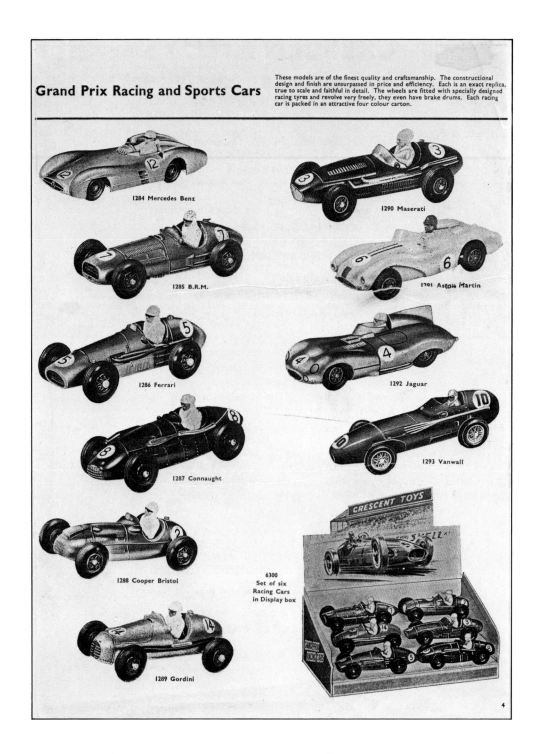

Grand Prix Racing and Sports Cars

These models are of the finest quality and craftsmanship. The constructional design and finish are unsurpassed in price and efficiency. Each is an exact replica, true to scale and faithful in detail. The wheels are fitted with specially designed racing tyres and revolve very freely, they even have brake drums. Each racing car is packed in an attractive four colour carton.

1284 Mercedes Benz

1290 Maserati

1285 B.R.M.

1291 Aston Martin

1286 Ferrari

1292 Jaguar

1287 Connaught

1293 Vanwall

1288 Cooper Bristol

6300
Set of six
Racing Cars
in Display box

1289 Gordini

A page from the 1960 Catalogue

TRI-ANG MINIC SHIPS
Accurately detailed waterline models

The catalogue is indebted to Mr Ian Clarke, the well known diecast model trader from Cumbria, for kindly compiling the model listing from the knowledge which he has built up over the past twenty years in the toy trade.

Brief History

The models were in the shops from about 1958-1964 having a comparatively short life, but production figures must have been high and this factor coupled with 'low play value' (they could not be raced like Dinky Toys!), has meant that from a collecting angle a reasonable number have survived in good condition.

Six sales catalogues were produced which nowadays are quite hard to find. No one catalogue shows the full range, as additions, deletions and alterations were a regular occurrence.

Minic ships were reintroduced in 1976 and these are now known as the second issues. The range was partly altered and they were painted in slightly different colours. Finally as if to guarantee the models demise, wheels were put on the bottom. As a consequence they didn't sell and are not collectable in the same way as the original issues. There are plenty about but as a guide to price comparison, an original example of say, CANBERRA is about £35-£40 and the second issues is £6-£9. All second issues have HONG KONG on the base.

GENERAL NOTES ON SPECIFIC MODELS (1st Issue)
M702, M703: Queens came with and without Funnel detail.
M708, M709: Saxonia/Ivernia, were slightly recast torwards the end of the run and renamed: Franconia and Carmania: Keeping the original catalogue number, they were slightly recast at the stern only to add a swimming pool, and remove cargo handling gear. They were finished in green with green masts and very few reached the shops. This alteration followed Cunards refurbishment of the actual ships. However this change by Tri-ang has created the two hardest models to find.

M754: Commando ship: Not generally known, and not appearing in any catalogues, or in the shops, this model was a type of publicity item produced, for the entire crew of a carrier in service at the time: Same casting as other carriers, it had a Helicopter landing deck in the form of a sticker, applied the full length of the ship. All produced in Grey. Again very rare.
M716, M717: Port Auckland/Port Brisbane: Short run: Scarce.
M783, M784, M785, M786: Hampshire/Kent/Devonshire/London: Missile Destroyers: Short run: Bit hard to find. Only ever seen in Grey.
M726: Pilot Boat: Hard to find.
M727: Lifeboat: Hard to find.
M743: Train Ferry: Never appeared in shops, only in catalogues.
M740: Barge: Designed to match up with M731 tugboat: Appears in catalogue but doubtful if ever actually issued.
M853: Factory: Hard to find.
M880: Whales: Grey and White types: Hard to find.

Also produced, but not appearing in any catalogue, is the Helicopter. It is possible this was designed to go with the limited issue Commando ship. It is a very small and basic item which was manufactured to a very high technological standard by taking an M880 Whale, and nailing a four bladed rotor arm to its head. (Same Rotor blade as used on missile destroyer).

OCEAN LINERS 1:1200 Scale (1″ to 100ft)

Ref. No.	Model Type	Model Features and Size	Rarity and Price Grading	
M701	R.M.S. Caronia	Green body, one plain Red/Black and one mast. 17.8 cms. "Painted in the correct Cunard Green she is a most striking vessel"	£30-£35	☐
M702	R.M.S. Queen Elizabeth	Black/White body, two plain Red/Black or detailed funnel, two masts 26.2 cms. "The worlds largest ship and the pride of the Cunard fleet"	£30-£35	☐
M703	R.M.S. Queen Mary. Plain Red Funnel	Black/White body, three plain Red/Black or detailed funnels, two masts 25.9 cms. "Her three funnels make her the most easily recognisable"	£20-£25	☐
M704	S.S. United States	Black/White body, two Red/White/Blue funnels. 25.2 cms. "The present holder of the Blue Ribband of the Atlantic"	£20-£25	☐
M705	R.M.S. Aquitania:	Black/White body, four Red/Black funnels, two masts. 23.1 cms.	NGPP	☐
M706	S.S. Nieuw Amsterdam	Grey/White body, two Yellow funnels, two masts	£35-£45	☐
M707	S.S. France	Black/White body, two Red/Black funnels, three masts. 26.2 cms. "The longest ship in the world 1035ft being 4ft longer than Queen Elizabeth"	NGPP	☐
M708	Saxonia	Black/White body, Red/Black or detailed funnel, 9 masts	£18-£24	☐
M708/2	Franconia	Green body, one Red/Black funnel, 9 masts. 15.5 cms.	NGPP	☐

Ocean Liners cont.

M709	Ivernia	Black/White body	£18-£24	
M709/2	Carmania	Green body, one Red/Black funnel, 9 masts. 15.5 cms.		NGPP
M710	R.M.S. Sylvania	Black/White body, one Red/Black funnel, 9 masts. 15.5 cms.	£18-£24	
M711	Carinthia	Black/White body, one Red/Black funnel, 9 masts. 15.5 cms.	£18-£24	
M712	N.S. Savanah	White body, no funnels, nuclear powered, 4 masts. 14.9 cms.	£35-£45	
M713	S.S. Antilles	Black/White body, one Red/Black funnel, 10 masts. 15.2 cms.	£38-£48	
M713	S.S. Antilles	White body, one Red/Black funnel, 10 masts. 15.2 cms.	£38-£48	
M714	S.S. Flandre	Black/White body, one Red/Black funnel, 10 masts. 15.2 cms.	£28-£35	
M714	S.S. Flandre	White body, one Red/Black funnel, 10 masts. 15.2 cms.	£28-£35	
M715	R.M.S. Canberra	White body, one Yellow funnel, 3 masts. 18.9 cms.	£40-£50	
M716	S.S. Port Brisbane	Grey/White body, one red/Black funnel, 7 masts. 14 cms.	£60-£90	
M717	S.S. Port Auckland	Grey/White body, one Red/Black funnel, 7 masts. 14 cms.	£60-£90	
M718	R.M.S. Amazon	White body, one Yellow funnel, 19 masts. 14.9 cms.	£45-£50	
M719	R.M.S. Orlanza	White body, one Yellow funnel, 19 masts. 14.9 cms.	£45-£50	
M720	R.M.S. Aragon	White body, one Yellow funnel, 19 masts. 14.9 cms.	£45-£50	
M721	H.M.S. Britannia, Royal Yacht	Blue/White body, Yellow/Black funnel, 3 masts. 10.5 cms.	£12-£15	
M712H	H.M.S. Britannia, Hospital Ship	White body, three masts. 10.5 cms.	£6-£9	

CHANNEL ISLAND STEAMERS

M722	Isle of Jersey	Black/White body, two Yellow/Black funnels, 2 masts. 7.8 cms.	£5-£7	
M723	Isle of Guernsey	Black/White body, two Yellow/Black funnels, 2 masts. 7.8 cms.	£5-£7	
M723	Isle of Sark	Black/White body, two Yellow/Black funnels, 2 masts. 7.8 cms.	£5-£7	
M726	Pilot Boat	Black/White/Yellow body, 'PILOTS'. 4.5 cms.	£35-£45	
M727	Lifeboat	Blue body.	£15-£20	

PADDLE STEAMERS

M728	Britannia Queen	Black/White body, two Black/Blue funnels, 2 masts. 7.8 cms.	£10-£15	
M729	Bristol Queen	Black/White body, two Black/Blue funnels, 2 masts. 7.8 cms.	£10-£15	
M730	Cardiff Queen	Black/White body, two Black/Blue funnels, 2 masts. 7.8 cms.	£10-£15	
		M728/9/30 also issued in White.		

TUGBOATS

M731	Tugboat	Black/Grey/Red body, Yellow/Black funnel. 3.8 cms.	£2-£3	
M731	Tugboat	Black/Blue/Red body, Yellow/Black funnel. 3.8 cms.	£2-£3	
M731	Tugboat	Black/Grey/Yellow body, Yellow/Black funnel. 3.8 cms.	£2-£3	

OIL TANKER

| M732 | S.S. Varicella | Black/White body, Black/Yellow funnel, 2 masts. 16.4 cms. | £25-£30 | |

WHITE FACTORY SHIP

| M733 | T.S.S. Vikingen | Grey body, six masts. 12.5 cms. | £15-£20 | |
| M734 | Whale Chaser | Grey body, Yellow/Black funnel. 3.9 cms. | £15-£20 | |

LIGHTSHIPS

M735	'SUNK'	Red body, White logo/name. 3.3 cms.	£3-£5	
M736	'SHAMBLES'	Red body, White logo/name. 3.3 cms.	£3-£5	
M737	'CORK'	Red body, White logo/name. 3.3 cms.	£3-£5	
M738	'VARNE'	Red body, White logo/name. 3.3 cms.	£3-£5	
M739	'ST. GOWAN'	Red body, White logo/name. 3.3 cms.	£3-£5	

WARSHIPS 1:1200 Scale (1″ to 100ft)

Ref. No.	Model Type	Model Features and Size	Rarity and Price Grading	
BATTLESHIP				
M741	H.M.S. Vanguard	Grey or Blue body, two masts. 20.6 cms.	£15-£20	
AIRCRAFT CARRIERS				
M751	H.M.S. Bulwark	Blue or Grey body, one mast. 18.6 cms.	£15-£20	
M752	H.M.S. Centaur	Blue or Grey body, one mast.	£15-£20	
M753	H.M.S. Albion	Blue or Grey body, one mast.	£15-£20	
COMMANDO SHIP				
M754		Grey body	£125-£140	
CRUISERS 14.5 cms.				
M761	H.M.S. Swiftsure	Blue or Grey body, one crane jib.	£10-£15	
M762	H.M.S. Superb	Blue or Grey body, one crane jib.	£10-£15	
FLEET ESCORT DARING CLASS DESTROYERS 9.8 cms.				
M771	H.M.S. Daring	Blue or Grey body, one mast.	£3-£5	
M772	H.M.S. Diana	Blue or Grey body, one mast.	£3-£5	
M773	H.M.S. Dainty	Blue or Grey body, one mast.	£3-£5	
M774	H.M.S. Decoy	Blue or Grey body, one mast.	£3-£5	
BATTLE CLASS FLEET DESTROYERS. 9.7 cms.				
M779	H.M.S. Alamein	Blue or Grey body, one mast.	£3-£5	
M780	H.M.S. Jutland	Blue or Grey body, one mast.	£3-£5	
M781	H.M.S. Anzac	Blue or Grey body, one mast.	£3-£5	
M782	H.M.S. Tobruck	Blue or Grey body, one mast.	£3-£5	

Minic Ships cont.

GUIDED MISSILE DESTROYERS COUNTY CLASS. 13.6 cms. COUNTY CLASS 13.6 cms.

M783	H.M.S. Hampshire	Grey body, two masts.	£20-£25	☐
M784	H.M.S. Kent	Grey body, two masts.	£20-£25	☐
M785	H.M.S. Devonshire	Grey body, two masts.	£20-£25	☐
M786	H.M.S. London	Grey body, two masts.	£20-£25	☐

'V' CLASS FAST ANTI SUBMARINE FRIGATES. 9.2 cms.

M787	H.M.S. Vigilant	Blue or Grey body, one mast.	£3-£5	☐
M788	H.M.S. Venus	Blue or Grey body, one mast.	£3-£5	☐
M789	H.M.S. Virago	Blue or Grey body, one mast.	£3-£5	☐
M790	H.M.S. Volage	Blue or Grey body, one mast.	£3-£5	☐

ANTI-SUBMARINE FRIGATES WHITBY CLASS 9.4 cms.

M791	H.M.S. Whitby	Blue or Grey body.	£3-£5	☐
M792	H.M.S. Torquay	Blue or Grey body.	£3-£5	☐
M793	H.M.S. Blackpool	Blue or Grey body.	£3-£5	☐
M794	H.M.S. Tenby	Blue or Grey body.	£3-£5	☐

MINESWEEPERS. Ton Class

M799	H.M.S. Repton	Blue or Grey body.	£2-£4	☐
M800	H.M.S. Dufton	Blue or Grey body.	£2-£4	☐
M801	H.M.S. Ashton	Blue or Grey body.	£2-£4	☐
M802	H.M.S. Calton	Blue or Grey body.	£2-£4	☐
M803	H.M.S. Picton	Blue or Grey body.	£2-£4	☐
M804	H.M.S. Sefton	Blue or Grey body.	£2-£4	☐
M805	H.M.S. Upton	Blue or Grey body.	£2-£4	☐
M806	H.M.S. Weston	Blue or Grey body.	£2-£4	☐
M810	H.M.S. Turmoil	Blue or Grey body.	£2-£3	☐

SUBMARINES 'A' CLASS 6.1 cms.

M817	Sub A Class	Blue	£7-£9	☐
M817	Sub A Class	Grey	£7-£9	☐
M818	Sub Recon	Blue	£7-£9	☐
M818	Sub Recon	Grey	£7-£9	☐

DOCKSIDE ACCESSORIES & MISCELLANEOUS

M827	B/Water Straights	Grey	£1-£2	☐
M828L	B/Water Angle left	Grey	£1-£2	☐
M828R	B/Water Angle right	Grey	£1-£2	☐
M829	B/Water end	Grey	£1-£2	☐
M836	Quay Straights	Tan	£1-£2	☐
M837	Crane Units	Tan Brown or Green cargo	£1-£2	☐
M838	Oil tanks	Grey or Silver	£1-£2	☐
M839	Customs Shed	Green	£1-£2	☐
M840	Warehouse	Brown	£1-£2	☐
M841	Ocean Terminal	White	£1-£2	☐
M842	Swing Bridge		£1-£2	☐
M843	Terminal extension	White	£2-£3	☐
M844	Lock Gates	Brown, pair	£1-£2	☐
M846	Lift Bridge	Silver/Tan	£1-£2	☐
M847	Pier centre section		£1-£2	☐
M848	Pier entrance section		£1-£2	☐
M849	Pier Head	White etc.	£6-£8	☐
M853	Factory Unit	Brown/Tan	£10-£15	☐
M854	Tanker Wharf set	Tan	£35-£40	☐
M857	26″ Sea	Blue (plastic)	£5-£7	☐
M857	52″ Sea	Blue (plastic)	£15-£18	☐
M861	Lifeboat set	Grey	£25-£30	☐
M878	Lighthouse	White	£3-£4	☐
M880	Whales	White or Plain Grey	£10-£12	☐
M882	Beacon		£3-£5	☐
M884	Statute of Liberty		£3-£5	☐
M885	Floating Dock		£20-£25	☐

GIFT SETS

M891	Q/Elizabeth	Gift set	£50-£60	☐
M892	U/States	Gift set	£100-£125	☐
M893	Task Force	Gift set	£50-£60	☐
M894	Royal Yacht	Gift set	£50-£60	☐
M895	N/Amsterdam	Gift set	£100-£125	☐

SPECIAL PRESENTATION PACKS

M702S	Queen Elizabeth		£35-£40	☐
M703S	Queen Mary		£25-£30	☐
M704S	S.S. United States		£25-£30	☐
M705S	Aquitania		NGPP	☐
M707S	S.S. France		NGPP	☐
M741S	H.M.S. Vanguard		£20-£25	☐

N.B. For collectors wishing to either start or build up their 'Minic' collections, Ian Clarke always has a fine selection on his mail order list — contact him at 78 Duke Street, Askham-in-Furness, Cumbria CA16 7AD (0229 66041).

The compiler will be delighted to learn any further information about this delightful series of models.

Lledo — Models of Days Gone

INTRODUCTION

A toy company formed by Jack Odell O.B.E. one of the founders of Matchbox Toys. The first models were produced in the summer of 1983, just as the first edition of this catalogue was going to the printers. Consequently printing was delayed just long enough to include details of the first six models LLEDO produced and what little beauties they were. What a lot has happened since those early days just five years ago. Consequently it is now a pleasure to provide collectors with full simplified listings of all the Code 1 models issued to the time of going to press in 1988. The catalogue is indebted to Ray Bush of the 'LLEDO CALLING' Specialist Collectors Club for supplying the information on which these lists are based. Full details of club membership are given at the end of the 'Lledo' chapter.

DG 001 Horse Drawn Tram.
DG 002 Horse Drawn Milk Float.
DG 003 Horse Drawn Delivery Van.
DG 004 Horse Drawn Omnibus.
DG 005 Horse Drawn Fire Engine.
DG 006 Model 'T' Ford Van.
DG 007 1930 Ford — Woody Wagon.
DG 008 Model 'T' Ford Tanker.
DG 009 Model 'A' Ford Open Car.
DG 010 1933 Albion Single Decker Bus
   with closed roof.
DG 011 Large Horse Drawn Van.
DG 012 1934 Fire Engine.
DG 013 1929 Ford Model 'A' Van.
DG 014 Model 'A' Ford Car.
DG 015 1932 A.E.C. Regent Double
   Decker Bus.
DG 016 1934 Dennis Heavy Goods Vehicle.

DG 017 1923 A.E.C. Regal Single Deck Coach.
DG 018 1937 Packard Enclosed Van.
DG 019 1931 Rolls Royce Phantom II.
DG 020 Ford Stake Truck.
DG 021 1934 Chevrolet Van.
DG 022 1933 Town Van.
DG 023 1954 Scenicruiser.
DG 024 1934 Rolls Royce Playboy Car.
DG 025 1925 Rolls Royce Silver Ghost Car.
DG 026 Chevrolet Delivery Van.
DG 027 Mack Breakdown Truck.
DG 028 Mack 'Canvas Back' Truck.
DG 029 Dodge Ambulance.
DG 030 Chevy Panel Van.

N.B.: Pictures reproduced from Lledo.

'Models of Days Gone' packaging.

MODEL LISTING INFORMATION

Only Code 1 models listed i.e. models 100% produced by Lledo and made available for sale through normal retail outlets or by mail order at the normal retail price. Models not listed will be Code 3 models i.e. models not sold through normal channels at normal retail prices but produced for promotional purposes. For further details of these models see the section on Promotionals which follows.

Unless described differently all the 'DAYS GONE' model designs are tampo printed. Normal Retail Price (NRP) shown alongside models in the price and rarity grading column indicates a model which has yet to attain a premium over and above the normal retail price. For models in this category assume a market price range of £2-£4.

The objective of this listing is to provide a simplified check list and price guide. For collectors requiring detailed information on the different types of castings, wheel hubs, tyres, grilles, seats and body colour variations, membership of the official Lledo Collectors Club (Lledo Calling) is strongly recommended. Details of how to join are given at the end of this chapter.

DG001 HORSE DRAWN TRAM. Model features a metal body with a plastic horse and seats. It has brass trim and includes a set of figures — 2 lady passengers, a male passenger, a girl and the driver.

001	1983	'WESTMINSTER' logo			
		i. With no strengtheners on end panel or shafts	£60	GP	☐
		ii. With strengtheners on shafts but not end panels	£60	GP	☐
		iii. With both strengtheners plus a Yellow or Cream crest	£15	NC	☐
		iv. With a White crest (Rerun in 1988 with deep Red seats)		NRP	☐
002		'MAIN ST' logo		NRP	☐
003		'NATIONAL TRAMWAY MUSEUM'		NRP	☐
004	1985	'DOWNTOWN' (No figures)		NRP	☐

(Rerun in 1987 with Darker Green seats)
N.B. DG-001 Models exist with reversed seats.

DG002 HORSE DRAWN MILK FLOAT. Model features a metal body with a plastic roof section, horse and 3 milk crates. It has brass 12 spoke wheels and a set of figures containing a lady, a man, the driver and a dog.

001	1983	'EXPRESS DAIRY'	NRP	☐
002	1984	'CHAMBOURCY'	NRP	☐
003	1984	'CLIFFORDS DAIRY'	NRP	☐
004	1984	'CELTIC DAIRY'	NRP	☐

N.B. 001 & 002 rerun in 1988 with no DG-2-3 on base.

DG003 HORSE DRAWN DELIVERY VAN. The model features a metal body with a plastic horse and roof section. Until 1985 a plastic set of figures was included — a lady, a boy and a driver.

001	1983	'WINDMILL BAKERY'	NRP	☐
002	1984	'PEPPERDENE FARM'	NRP	☐
003		'STAFFORD SHOW'	NRP	☐
004		'MATHEW NORMAN CLOCKS'	NRP	☐
005		'FINE LADY BAKERIES'	NRP	☐
006		'ROBERTSONS MARMALADE'	NRP	☐
007		L.S.W.R. — watercress hunt	NRP	☐
008		'HAMLEYS TOY SHOP' — special box	NRP	☐
009	1985	'TRI-SUM CRISPS'	NRP	☐
010		'COCA-COLA'	NRP	☐
011		'ROYAL MAIL'	NRP	☐
012		'LLEDO WORLDWIDE CLUB'	NRP	☐
	1988	'SMITHFIELD MARKET' 'Eastenders' set model	NRP	☐

N.B. 001, 002 & 006 rerun in 1988 with no DG2-DG3 on shafts.

DG004 HORSE DRAWN OMNIBUS. The model features a metal omnibus with plastic horses and seats. It has a set of Cream figures containing 2 ladies, a man, the driver, a conductor and a number four.

001	1983	'VICTORIA — KINGS CROSS'			
		i) Red body with Green 'LIPTONS' logo on an off White panel and rear axle visible from rear	£20	NC	☐
		ii) With 'LIPTONS' logo on White panel and no view of rear axle	£20	NC	☐
		iii) With White 'LIPTONS' logo on Green panel		NRP	☐
002	1984	'BOWERY TO BROADWAY' Brown or green body		NRP	☐
003	1984	'OAKEYS POLISH'		NRP	☐
004	1984	'PEARS SOAP'		NRP	☐
005	1984	'MADAM TUSSAUDS'		NRP	☐
006	1984	'HAMLEY'S TOYS'		NRP	☐
007	1985	MASONS PANTRY		NRP	☐
008	1986	'HIGH CHAPPARAL'		NRP	☐
	1988	'BALMORAL' SBX Ruby Wedding set model		NGPP	☐
	1988	'LIPTONS TEAS' (reissue)		NRP	☐
	1988	'RADIO TIMES' 'Eastenders' set model in 3 liveries:-		NRP	☐
		i) 'A million copies a week!'			
		ii) 'T. Tilling Ltd'			
		iii) 'News of the World'.			

DG005 HORSE DRAWN FIRE ENGINE. The model features a metal main body with plastic horses. It contains a set of Cream figures — 1 driver and 2 seated firemen. No figures issued after 1985.

001	1983	'LONDON FIRE BRIGADE'	£10	NC	☐
002	1983	'CHICAGO FIRE BRIGADE'		NRP	☐
003	1983	'GUILDFORD FIRE BRIGADE' Black boiler 288 issued	£150	GP	☐
		Gold boiler		NRP	☐
004	1984	'HONG KONG' Red boiler 288 issued	£150	GP	☐
		Gold boiler		NRP	☐
005	1984	'G.W.R. (Swindon)'			
		With Gold wheels/Black horses	£10		☐
		With Gold wheels/Beige horses	£10		☐
006	1984	'PHILADELPHIA FIRE' Bright Red body	£45	NC	☐
		Plain Red body		NRP	☐
007	1984	'B.I.F.B.A.C. II'		NRP	☐
008	1985	'LAKE CITY'		NRP	☐
	1988	'LONDON FIRE BRIGADE, EAST HAM' 'Eastenders' set model		NRP	☐

DG006 MODEL 'T' FORD VAN. The model features a metal main body with brass radiator with 'FORD' on the surround.

It has a plastic roof section, header board and seats plus a set of Blue figures enclosed with models 001-035 containing a policeman, a man with a starting handle plus a dog and a girl with her teddy. Later issues cast with no cab door imprint. There are three different baseplate (BP) types.

1st DG6-DG   2nd DG6-DG8   3rd DG6-8

001	1983	'OVALTINE'			
		1st baseplate	£8	NC	☐
		2nd or 3rd baseplate		NRP	☐
002	1983	'YORKSHIRE POST'		NRP	☐
003	1984	'COOKIE COACH Co'			
		Yellow logo	£9	NC	☐
		White logo		NRP	☐
004	1984	'BRITISH MEAT'			
		1st baseplate	£25	NC	☐
		2nd baseplate without rear door design	£20	NC	☐
		With rear door design		NRP	☐
005	1984	'MARCOL'			
		Red dragon on rear door	£15	NC	☐
		No dragon on rear door		NRP	☐
006	1984	'POLICE AMBULANCE'			
		Numbered 5000 issue	£45	NC	☐
007	1984	'AEROPLANE JELLY'		NRP	☐
008	1984	'I.P.M.S.'	£12	NC	☐
009	1984	'ILLINOIS TOY SHOW'		NRP	☐
010	1984	'LIVERPOOL FESTIVAL'		NRP	☐
011	1984	'STRETTON MINERAL' —			
		Black CH		NRP	☐
		With Green chassis & roof	£12	NC	☐
012	1984	YORKSHIRE EVENING POST		NRP	☐
013	1984	'COCA-COLA'			
		'SODA FOUNTAINS' logo	£8	NC	☐
014	1984	'COCA-COLA'			
		'EVERY BOTTLE' logo	£8	NC	☐
015	1984	'BRITISH BACON'		NRP	☐
016	1984	'LLEDO CALLING'			
		Collectors Club Model	£17		☐
017	1984	'YORKSHIRE BISCUITS'		NRP	☐
018	1984	'WONDERBREAD'		NRP	☐
019	1984	'RAILWAY EXPRESS AGENCY		NRP	☐
020	1984	'PHILADELPHIA' 'FIRE/RESCUE'		NRP	☐
021	1984	'PHILADELPHIA', 'FIRE/AMB.'		NRP	☐
022	1984	'HARRY RAMSDENS'		NRP	☐
023	1984	'AUSTRALIAN AUTOMODIA'		NRP	☐
024	1984	'EXPRESS NEWS'		NRP	☐
025	1984	'PERRIER JOUET'		NRP	☐
026	1984	'MARKS & SPENCERS'		NRP	☐
027	1984	'HAMLEYS TOY SHOP'		NRP	☐
028	1984	'MAGASIN DU NORD' (normal)		NRP	☐
		White letters on headboard	£20	NC	☐
029	1984	'ECHO NEWSPAPER'		NRP	☐
030	1984	'MURPHYS POTATO CRISPS'		NRP	☐
031	1985	'OVALTINE 75th'			
		2nd baseplate/special box	£20	NC	☐
		3rd baseplate/normal box		NRP	☐
032	1985	'HOME ALES' all Green		NRP	☐
		Two tone Green body	£20	NC	☐
033	1984	'BARCLAYS BANK'			
		2nd BP, Blue logo on headboard	£20	NC	☐
		3rd BP, Cream logo on headboard	£20	NC	☐
		Other issues		NRP	☐
034	1985	'KODAK'		NRP	☐
035	1985	'LINDT CHOCOLATE'			
		TT Blue body and roof		NRP	☐
		Pale Blue body and roof	£20	NC	☐
036	1985	'WELLS DRINKS'		NRP	☐
037	1985	AUSTRALIAN 'DG' CLUB			
		Brown chassis and roof		NRP	☐
		TT Brown chassis and roof	£20	NC	☐
		With '1985 CONVENTION' logo	£200	GV	☐
038	1985	'ALTON TOWERS'		NRP	☐
039	1985	'EVENING CHRONICLE'			
		2nd BP	£20	NC	☐
		3rd BP		NRP	☐
040	1985	'WOODWARDS'		NRP	☐
041	1985	'ROYAL MAIL' red body			
		2nd baseplate	£50	NC	☐
		3rd baseplate		NRP	☐
		Late 3rd BP - no side doors	£20	NC	☐
042	1986	'JOHN SMITHS'		NRP	☐
043	1986	'CWM DALE SPRING' (Blue CH)		NRP	☐
		3rd BP and Red chassis	£20	NC	☐
044	1986	'NORTHERN DAILY MAIL'		NRP	☐
045	1986	'TOY FAIRS 1986'			
		Not sold to public — trade gift		NGPP	☐
046	1986	'CADBURYS COCOA'		NRP	☐
047	1986	'TIZER'		NRP	☐
048	1986	'HARDWARE JOURNAL'			
		Blue body	£40	NC	☐
049	1986	'HERSHEYS'		NRP	☐
050	1986	'COCA-COLA'		NRP	☐
051	1986	'COCA-COLA'		NRP	☐
052	1986	'BAY TO BIRDWOOD'		NRP	☐
053	1986	CANADA CRAFT & HOBBY — Scarce		NGPP	☐
054	1986	CANADA — TRAVEL — Scarce		NGPP	☐
055	1986	'CADBURYS DRINKING CHOCOLATE'			
		3rd baseplate with doors. SPB	£100	GV	☐
		3rd baseplate — no cab doors		NRP	☐
056	1987	'1987 TOY FAIR' Not sold to public — trade gift	£10	NC	☐
057	1987	HEDGES & BUTLER		NRP	☐
058	1987	'WELLS — BLACK VELVET'		NRP	☐
059	1987	'FAIRY SOAP'		NRP	☐
060	1988	'ROSE & CROWN'		NRP	☐
061	1988	'ROYAL FLYING CORPS'		NRP	☐
	1988	'GOLDEN SHRED'		NRP	☐
	1988	'CHARRINGTON'		NRP	☐
	1988	'1988 TOY FAIR'	£10	NC	☐

DG007 WOODY WAGON — 1930 FORD. The model features a metal body with a plastic baseplate, roof blade and seats. Designs are tampo printed and a set of figures was issued with models 001-007 containing a woman and 3 poodles.

001	1984	Pats Poodle Parlour		NRP	☐
002	1984	'COCA-COLA'		NRP	☐
003	1984	'FORD CAR SALES'		NRP	☐
004	1984	'WEST POINT TOY SHOW'			
		DG7-DG9 on BP	£20	NC	☐
		DG13 and DG14 on axles		NRP	☐
005	1984	'HAMLEYS TOYS'		NRP	☐
006	1985	'GODFREY DAVIS'		NRP	☐
007	1986	'DELLA CHOCOLATES'		NRP	☐
008	1986	'COMMONWEALTH GAMES'		NRP	☐
	1988	'CASTROL'		NRP	☐

DG008 MODEL 'T' FORD TANKER. The model features a metal body with a plastic roof section, seats and tank. Included with models 001-008 is a set of figures containing a policeman, a man with a starting handle plus a dog and a girl with her teddy.

001	1984	'ESSO PETROL'	BP-A & B	NRP	☐
022	1984	'COCA-COLA'	BP-A	NRP	☐
003	1984	'PHILADELPHIA FIRE'	BP-A	NRP	☐
004	1985	'HOFMEISTER'	BP-A & B	NRP	☐
005	1985	'CASTROL'	BP-B	NRP	☐
006	1985	'PENNZOIL'	BP-B	NRP	☐
007	1986	'BLUE MOUNTAIN'	BP-B	NRP	☐
008	1986	'HERSHEYS'	BP-B	NRP	☐
009	1987	'CROW CARRYING Co'	BP-B	NRP	☐
010	1987	'WATER WORKS'	BP-B	NRP	☐
011	1987	'ZEROLENE' 2500 only	BP-B	NGPP	☐
	1988	'HOME PRIDE'	BP-B	NRP	☐
	1988	'SHELL'	BP-B	NRP	☐

N.B. Baseplates (BP) Types
A-DG6, B-DG8, C-DG6-8

DG009 MODEL 'A' FORD OPEN CAR. The model features a metal body with a plastic baseplate and seats.

A set of figures is included containing 2 robbers, 1 police driver plus handgun.

001	1984	'POLICE' Car			
		Two tone Blue with DG7-DG9			
		on baseplate	£35	NC	☐
		All Blue version		NRP	☐
002	1984	'NEW YORK-RIO RACE'			
		DG7-DG9 on baseplate	£20	NC	☐
		DG13 & DG14 on axles		NRP	☐
003	1984	'PHILADELPHIA FIRE'		NRP	☐
004	1985	'15th MILLIONTH FORD'		NRP	☐

DG010 1933 ALBION SINGLE DECKER BUS WITH CLOSED ROOF. The model features a metal body with a plastic roof section. The set of figures contains a man and woman with boy, a lady with dog plus man leaning on bus stop.

001	1984	'BRIGHTON BELLE'		NRP	☐
002	1984	'SCHOOL BUS' Gold radiator		NRP	☐
		Silver radiator	£15	NC	☐
003	1984	'TILLINGBOURNE BUS'		NRP	☐
004	1984	'POTTERIES' Cream roof		NRP	☐
		Red roof	£15	NC	☐
005	1984	'SOUTHERN VECTIS'			
		Cream roof	£5	NC	☐
		With White logo	£15	NC	☐
006	1984	'HAMLEYS TOY SHOP'		NRP	☐
007	1985	'BARTONS'		NRP	☐
008	1985	'TARTAN TOURS'		NRP	☐
009	1985	'G.W.R.'		NRP	☐
010	1985	'TRAILWAYS'		NRP	☐
011	1985	'IMPERIAL AIRWAYS'		NRP	☐
012	1986	'REDBURNS'		NRP	☐
013	1986	'HERSHEYS' Cream chassis		NRP	☐
		Dark Cream chassis	£15	NC	☐
014	1986	'COMMONWEALTH GAMES'		NRP	☐
015	1986	'LONDON COUNTY'		NRP	☐
016	1987	'SILVER SERVICE'			
		White 'MATLOCK' logo		NRP	☐
		Silver 'MATLOCK' logo	£30	NC	☐
017	1987	'OAKRIDGE SCHOOL'		NRP	☐
	1988	BILLINGSGATE MARKET'			
		'Eastenders' set model		NRP	☐

N.B. No figures issued after 1985

DG011 LARGE HORSE DRAWN VAN. Model features a metal body with a plastic roof section and 2 horses.

The set of figures contains driver, woman, girl with hoop and boy with dog.

001	1984	'TURNBULL & Co'		NRP	☐
002	1985	'BIG TOP CIRCUS BP-A & B		NRP	☐
003	1985	'ABELS REMOVALS' BP-A		NRP	☐
004	1985	'STAFFORDSHIRE SHOW' BP-A		NRP	☐
005	1985	'WILLIAMS & GRIFFIN' BP-A		NRP	☐
006	1985	'ROYAL MAIL' BP-A		NRP	☐
007	1986	'MacCOSHAM' BP-B		NRP	☐
008	1986	'COCA-COLA' BP-B		NRP	☐
	1988	'RIDGEWAY'S TEA' BP-B		NRP	☐

BP Types: A-DG 11 near front axle
B-DG 11 near rear axle

N.B. No figures issued after 1985

DG012 1934 FIRE ENGINE. Model features a metal body with a plastic baseplate and ladder. The set of figures contains a fireman driver and 2 seated firemen in Blue plastic. No figures after 1985.

001	1984	'LUCKHURST COUNTY'	NRP	☐
002	1985	'CARDIFF CITY'	NRP	☐
003	1985	'BERMUDA'	NRP	☐
004	1986	'LONDON' (L.C.C.)	NRP	☐
005	1986	'CHELMSFORD TOWN'	NRP	☐
006	1987	'AUXILIARY SERVICE'	NRP	☐
007	1987	'ESSEX COUNTY'	NRP	☐
008	1987	'WINDSOR' SBX		
		Ruby Wedding set model	NRP	☐
009	1987	'WARE FIRE SERVICE'	NRP	☐

N.B. From 1986 the ladder has wheels.

DG013 1929 Ford MODEL 'A' VAN. The model features a metal body with a plastic roof and roof blade (when fitted). The 12 spoke wheels fitted may be brass, Red, Brown or Cream or Yellow 20 spoke. The set of figures contained in 001-010 includes a boy, a man and a delivery man.

001	1984	'EVENING NEWS' BP-A & B		NRP	☐
002	1984	'ROYAL MAIL VAN' BP-B		NRP	☐
003	1984	'MARY ANN BREWERY' BP-B		NRP	☐
004	1984	'HAMLEYS TOY SHOP'			
		SPB BP-B		NRP	☐
005	1985	JERSEY EVENING POST BP-B		NRP	☐
006	1985	'COCA-COLA' BP-B		NRP	☐
007	1985	'BASILDON BOND' — gloss		NRP	☐
		with matt paint finish BP-B	£15	NC	☐
008	1985	'MICHELIN TYRES' BP-B & C		NRP	☐
009	1985	'STROH'S BEER' BP-B & C		NRP	☐
010	1985	'COCA-COLA' BP-B & C		NRP	☐
011	1985	'LIVERPOOL GARDEN			
		FESTIVAL' BP-C		NRP	☐
012	1985	'TUCHER BEERS' BP-C		NRP	☐
013	1985	'EVENING SENTINEL' BP-C		NRP	☐
014	1985	'ROYAL MAIL 350th' BP-C		NRP	☐
015	1986	'ROBINSONS SQUASHES' BP-C		NRP	☐
016	1986	'CAMP COFFEE' BP-C		NRP	☐
017	1986	'MITRE 10' BP-C	£20	NC	☐
018	1986	'HERSHEYS KISSES' BP-C		NRP	☐
019	1986	'HERSHEYS' BP-C		NRP	☐
020	1986	'COCA-COLA'			
		(Yellow/Black) BP-C		NRP	☐
		With all Yellow body		NGPP	☐
021	1986	'F.D.B.' (Danish Co-op) BP-C	£20	NC	☐
022	1986	'RYDER TRUCK' BP-C		NRP	☐
023	1987	'H.P. SAUCE' BP-C		NRP	☐
024	1987	'J. LYONS & Co Ltd' BP-C		NRP	☐
	1988	'EXCHANGE & MART'			
		with 'DAYS GONE' Base		NRP	☐
	1988	'HEINZ TOMATO SOUP' BP-C		NRP	☐
	1988	'Eastenders' set model logo			
	1988	'EVER READY' BP-C		NRP	☐

BP Types A. DG7, DG9.
B. Same plus DG13 & DG14 on axles.
C. DG7 9-13-4 no axle numbers.

DG014 1930 MODEL 'A' FORD CAR. Model features a metal body with a plastic roof, baseplate and seats. The set of figures with only 001 contains 1 U.S. cop and 2 U.S. firemen.

001	1985	"SAN DIEGO 'FIRE CHIEF'" BP-B		NRP	☐
		With 'FIRE CHIEF' in Gold BP-A	£50	GP	☐
002	1985	'TAXI' BP-B		NRP	☐
003	1985	'ACME CLEANERS' BP-B		NRP	☐
004	1986	'GRAND HOTEL' BP-B		NRP	☐
005	1986	'HAMLEYS TOY SHOP' SPB BP-B		NRP	☐
006	1987	'STATE PENITENTIARY' BP-B		NRP	☐

BP Types. A. DG13 & DG14 on axles.
B. No numbers on axles.

DG015 1932 A.E.C. REGENT DOUBLE DECKER BUS. Model features a White or Cream plastic upper window section. No figures issued.

001	1985	'HALLS WINE' Red body			
		Silver roof — smooth underpiece	£45	GP	☐
		Silver roof — ribbed underside			
		and brass radiator grille	£45	GP	☐
		Silver roof — chrome grille		NRP	☐
		Brown body — Grey roof	£30	NC	☐
		Display case model	£45	GP	☐
002	1985	'COCA-COLA'		NRP	☐
003	1985	'FESTIVAL GARDENS'		NRP	☐
005	1985	'CINZANO'		NRP	☐
006	1985	'CASTLEMAINE XXXX'		NRP	☐
007	1986	'EVENING ARGUS'		NRP	☐
008	1986	'ROYAL WEDDING' SPB		NRP	☐
009	1986	'COMMONWEALTH GAMES'		NRP	☐
010	1986	'SWAN VESTAS'		NRP	☐
011	1987	'MADAME TUSSAUDS'		NRP	☐
012	1987	'HEINZ 57'		NRP	☐
013	1987	'RADIO TIMES' SBX			
		Ruby Wedding Set model		NGPP	☐
014	1987	'TV TIMES'		NRP	☐
	1988	'GOLDEN WONDER CRISPS'		NRP	☐
	1988	'THE BIRMINGHAM MAIL'		NRP	☐

DG016 1934 DENNIS HEAVY GOODS VEHICLE. Model features a metal body with a plastic baseplate and roof section. No figures.

001	1985	'MAYFLOWER'		NRP	☐
002	1985	'CROFT SHERRY'		NRP	☐
003	1985	'ROYAL MAIL'		NRP	☐
004	1985	'BUSHELLS TEA'		NRP	☐
005	1986	'TREBOR'		NRP	☐
006	1986	'L.N.E.R.'		NRP	☐
007	1986	'HAMLEYS'		NRP	☐
008	1986	'HERSHEYS-KRACKEL		NRP	☐
009	1986	'HERSHEYS MR GOOD BAR'		NRP	☐
010	1986	'COCA-COLA'		NRP	☐
011	1986	'KIWI POLISHES'		NRP	☐
012	1987	'FYFFES'		NRP	☐
013	1987	'CADBURYS CHOCOLATE'		NRP	☐
014	1987	'LLEDO WORLDWIDE C'TORS CLUB'		NRP	☐
015	1988	'PICKFORDS REMOVERS'		NRP	☐
	1988	'ABELS'		NRP	☐

DG017 1932 A.E.C. REGAL SINGLE DECK COACH. Model features a metal body with a plastic baseplate, seats and window section. No figures.

001	1985	'SOUTHEND' (Blue body)			
		Casting with filler cap	£45	GP	☐
		Casting without filler cap		NRP	☐
		With Red body	£75	GP	☐
002	1985	'CORPORATION TRANSPORT' - 'B.O.A.C.'		NRP	☐
003	1985	'EURO TOURS'		NRP	☐
004	1985	'LONDON TRANSPORT'		NRP	☐
005	1986	'COMMONWEALTH GAMES'		NRP	☐
006	1986	'STRATFORD BLUE' (Chrome rad.)		NRP	☐
		With brass radiator	£10	NC	☐
007	1986	'OXFORD' 'MORRELL'S ALES'		NRP	☐
008	1986	'HAMLEYS TOY SHOP' SPB		NRP	☐
009	1986	'BIG TOP CIRCUS'		NRP	☐
010	1987	'BURNLEY CORPORATION'		NRP	☐
011	1987	'PENNINE COACHES'		NRP	☐
012	1987	'ROYAL AIR FORCE'		NRP	☐
013	1988	'HANTS & DORSET'		NRP	☐

DG018 1937 PACKARD ENCLOSED VAN. Model features a metal body with a plastic baseplate and roof section. No figures.

001	1985	'AMBULANCE' BP-A		NRP	☐
002	1985	'AMERICAN AMBULANCE' BP-A		NRP	☐
003	1986	'RAPID CASH TRANSIT' BP-A		NRP	☐
004	1986	'COMMONWEALTH GAMES' A & B		NRP	☐
005	1986	'FIRESTONE TYRES' BP A & B		NRP	☐
006	1986	'CAMPERDOWN' (3000) A & B	£60	GP	☐
007	1987	'WHITE STAR LINE' BP-B		NRP	☐
008	1987	'COLMANS MUSTARD' BP-B		NRP	☐
009	1987	RAF AMBULANCE BP-B		NRP	☐
	1988	NATIONAL WESTMINSTER BANK BP-B		NRP	☐

N.B. 3 BP types as per DG 024

DG019 1931 ROLLS ROYCE PHANTOM II

001	1985	Burgundy body, Black roof		NRP	☐
002	1985	All Cream model - not sold to general public		NGPP	☐
003	1986	Yellow body, Brown roof		NRP	☐
004	1986	Two tone Beige body		NRP	☐
005	1987	Metallic Gold body, White roof		NRP	☐
	1987	Ruby body, Cream roof. SBX.		NGPP	☐
006	1988	Silver lustre body, Black roof		NRP	☐

N.B. 3 BP types as per DG 024

DG020 1936 FORD STAKE TRUCK

001	1986	'EAGLE ALES'		NRP	☐
002	1986	'COCA-COLA'		NRP	☐
003	1986	'WHITBREAD'		NRP	☐
004	1986	'GOODRICH'		NRP	☐
005	1986	'STROHS BEERS'		NRP	☐
006	1987	'UNIROYAL'		NRP	☐
007	1988	'AULD SCOTCH GINGER'		NRP	☐
	1988	'IND COOPE'		NRP	☐

DG021 1934 CHEVROLET VAN

001	1986	'SHARPS TOFFEES'		NRP	☐

002	1986	'LEICESTER MERCURY'		NRP	☐
003	1986	'COCA-COLA'		NRP	☐
004	1986	'HOSTESS CAKE'		NRP	☐
005	1987	'DR PEPPER'		NRP	☐
006	1987	'LLEDO WORLDWIDE CLUB'		NRP	☐
	1988	'W. H. SMITHS'		NRP	☐

DG022 1933 TOWN VAN

001	1986	'STAG WHISKY' BP-A, B, C		NRP	☐
002	1986	'LORD TED CIGARS' BP-B, C		NRP	☐
003	1987	'INTERFLORA U.S.A.' BP-C		NRP	☐
004	1987	'WHITMANS CHOCOLATES' BP-C		NRP	☐
005	1987	'LLEDO WORLDWIDE CLUB' BP-C		NRP	☐
	1988	'TESCO's' BP-C		NRP	☐

N.B. 3 BP types as per DG 024

DG023 1954 SCENICRUISER

001	1987	'GREYHOUND' (Dark Smoke WDS)		NRP	☐
		With Pale Smoke windows	£50	GP	☐
002	1987	'GOLDEN WEST TOURS'		NRP	☐
003	1987	'BUFFALO'		NRP	☐

DG024 1934 ROLLS ROYCE PLAYBOY CAR

001	1987	Yellow/Black body, Tan roof.			
		A. DG-18-19-22 on baseplate		NGPP	☐
		B. DG18/19/22/24/25 on baseplate & small luggage boot flange		NGPP	☐
		C. With large luggage boot flange		NRP	☐
		Models i & ii were TV Times direct mail offer models. A few were fitted with Packard radiators.			
		Two tone Lilac body, White roof (3 Lilac shades exist)		NRP	☐
		Red/White body, White roof	£7-£9	MPR	☐
	1988	Silver lustre body, Black roof		NRP	☐

DG025 1925 ROLLS ROYCE SILVER GHOST CAR

001	1987	Dark Blue body chassis/roof			
		A. With DG18-19-22 on baseplate and large D flange		NGPP	☐
		B. With DG/18/19/22/24/25 on baseplate and small luggage boot flange		NGPP	☐
		C. With DG/18/19/22/24/25 on baseplate & large luggage boot flange		NRP	☐
		NB. TV Times direct mail offer Silver body, Blue chassis & roof		NRP	☐
		White body, Black roof		NRP	☐
		Silver lustre body, Black roof		NRP	☐
	1988	New colour to be issued			

DG026 CHEVROLET DELIVERY VAN — DRINKS

001	1987	'SCHWEPPES'			
		Lemon body, Tan load	£25	NC	☐
		Yellow body, Black load		NRP	☐
002	1987	'COCA-COLA'		NRP	☐
003	1987	'LLEDO WORLDWIDE CLUB'		NRP	☐
004	1988	'BARRS IRN BRU'		NRP	☐
	1988	'TIZER'		NRP	☐

DG027 1938 MACK BREAKDOWN TRUCK

001	1987	'A1 24-HOUR RECOVERY'		NRP	☐
002	1988	'HANKS AUTO SERVICES'		NRP	☐
	1988	'MOBIL OIL'		NRP	☐

DG028 1937 MACK 'CANVAS BACK' TRUCK

001	1988	'TYPHOO TEA'		NRP	☐
	1988	HEINZ BEANS		NRP	☐

DG029 DODGE AMBULANCE

001	1988	U.S. Military Field Ambulance		NRP	☐

DG030 CHEVY PANEL VAN

001	1988	JOHN BULL TYRES		NRP	☐

Collector Packs

Ref. No.	Dates	Model Type	Model Features and Size	Rarity and Price Grading	
GS1	1984		006 'RAILWAY EXPRESS, 007 'FORD SALES & SERVICE', 009 NEW YORK-RIO	£10-£15	MPR ☐
CP1	1984		003 'ROBERTSONS', 004 'PEARS SOAP', 006 'DAILY EXPRESS'	£10-£15	MPR ☐
CP2	1985		010 'TRAILWAYS', 015 'CASTLEMAINE XXXX', 017 'EUROTOUR CRUISES'	£5-£8	MPR ☐
?	1985		006 'BARCLAYS', 011 'ABELS', 013 'MICHELIN'	£5-£8	MPR ☐

SETS OF MODELS

	1984	'COCA-COLA'	013, 016, 020, 021		NRP ☐
	1984	'PHILADELPHIA FIRE BUREAU'	005, 006 (Red), 006 (White), 008, 009		NRP ☐
	1984	'HAMLEYS TOY SHOP'	003, 004, 006, 007, 010, 013		NRP ☐
	1985	'ROYAL MAIL'	003, 006, 011, 013, 016		NRP ☐
	1986	'COMMONWEALTH GAMES'	007, 010, 015		NRP ☐
	1986	'COCA-COLA'	006 (Red), 006 (Green), 011, 013, 016, 020, 021		NRP ☐
	1986	'HERSHEYS'	006, 008, 010, 013 (White), 013 (Blue), 016 (Red), 016 (Yellow)		NRP ☐
	1987	'ROYAL FLYING CORPS'	006, 017, 018		NRP ☐
	1988	'VINTAGE ROLLS ROYCE COLLECTION'	Silver lustre finish 019, 024, 025	£14.95	NC ☐
	1988	'BUDWEISER'	006, 011, 020, 021, 022, 026 USA release 1988 — UK & EUROPE 1989	£28.50	NC ☐

Fantastic Set-O-Wheels by Lledo (London) Ltd.

Ref. No.	Model Type	Model Features and Size	Rarity and Price Grading	
A series of models introduced in 1985 and aimed at the children's market in the USA and sold by Hartoy Inc of Florida.				
DG006/001	'MALIBU OR BUST'		NRP	☐
DG007/001	'TRI STAGS DEALER'		NRP	☐
DG008/001	'LIQUID BUBBLE'		NRP	☐
DG010/001	'OAKRIDGE SCHOOL'		NRP	☐
DG012/001	'BOSTON FIRE DEPT'		NRP	☐
DG013/001	'JOLLYTIME'		NRP	☐
DG014/001	'POLICE CAR'		NRP	☐
DG014/002	'SAN DIEGO FIRE'		NRP	☐

Edocar Models by Lledo (London) Ltd

Models made solely for sale through a Netherlands outlet trading as Edor BV (Fred Beheer BV). 'EDOCAR' on baseplate.

Ref. No.	Model Type	Model Features and Size	Rarity and Price Grading	
DG008	'ESSO BLUE' — Red or Blue		NRP	☐
DG012		All Red body	NRP	☐
DG014	'TAXI'	Yellow body	NRP	☐
DG016/17	'HUMBROL'	Green or White	NRP	☐
DG018	'AMBULANCE'	White body	NRP	☐
DG019	'AMBULANCE'	Silver body	NRP	☐
DG021	'EDOCAR'	Blue body	NRP	☐

'Marathon' Models by Lledo (London) Ltd

Ref. No.	Dates	Model Type	Model Features and Size	Rarity and Price Grading	
A new series introduced in 1987.					
MM1 LEYLAND OLYMPIAN DOUBLE DECKER					
01	1987	'LONDON PRIDE — ENSIGN BUS'		NRP	
03	1987	'TODAY'S PAN AM'		NRP	☐
MM2 SETRA COACH					
01	1987	'AIR CANADA COURTESY BUS'		NRP	☐
02	1987	'PAN AM CREW BUS'		NRP	☐
03	1987	'GHANA AIRWAYS'		NRP	☐
MM3 NEOPLAN SPACELINER					
01	1987	'GATWICK FLIGHTLINE'		NRP	☐
02	1987	'SPEEDLINK HARROW — GATWICK'		NRP	☐
03	1987	'ISLAND TOURS'		NRP	☐
1988 new model to be issued 'SHELL' Petrol Tanker					

LLEDO — Promotional Models

Collectors will find models which are not listed in this Catalogue. These models have been produced for promotional purposes and have not been offered for sale through the normal retail shops unlike the code 1 models which have been listed.

These promotional models may or may not have been 100% produced by Lledo e.g. the 'View Van' series where the 'Views' have been applied by a different firm.

The prices for most promotional models are around £5 although higher prices are asked for models where perhaps only a very few are available to collectors ie 95% of the models produced having been given to trade customers.

Examples of Prices Asked For the Rarer Promotionals

Ref. No.	Model Type	Model Features and Size	Rarity and Price Grading	
LP003	'PHOENIX STEAM DRY' (1000)		£25	NC ☐
LP004	'BRIDLINGTON' (500)		£25	NC ☐
LP005	'HULL FIRE BRIGADE (1000)		£35	NC ☐
LP006	'FARNHAM MALTINGS' (990)		£10	NC ☐
	'SALVATION ARMY (1000)		£15	NC ☐
	'FRANKLIN PRO AM (1500)		£7.50	NC ☐
LP013	'BUCKTROUT' (2000)		£5.50	NC ☐
	VECTIS MODELS (500)		£6.50	NC ☐
LP015	Canadian set of 5 models	EDMONTON, TORONTO, MONTREAL, VANCOUVER, QUEBEC	£75	GP ☐
LP016	'KLEEN-E-ZE' (10000)		£9	NC ☐
LP021	DR BARNARDO'S (1000)		£8.50	NC ☐
LP022	'PACKARD MOTOR COMPANY'		£5.50	NC ☐
	'SCOTSBURN'	Canadian Sets of Promotional Models, e.g. 'PERSIL', 'DUNDEE BUS', 'CASTROL', 'KLM'	£11-£14	MPR ☐

'DAYS GONE' collectors should be aware that some of the early early promotional models had 'DAYS GONE' on the BP eg DG003 Horse Drawn Delivery Vans and DG005 Horse Drawn Fire Engines, which had special 'HULL', 'METROPOLITAN' and 'GUILDFORD' promotional tampo printed liveries. These are not short run 'DAYS GONE' models but promotional models having had their designs added by an external firm.

Some early promotionals were actually issued in 'DAYS GONE' boxes but may be easily recognised for they had adhesive labels attached outside the Lledo factory instead of the tampo print designs. One exception to this rule is the 'HALE END SCHOOL' promotional which has 'DAYS GONE' on the baseplate plus a tampo print design put on by an outside firm.

Lledo's very first attempt at producing a promotional model was a Model 'T' Ford Van 100% produced in the Lledo factory with DG6-DG8 on its base. In addition it had labels affixed (W. HAYDON) and was mounted on a wooden plinth. The models were eventually distributed to the public through a dealer outlet and hence instead of being a promotional model it became the only Code 1 model with labels affixed.

Early promotionals may also be recognised by having either just 'MADE IN ENGLAND by Lledo' on the BP, or by simply not having 'DAYS GONE' on the BP. Nowadays it is clearly indicated on both the model and the box that a model is a promotional.

Collectors requiring a full listing of promotional models should contact the LLEDO CALLING Collectors Club (see next page for details).

It is often said that collectors collect what they like and this is very true of promotional models.

For those interested in having Lledo (London) Ltd produce a promotional model bearing their own particular promotional message the address to write to is:-

Lledo (London) Ltd, Woodhall Road, South Street, Ponders End, Middlesex EN3 4LE.

Lledo Calling

'MODELS OF DAYS GONE' Collectors Club

Whilst it is the intention of this catalogue to provide collectors with listings of this most exciting range of die-cast models the listings must of necessity be of a relatively simplified nature. It is not therefore the objective of this catalogue to describe the models in detail so consequently collectors requiring more information would be well advised to join the 'MODELS OF DAYS GONE' Collectors Club.

The 'LLEDO CALLING' Collectors Club was founded by Ray Bush in 1985 and already encompasses a large worldwide membership. It is the only official LLEDO 'MODELS OF DAYS GONE' Collectors Club authorised by LLEDO (LONDON) LTD.

A Club magazine is issued four times a year to members and it is full of interesting information which ideally supplements this catalogue.

Ray is always happy to answer club members queries providing they are put to him during normal office hours Mon-Fri unless it's something particularly urgent, so why not drop him a line about membership to the address given below. Please remember though that all correspondence requiring a response must include a reply paid envelope.

'LLEDO CALLING' Collectors Club,
1 Torr Road,
Hartley,
Plymouth,
Devon,
PL3 5TD,
ENGLAND.

LLEDO PROMOTIONAL MODELS

The aim of the 'LLEDO CALLING' Collectors Club has been to encourage the collecting of 'DAYS GONE' models through its club magazine. Consequently details of 'LLEDO PROMOTIONAL' models models are not included. To fill this gap a new publication was launched in the summer of 1988 only concerned with the models designated 'LLEDO PROMOTIONAL'. The publication will be issued quarterly at the same time as the 'LLEDO CALLING' magazine. For further details write to the above address enclosing a stamped addressed envelope. NB. The publication has nothing in common with LLEDO CALLING and has its own editor Bill Lynas of Middlesbrough.

CATALOGUE PHOTOGRAPHS

All the models used in the photographs form part of the British Die-cast Model Toys Catalogue's own collection unless differently described.

ADVERTISERS PHOTOGRAPHS

Vectis Models have included the following models from the display at the Cowes Toy & Model Museum:

i) Dinky Garage No. 45 and No. 49 Petrol Pumps, parked outside is 306 Rolls Royce (post-war) and 36a Armstrong Siddeley (post-war).

ii) Dinky Set No. 50 in Box 'Ships of the British Navy' issued 1934-1942.
Unboxed set Dinky Toys Set No. 51 — Famous Liners

iii) Station Bookshop picture includes Dinky pre-war Dinky passenger accessories from Set No 3.

iv) The three commercial vehicles are of course Dinky Guy Vans No. 514 'LYONS SWISS ROLLS' and 'WEETABIX' plus 25v Bedford Refuse Wagon.

Mecca Models' advertisement features a Dinky Guy Van No. 918 'EVER READY'.

Past Present Toys have included the superb 941 (504) Dinky Toys 'MOBILGAS' Tanker in their advertisement.

David Hinams advertisement include features Dinky Toys Nos. 156 Rover 75, 108 MG Midget (Competition Finish) and 31d Trojan Van 'OXO'.

Corgi Toys feature a tremendous selection from their current range.

Model Motors feature the 'Models of Yesteryear' Y13 U.K. Matchbox Club Code 2 Model, plus the Y1 'ZEROLENE' Tanker and the Dinky Toy Model 485 'SANTA SPECIAL' Model 'T' Ford.

Jonscot Collection features the 'Models of Yesteryear' Y6 AEC 'OSRAM' truck and the Dinky Toy 30j/412 Austin Wagon.

The front cover displays many models — a magnifying glass will assist in their identification.

The rear cover displays many models — less experienced collectors might like to identify each one:—
Dinky Toys: 295, 954, 450, 504/941, 581/981, 514, 984, 491, 292, 514/917, 968, 443, 25h/250, 260, 261, 472, 274, 784, 36g, 308, 716, 62x, 736, 62k, 073, 067, 065, 52e.
Corgi Toys: C11, 1101, 301, 302, 468, 266, 9004, 9002.
Spot On Models: 281, 263, 266, 118.
Matchbox Toys: Early Lesney (one model) Major Models M2a, M6a.
Models of Yesteryear: Y5-4, 3 x Y12-3, Y11-1. Y9-1, Y12-1, 2 x Y4-2, Y13-1, Y5-2.
Matchbox Miniatures: 1b, 5c, 7a, 9a, 10c, 19a.
Lledo 'Models of Days Gone': DG001, DG006.

N.B.: The compiler regrets that owing to printing deadlines only photographic copy which was with us by 1st August 1988 could be included for mention in this section.

A PRACTICAL GUIDE TO COLLECTING BRITISH DIE-CAST MODEL TOYS
BY ROGER MAZILLIUS

From the humble and crude beginnings of the pre-war "slush cast" Britains, Taylor & Barrett, Johillco etc, and the earliest die-cast Meccano Modelled Miniatures, to the more sophisticated and detailed Dinky, Corgi Toys, Lesney and Spot-On models some 30 years later, the British die-cast model toy has today encapsulated the nostalgic memories of thousands of middle-aged "boys" with the desire to own an appreciating collectable asset.

As readers of this catalogue will have noted, the increase in value of most of the thousands of models described therein is nothing short of remarkable. The continued strength of demand from an increasing number of collectors coupled with the scarcity of fine original models can only give confidence to both collector and dealer alike.

As most users of this book are well acquainted with the collecting market place, I trust they will forgive me for stating what to them is the obvious, in the following paragraphs — which are written as a well-intentioned guide for the new collector.

What do you want to collect? For example, is it Dinky Toys across the board or only post-war production, or just military models, or American cars, or British cars or aeroplanes etc, etc. Then what condition do you require, is it mint with box, or mint or any condition. What about price? Many collectors have a limit they will pay for a model so will it be £5, £10, £50 etc?

Or will you want to collect the models you remember playing with as a child irrespective of make or condition? I have seen many a collector grow misty-eyed as he recalled playground encounters with his speedy Austin Atlantic which somehow kept its feet while all around were losing theirs!

Or are you the investing type with a few thousand pounds to spare who, attracted by recent media hype about the investing possibilities in old toys, is looking for a financial return rather than a trip down memory lane?

Well gentlemen, and a few ladies, there are plenty of full and part-time dealers in the world of old toys and models who are ready and willing to assist you in the spending of a few pounds up to many thousands in the pursuit of your personal collecting habit.

Some will have advertised in this book, others in The Collector's Gazette, The Model Collector, Model Auto Review and other monthly or bi-monthly specialist publications.

Many advertise specific items for sale with details of their condition, e.g. "Dinky Toy No. 111 Triumph TR2 — Pink — M/B — £60" — The M/B of course stands for "Mint Boxed". And here is your first problem. What is "Mint Boxed". Well what it isn't is a model with chipped paint-work, however slight or a box either torn or creased, again however slight. Of course the likelihood of finding perfection in both model and box is remote thus many items are advertised as Mint and Boxed which do have faults. As a consequence of this there are dealers who advertise models as "Boxed" giving a no quibble money-back refund if the purchaser considers the model unworthy of the price or description.

If you buy from an advertised list and are unhappy with the model received then a rational request to the advertiser should result in a satisfactory refund — if not, write to the Editor of the publication concerned; see your solicitor or never deal with the trader again!

Of course many collectors prefer to see before they buy, and thus a personal visit to the premises of the advertisers is a must. Where this is not possible, e.g. the business is part-time postal only or you live in Devon and the trader in Berwick-on-Tweed, you have a problem.

This is easily solved however by the popularity of "Swapmeets". These public old toy and train collectors' fairs, which is what Swapmeets have become since little "swapping" actually now occurs, take place all over the country every weekend and many mid-week evenings, bringing together a good selection of dealers and their wares for public perusal.

Here in the spotlight of competitiveness, the careful purchaser can buy after, not only a careful perusal of the model concerned, but a check on the prices of other dealers. This is particularly possible at the bigger events where the contents of perhaps two hundred tables are available for inspection.

A list of such events are published in most of the collectors' magazines with the telephone number of the organisers, most of whom are only too pleased to give details of the event to enquirers. After all there is usually an admission charge — between 50p–£1, so every customer is welcomed.

Anyway to return to your collection. Having decided what you want to collect and of course this will also depend on the amount of money you have available for this purpose, plan your purchases carefully.

For example, what Swapmeets can you attend; whether any dealers whose lists you have are attending any of these events, how much you intend to spend etc...

By carefully planning, you should avoid the pitfall of impulse buying, or even worse, panic buying — that is, seeing someone else admiring a model you are uncertain about and buying this just in case the other person does! The next day you realise that you did not really want the model in the first place.

Having decided what to buy, can you do anything about the asking price. Well usually you can as most dealers are prepared to haggle — that is the tradition at Swapmeets — particularly if you are buying more than one piece and paying in cash!

Of course established dealers will take a cheque with a valid card and credit cards as well (but are not so keen to give a price reduction on credit cards).

So the choice is yours — be careful, be vigilant, ask for a written guarantee of authenticity if the model is a rare or expensive one, beware of repainted or touched up models, particularly the Dinky Supertoy Vans and Lorries as these can be "restored" and then confused with original mint examples by even quite knowledgeable collectors. If in doubt — ask for a second opinion or don't buy!

Finally, congratulations on entering such a world-wide, friendly and interesting hobby — may all your purchases be good ones, including your fair share of bargains and remember, most wives, girlfriends etc. cannot understand our fascination with collecting our old toys — particularly the money we spend on them, so be prepared for a bit of flak when the extent of your interest is known!

ABBREVIATIONS

EXAMPLE OF USE

Early Dinky Cars
Model 366 Bentley Two Seater Sports Coupe.
Yellow/Black or Cream/Black body, OC
SBL (3 + 9)/SBP/SDL/MCH/BR/1SDW/S

Non Abbreviated Form
Yellow and Black or Cream and Black body, other
colours also thought to exist. Slanting bonnet louvres
(group of three, plus a group of nine), Slots in Base
Plate, Sidelights, Moulded Chassis, Bentley
Radiator, one sidewindow, seats.

A	Aerial
AA	Automobile Association
AB	Aveling Barford
AC	Aircraft
AD	Army Driver
ADS	Advertisements
A.E.C.	Not an abbreviation but the name of a vehicle type
AF	Aerofoil
AFO	Air Force
AFT	Adjustable Feet
AIM	Australian Issue Model
ALO	Attendant Leans Out
AM	Ambulanceman (men)
AMB	Ambulance
AMP	Anti Mist Panel
AN	Animal(s)
AOV	All Other Variants
AP	Airport
ARDT	Authentic Radiator
ARB	Anti Roll Bar
ARBB	Anti Roll Bar and Bumpers
ARC	Armoured Car
AS	Adjustable Seats
ASIC	As Shown in Catalogue
ASM	Auto Steer Mechanism
ASR	Armstrong Siddeley Radiator
AU	Authentic
AUTO	Automobile
ATT	Arrow Tread Tyres
AV	Articulated Vehicle
AVI	Also Version Issued
AX	Axle
B	Body
BB	Black Base
BC	Black Crosses
BCR	Bedford Carrimore
BCT	Black Tyres
BCV	Battery Cover
BD	Boiler Door
BDT	Breakdown Truck
BEM	Bonnet Emblem
BEPL	Beige Plastic
BGPT	Black or Grey Plastic Tyres
BK	Building Kit
BLB	Bill Boards
BLM	Black Metal
BLP	Black Plastic
BLPS	Black Plastic Seats
BLSP	Blister Pack
BM	Bumper(s)
BMBP	Bare Metal Base Plate
BMS	Boom(s)
BN	Bonnet
BNB	Bonnet Badge
BO	Battery Operated
BOCTV	Battery Operated Colour TV Set
BOF	Battery Operated Features
BOFL	Battery Operated Flashing Lights
BOMCA	Battery Operated Micro-chip Action
BOWL	Battery Operated Working Lights
BP	Base Plate (or British Petroleum)
BPCL	Black Plastic Coal Load

BPBP	Black Painted Base Plate
BPR	Black Plastic Rollers
BPk	Buyers Premium
BPS	Base Plate Solid
BPT	Black Plastic Tyres
BPW	Black Plastic Wheels
BR	Bentley Radiator
BRB	Battery on Running Board
BRR	Brass Radiator
BRPL	Brown Plastic
BRS	Bristol
BRT	Brass Trim
BRW	Brass Wheels
BS	Bonnet Strap
BSR	British Salmson Radiator
BT	Boot
BUP	Bubble Pack
BW	Bogey Wheel
BX	Boxed
BXV	Box Van
CA	Crimped Axles
CCC	Contains Collector Card
CCH	Colour Change
CCCH	Criss Cross Chassis
CCM	Collector Club Member
CCR	Criss Cross Radiator
CD	Civilian Driver
CDG	Corgi Dog
CDS	Conductress
CEM(S)	Company Emblem(s)
CEQ	Crane Equipment
CF	Competition Finish
CFL	Cab Floor
CH	Chassis
CHEVVY	Chevrolet
CHIP	Chipperfields
CHVR	Combine Harvester
CHS	Coloured Hubs Seen
CHT	Chain Tracks
CHW	Chrome Wheels
CI	Cast In
CIR	Circle
CIRD	Cast In Rear Door
CISPKW	Cast In Spoke Wheels
CL	Carriage Lamps
CLS	Coach Lines
CLW	Clover Leaf Wheels
CM	Camouflage
CMC	Command Centre
CMN	Camouflage Net
CMX	Concrete Mixer
CND	Conductor
CNP	Canopy
CNT	Container
CNTT	Container Truck
CO	Crane Operates
CP	Chrome Parts
CPC	Clear Plastic Cover
CPL	Cream Plastic Load
CPM	Collector Pack Model
CPT	Cream Plastic Tyres
CR	Crane
CRA	Crimped or Riveted Axles
CRF	Cab Roof
CRS	Crew Seats
CRT	Current
CRPL	Cream Plastic
CRV	Caravan
CRWH	Closed Rear Wheel Housing
CS	Cab Streamliner
CSP	Canopy Supports
CT	Contains
CTP	Correct Tyre Pattern
CTR	Chrome Trim
CTS	Collapsible Tiers
CV	Convertible
CVB	Conveyor Belt
CW	Clear Windows
CWK	Cat Walk
CWS	Celluloid Windscreen

D	Driver
DAT	Detachable Ammunition Trailer
DB	Dashboard
DBD	Destination Boards/Blinds
DBL	Dozer Blade
DBG	Door Badge
DC	Die-cast
DCH	Detailed Chassis
DCFB	Dropping Cap Firing Bombs
DCI	Drive Cast In
DCNT	Detachable Container
DCS	Decals
DCST	Driver Controlled Steering
DCV	Detachable Canvas
DD	Double Decker
DDB	Detailed Dashboard
DDC	Detachable Driver's Cab
DDR	Drop Down Ramp
DDS	Door Design
DDTB	Drop Down Tailboard
DDTG	Drop Down Tailgate
DE	Detailed Engine
DEL	Deleted
DEX	Detailed Exhaust
DH	Driver's Helmet
DHT	Detachable Hood and Tonneau
DI	Detailed Interior
DIA	Diarama Box
DIIT	Detailed Interior Includes Toilet!
DK	Dark
D/L	Decal/Logo
DL	Double Line
DLD	Detachable Ladder
DLG	Detachable Luggage
DMB	Dumper Blade
DMP	Dumper
DPBA	Detailed Propshaft and Back Axle
DPHD	Detachable Plastic Hood
DR	Decal Reads
DRAXW	Detachable Rear Axle and Wheels
DRF	Detachable Roof
DRL	Diesel Roller
DRMDW	Detachable Roof Mounted Driving Wheel
DRS	Driver's Seat
DS	Detailed Suspension
DSC	Driving School Car
DSI	Driver Slotted In
DSPOM	Direct Sale Pack Offer Model
DSPW	Detachable Spare Wheel
DST	Driver Standing
DT	Detail
DTA	Detachable
DTC	Detachable Truck Cover
DTH	Detachable Hood
DTR	Dump Truck
DW	Double Wheels
E	Engine
EAX	Early Axle type
EBD	Exposed Brake Drums
EC	Engine Cover
EE	Exposed Engine
EG	Elevating Gun
EHBL	Equal Horizontal Bonnet Louvres
EI	Early Issue
ELD	Extension Ladders
ELS	Electronic Siren
EM	Emblem(s)
EMBS	Elevating Booms
EMR	Early Models had no Rivets
EOI	Explodes On Impact
EQ	Equipment
ERE	Exposed Rear Engine
EX	Exhaust
EXCO	Exclusive to Company
EXP	Exhaust Pipes
EXPM	Export Model
EXPS	Export Set

F	Front
FAS	Front Axle Swivels
FC	Forward Control
FCP	Filler Cap(s)
FD	Fender(s)
FDR	Female Driver
FE	Fire Engine
FEX	Fire Extinguisher
FFS	Flat Float with Sides
FFWS	Flat Float without Sides
FHC	Fixed Head Coupe
FHD	Folded Hood
FI	French Issue
fig(s)	figure(s)
FL(s)	Flash(es)
FLB	Flat Bed
FLD	Flanged
FLL	Flashing Light
FLLB	Flashing Light Bar
FM	Fireman (men)
FMS	Fires Missiles
FMW	Front Metal Wheels
FN	Funnel(s)
FNZ	Foam Nozzles
FP	Fire Pump
FR	Front and Rear (also F and R)
FRK	Fires Rockets
FS	Fingertip Steering
FSH	Fires Shells
FT	Flat Truck
FW	Forward
FWL	Flywheel
FWM	Friction Wheel Motion
FWS	Folded Windscreen
FWT	Folding Wing Tips
G	Grille
GBT	Globe Trotter
GBPW	Grey or Black Plastic Wheels
GDR	Guard Rails
GEN	General
GIM	German Issue Model
GJ	Golden Jacks — a jacking system
GL	Glass Load
GLV	Gear Lever
GMS	Guided Missile
GP	Grand Prix
GPL	Grey Plastic
GPT	Grey Plastic Tyres
GPW	Grey Plastic Wheels
GRL	General Release
GS	Gift Set
GSBPW	Grey Silver or Black Plastic Wheels
GSPW	Grey or Silver Plastic Wheels
GTR	Gold Trim
GV	Guidance Value (see Price & Rarity Grading)
H	Hook
HA	Handling Attachment
HB	Hatchback
HBD	Headboard
HBL	Horizontal Bonnet Louvres
HBR	Handbrake
HCLP	Hackney Carriage Licence Plate
HD	Hood
HDS	Hood Supports
HDT	Heavy Duty Tyres
HG	Headlight Guard
HGV	Heavy Goods Vehicle
HH	Hooter Horn(s)
HL	Headlights
HLPW	Highlift Plastic Wheels
HLC	Helicopter
HLF	Hydraulic Lifter
HM	Helmet
HNS	Horns
HP	Hand Painted
HPC	High Peaked Canopy
HPS	Hinged Parcel Shelf
HRS	Hinged Rear Shelf
HS	Horse
HSB	Horsebox
HSL	Headlights and Sidelights
HST	Hoist
HTBD	Hinged Tailboard

HVR	Humber Vogue Radiator
IDN	Identity Number
INT	Interior
INTER	International
JB	James Bond
JIM	Japanese Issue Model
JW	Jockey Wheel
K	Kangaroo
KB	Karrier Bantam
KC	Kings Cross
KNT	Knobby Tyres
L	Lights
LB	Label
LC	Lead Construction
LD	Ladder
LDB	Lifting Dozer Blade
LE	Limited Edition
LFB	Large Front Bumper
LG	Luggage
LGB	Luggage Boot
LGR	Luggage Rack
LHD	Left Hand Drive
LLD	Low Loader
LM	Lifting Mechanism
LMDG	Lledo Models of Days Gone
LMS	Lifting Mid Section
LMN	Luminous
LMGW	Luminous 'Glo' Windows
LOB	Lift Off Body
LORC	Large Open Racing Car
LP	Licence Plate
LPS	Lady Passenger(s)
LR	Land Rover
LRF	Lowered Roof
LRP	Launching Ramp
LRS	Lifting Rear Section
LRW	Large Racing Wheels
LS	Loudspeaker(s)
LSM	Large or Small
LT	Light
LTR	London Transport
LTRL	Loading Trolley
LTS	Letters
LUS	Luminous Seats
LV	Later Version
LWB	Lower Body. (Refers to Chassis Mudguards, Base Plate and Running Boards)
LWBS	Long Wheel Base
LWD	Lower Deck
MB	Main Body (The Major Body Colour Section)
M/B	Mint Boxed
MBENZ	Mercedes Benz
MC	Motor Cycle
MCA	Micro Chip Action
MCBV	Minor Colour and Body Variations exist
MCH	Moulded Chassis
MECH	Mechanical
MET	Metallic
MF	Massey Ferguson
MG	Military Green
MGBN	MG Badge on Nose
MGC	Military Green Camouflage
MGBPW	Metal or Grey or Black Plastic Wheels
MGM	MG Magnette
MGPW	Metal or Grey Plastic Wheels
MGRB	Mud Guards and Running Boards
MGSBPW	Metal or Grey or Silver or Black Plastic Wheels
MH	Mechanical Horse
MICCS	Model Issued with Connoisseurs Collection Set
MIECI	Made in England Cast In
MK	Markings
MLCD	Multicoloured
MLG	Moulded Luggage
MLL	Machinery Low Loader
MM	Merryweather Marquis
MN	Model Number

MNP	Military Number Plate
MNP	Manifold Pipes
MOCM	Mail Order Catalogue Model
MOM	Mail Order Model
MOV	Many Other Variations
MOY	Models of Yesteryear
MPR	Market Price Range (see Price & Rarity Grading)
MPS	Male Passenger(s)
MPSW	Metal or Plastic Steering Wheel
MRER	Mobile Ram Expels Rubbish
MRN	Maroon
MRW	Metal Roller Wheel
MSPKW	Metal Spokes Wheels
MSPW	Moulded Spare Wheel
MSW	Metal Steering Wheel
MT	Metal Tyres
MTBP	Moulded Tinplate Base Plate
MTC	Monte Carlo
MTP	Metropolitan
MW	Metal Wheels
N	Nose
NB	News Board
NC	Not Common (see Price & Rarity Grading)
NCI	Number Cast In
NFB	No Front Bumper
NGR	Not Generally Released
NGPP	No Grading Possible at Present (see Price & Rarity Grading)
NH	No Hook on early types
NMP	Number Plates
NN	No Number
NP	Number Plates
NPE	No Price Estimate (see Price & Rarity Grading)
NPP	No Price Possible (see Price & Rarity Grading)
NRP	Normal Retail Price (see Price & Rarity Grading)
NS	Nearside
NSTW	Non See Thru' Windows
OBB	Opening Bonnet and Boot
OBN	Opening Bonnet
OBNHB	Opening Bonnet and Hatchback
OBT	Opening Boot
OC	Other Colours
OCATD	Open or Closed Access to Top Deck
OCCSA	Other Colours and Compounds same as (?)
OCCSAMP	Other Colours/Components same as previous Model
OCH	Open Chassis
OCP	Opening Cockpit Cover
OCR	Open or Closed Roof
OD	Opening Door(s)
ODBB	Opening Door(s), Bonnet and Boot
ODBN	Opening Door(s) and Bonnet
ODBNHB	Opening Door(s), Bonnet and Hatchback
ODBT	Opening Door(s) and Boot
ODHB	Opening Door(s) and Hatchback
ODS	Opening Dicky Seat
ODT	Opening Door(s) and Tailgate
OEC	Opening Engine Cover
OH	Opening Hatch
OHB	Opening Hatchback
OL	Operating Lift Forks
OOS	On Off Switch
OPC	One Piece Casting
OPWDS	Open Windows
ORC	Opening Rear Cover
ORD	Opening Rear Door
ORDBN	Opening Rear Door and Bonnet
OREC	Opening Rear Engine Cover
ORF	Opening Roof
ORG	Original Radiator Grille
ORGN	Other Registration Numbers
ORS	Opening Rear Shutter
ORWH	Open Rear Wheel Housing
OS	Offside
OSR	Open Sunshine Roof
OTE	Opening Tipper End

OTG	Opening Tailgate
OWD(S)	Opening Window(s)
OWP	Operating Water Pump
OWS	Open Windscreen
P	Plastic
PB	Propeller Blades
PBP	Plastic Base Plate
PBM	Plastic Bumper(s)
PC	Petrol Cap
PCD	Pack Design
PCH	Plastic Chassis
PCR	Police Crest
PDS	Press Down Start
PFC	Petrol Filler Cap(s)
PH	Plastic Hook
PHD	Plastic Hood
PHT	Plastic Hard Top
PI	Pipes
PL	Plain
PLD	Plastic Ladder
PLL	Pallet Load
PLP	Plastic Parts
PLR	Plain Radiator
PM	Policeman
PMG	Plastic Mudguards
PN	Painted
PNB	Panelled Body
PNS	Panniers
PP	Plated Parts
PPX	Perspex
PRB	Plastic Running Board
PRM	Promotional Model (or PRO)
PRR	Plastic Replica Radiator
PRS	Plastic Roof Section
PRSN	Plastic Roof Siren
PRW	Plastic Roller Wheels
PS	Passenger
PSD	Plastic Sliding Door
PSPKW	Plastic Spoke Wheels
	(Number of spokes shown)
PST	Piston
PSW	Plastic Steering Wheel
PSWH	PLastic Spoked Wheel Hubs
PT	Plastic Tyres
PTF	Plastic Trailer Fittings
PTK	Petrol Tank
PTKR	Petrol Tanker
PTL	Painted Tail Lights
PTR	Plastic Tracks
PTT	Pattern Tread Tyres
PU	Pick-Up
PUS	Plastic Upper Section
PV	Platform Vehicle
PW	Plastic Wheels
PWH	Plastic Wheel Hubs
PWS	Plastic Window Section
(R)	Indicates the rarer colour issued
R	Radiator
RA	Riveted Axles
RAC	Royal Automobile Club
RAHBP	Rear Axle held by Base Plate
RAP	Rear Axle Pillars
RAR	Ribbed at Rear
RAXWR	Rear Axle and Wheels Removable
RB	Radiator Badge
RBD	Ribbed
RBDB	Ribbed Bed
RBM	Rear Bumper
RBT	Ridged Boot
RBW	Rubber Wheels
RC	Racing Car
RCL	Remote Control
RCD	Racing Driver
RCS	Red Cross(es)
RCT	Racing Tyres
RCTLD	Remote Control Telescopic Ladder
RCW	Racing Wheels
RD	Rear Door
RDD	Rear Door Design
RDLS	Roundels
RDT	Radiator
RDBP	Rear Differential on Base Plate
RE	Racing or Rally Emblem
REC	Rear Engine Cover

RF	Roof
RG	Radiator Grill
RGN	Registration Number
RGT	Revolving Gun Turret
RH	Roof Hatch
RHD	Right Hand Drive
RHL	Retractable Headlights
RHT	Removable Hard Top
RLB	Roof Light Bar
RLM	Rolomatic
RLT	Rear Lights (or RL)
RM	Routemaster
RMV	Removable
RMW	Rear Metal Wheel
RN	Racing or Rally Number
RNBS	Running Board(s)
RPL	Red Plastic
RPR	Replica Radiator
RR	Roof Rack or Rolls Royce
RSJ	Retractable Support Jacks
RSL	Roof Spot Light
RS	Radiator Surround
RT	Route or Rubber Tyres
RTB	Rotating Barrel
RTR	Rubber Tracks
RTRT	Rotating Turret
RTT	Retractable
RTW	Retractable Wheels
RV	Rare Version
RVD	Revolving Drum
RVM	Rear View Mirror
RVR	Rover Radiator
RW	Racing Wheel
RWD(S)	Rear Window(s)
RWS	Rear Window Slats
RWT	Rear Wheel Treads
RWWT	Racing Wide Width Tyres
S	Seats
SAA	Self Adhesive Accessories
SAPM	Same as Previous Model
SB	Stake Body
SBL	Slanting Bonnet Louvres
SBP	Slots in Base Plate
SBPT	Smooth Black Plastic Tyres
SBMU	Separate Bumper Unit
SBPRW	Silver or Black Plastic Roller Wheels
SBPT	Solid Black Plastic Tyres
SBPW	Solid Black Plastic Wheels
SBX	Special Box
SC	Sidecar
SCD	Sliding Door(s)
SCP	Scaffolding
SCP	Sleeping Compartment
SCS	Self Centering Steering
SCT	Scooter
SCW	Side Cab Window
SD	Side
SDB	Strapped Down Bonnet
SDH	Simulated Delivery Hoses
SDL	Sidelight(s)/Lamp(s)
SDW	Side Windows(s)
SDWT	Straight or Diagonal Wheel Tread
SE	Shaded Edging
SF	Superfast Wheels
SGL	Single Line
SFMW	Solid Front Metal Wheels
SGMW	Solid Grey Metal Wheels
SGPT	Smooth Grey Plastic Tyres
SGW	Single Wheel(s)
SH	Shells
SIL	Silver
SHOD	Shields on Doors
SL	Special Lights eg. jewelled headlights & emergency services roof lights
SLC	Sleeping Compartment
SLDS	Soldiers
SLD	Sliding Door
SLGB	Smooth Luggage Boot
SLWS	Solid Windscreen
SLW	Solid Wheels
SM	Smooth
SMB	Smooth Bed
SMS	Smoke Stack
SNP	Snowplough

SOD	Switch Operated Door
SOF	Set of Figures
SP	Spares
SPH	Super Hauler
SPL	Spoiler
SPN	Side Panel(s)
SPR	Silver Plastic Rollers
SPTR	Spare Tyre
SPKW	Spoke Wheels
SPT	Smooth Plastic Tyres
SPW	Spare Wheel(s)
SPWB	Spare Wheel on Bonnet
SPWBC	Spare Wheel Behind Cab
SPWBD	Spare Wheel Behind Driver
SPWH	Spare Wheel Housing
SPWR	Spare Wheel on Right
SPWRE	Spare Wheel at Rear
SPWS	Spare Wheel on some
SPWW	Spare Wheel(s) in Wing
SQM	Squadron Marking
SR	Steering Rods
SRF	Smooth Roof
SRMW	Solid Rear Metal Wheel
SS	Suspension
SSR	Shield Shaped Radiator
SST	Side Struts
SSW	Solid Spoke Wheel(s)
SSWL	Separate Steering Wheel
ST	Supertoy
STB	Stabilizers
STC	Steering Control
STCS	Staircase
STH	Starting Handle
STRC	Stretcher
STR	Silver Trim
STRP	Stripes
STRL	Standard Release
STW	Station Wagon
SW	Steering Wheel
SWC	Spare Wheel Cover
SWCI	Steering Wheel Cast In
SWOS	Steering Wheel Open or Solid
SWS	Speed Wheels
SWV	Swivels
SWW	Solid Wire Wheels
T	Tyre(s)
TB	Towbar
TBA	Turbo Assisted
TBD	Tailboard
TBDHD	Tailboard Hinges Down
TBMS	Turntable Booms
TBX	Tool Box
TC	Tonneau Cover
TCB	Tilt Cab
TCC	Tinted Cockpit Cover
TCNP	Tilt Canopy
TD	Top Deck
TF	Touring Finish
TFN	Tailfin
THW	Thin Wheels
TK	Tank or a Vehicle Type
TL	Tail Lights
TN	Tonneau
TOL	Trans-O-Lite — Corgi light ray system to illuminate headlights
TOW	Take Off Wheels
TP	Tinplate
TPBP	Tinplate Base Plate
TPD	Tampo Print Design
TPR	Tipper
TPTR	Transporter
TR	Trim — this can include: Radiator Shell, Head and Sidelights, Petrol Tank, Battery Cover, Bumpers, Outside Handbrakes and Horns, Spare Wheel Housing and Luggage Racks etc.
TRL	Trailer
TRT	Tractor
TRM	Transmission
TS	Tilt Seats
TSP	Tommy Spot
TSV	Transit Van
TT	Two Tone

TU	Trailer Uncouples	VBY	Van Body	WPEM	Working Pallet Ejection Mechanism
TUT	Turntable	VD	Various Decals	WRL	Working Rear Lights
TW(S)	Tinted Window(s) (or Toned)	VN	Vehicle Number	WRRT	Wide Rimmed Racing Tyres
TQ	Turquoise	VRF	Van Roof	WRW	Wire Wheels
		VRN	Various Rally Numbers	WS	Windscreen
UB	Unboxed	VS	Various Shades	WST	Woman Standing
UD	Upper Deck	VSN	Version	WSTR	Water Slide Transfer
UDC	Undercarriage	VW	Volkswagen	WSW	Windscreen Wipers
(UDD)	Unless Described Differently			WT	White Tyres
UF	Underframe	W	Wheel(s)	WTF	Warrior Type Front
UJ(s)	Union Jack(s)	WBL	Working Brake Lights	WW	With or Without
UNP	Unpainted	WC	White Circle	WWCLW	With or Without Crane Lattice Work
UPB	Upperbody	WCD	Without Cab Doors		
UPD	Upperdeck	WDSC	Window Section	WWPTL	With or Without Painted Tail-lights
UPF	Unpainted Plastic Figures	WDS	Windows	WWS	Wire Windscreen
UPN	Upper Panel(s)	WDW	Wide Wheels	WWT	Whitewall Tyres
US	United States	WGS	Wagon Sides	WKP	Working Parts
USDW	Upper Side Windows	WGS	Wings	WZW	Whizz Wheels
USIM	Model Issued in USA	WH	Wire Hook		
		WHB	Wheel Hub(s)	YEL	Yellow
V	Vehicle	WHS	White Horses	YPCHBD	Yellow Pages Correct on Headboard
VADS	Various Advertisements	WM	Wing Mirrors		
VB	Venetian Blinds	WO	Winch Operates	YPRHBD	Yellow Pages in Reverse on Headboard
VBL	Vertical Bonnet Louvres	WPD	White Plastic Dogs		

TRADE SOURCES OF INFORMATION

The catalogue compiler would like to express his appreciation to the following dealers who so kindly supplied information in connection with the market survey:

John Gay, 7 Horsham Lane, Upchurch, Sittingbourne, Kent.
Long established International Mail Order specialist and Toyfair trader.

David Hinam, 278 Ashgate Road, Chesterfield, S40 4AW.
Well known International Mail Order specialist and Toyfair trader.

John Webb, Rosebank House, Station Road, Bardney, Lincs, LN3 5UF.
Well known Toyfair promoter and trader.

Graham Ward, Promod Ltd, Vivian Road, Fenton, Sheffield.

Ray Laycock, 227 Abbeydale Road, Sheffield.
Long established shopkeeper, Mail Order specialist and Toyfair trader.

Mike Richardson, 15 Ball Lane, Eaten Wick, Windsor, Berks.
Specialist die-cast trader of international repute.
Co-author with his wife Sue of 'Dinky Toys and Modelled Miniatures', the Bible for all Dinky Toy collectors.

Roger Mazillius of Vectis Models, 96 High Street, Cowes, Isle of Wight.
Long established specialist shopkeeper and Mail Order dealer.
Well known Toyfair promoter and owner of the Cowes Toy & Model Museum.

Trevor Morgan, Cheltenham Model Centre, 39 High Street, Cheltenham, GL50 1DY.
Shopkeeper and International Mail Order trader, co-organiser of the Gloucester Toyfair.

Ian Clark, 78 Duke Street, Askam in Furness, Cumbria, LA16 7AD.
Long established International Mail Order specialist and Toyfair trader.

Peter and Mary Wheatley, Hamilton Road, Felixstowe, Suffolk.
Long established shopkeepers, Mail Order traders and specialists on modern die-casts.

Jon Scot Collections, 56 Doddington Road, Wimblington, March, Cambs.
Specialist dealer in the older, collectable die-casts.

Graham Ward, Models and Hobbies, 256 Uttoxeter Road, Stoke-on-Trent.
Shopkeeper, International Mail Order and Toyfair trader.

Victor Bailey, Veteran and Vintage Models, Old Portslade Village, Brighton.
Long established.

Stewart Orr and Kevin McGimpsey, Chester Toy Museum, 42 Bridge Street Row, Chester CH1 1NQ.
Co-editors of the Matchbox International Collectors Association (M.I.C.A.)

John King and Geoff Curran, Mecca Models, 11 St Gregory's Alley, Norwich.
Specialist Lledo and Corgi trader.

Philip Bowdidge, 8 Melrose Court, Ashley, New Milton, Hants, BH25 5BY.
Renowned Matchbox collector and International Mail Order specialist, for special assistance with the 'Matchbox Miniatures' listings.

John Marshall, J & J Models, 941 East 4th Street, Box 147, Santa Ana, California 92702, U.S.A.
For in-depth research and information on British Diecast Toys in the U.S.A.

David Cooper, Timbercraft Cabinets, 20 Duke Street, Northampton.

Nigel Mynheer, Phillips, Son & Neale, Blensbek House, 7 Blenheim Street, New Bond Street, London, W1Y 0AS.

Peter Crichton, Lacy Scott & Co, The Auction Centre, Bury St Edmunds, Suffolk.

Hilary Kay, Sotheby Parke, Bernet, 34 New Bond Street, London, W1A 2AA.

Tim Matthews, Christies & Co, 85 Old Brompton Road, London, SW7 3LD.

PERSONAL ACKNOWLEDGEMENTS

The catalogue compiler would like to express his appreciation to the following for all the help received:

To Susan Pownall of Corgi Toys.

To Tony Beacock, 1 Stone Cottage, Claygate, Shepway, Maidstone.

To John Plume, 'Ashlea', Cecil Road, Iver, Bucks.

To David Gilbert, 101 Erville Road, Knowle, West Midlands.

For assistance with the Budgie and Morestone listings.

To Mike Richardson for allowing use to be made of a Budgie Toys article in 'Modellers World'.

For assistance with the Crescent Toy listings:

Ray Strutt, The Rosery, New Place, Uckfield, East Sussex, TN22 5DP.

Mr J.D. Schneider former Managing Director of Crescent Toys Ltd.

For assistance with the Dinky Toy listings:

John Watson of the 'Dinky Die-Cast Club', 29 Fairfield Avenue, Leckhampton.

Ray Holcroft, 157 Burnley Road, Padiham, Burnley, Lancs.

Mr A.J. Grahame, 47 Devonshire Road, Aberdeen.

Steve Bradley, 26 Chancet Ward Drive, Sheffield.

Antony Payne, 77 Bramley Way, Ashstead, Surrey, of the Surrey Die-Cast Model Club.

To Derek Barratt, 230 Earlham Road, Norwich, for much technical information on Dinky aircraft.

To Dave Towl, 88 Cedar Avenue, Spixworth, Norwich, for special help with Models of Yesteryear.

To Mr G. Tekerian, Marketing Manager of Matchbox Toys, for giving permission to quote his company's trademarks.

To Mr M. Rosser, Managing Director of Corgi Toys, for giving permission to quote his company's trademarks.

To Paul Robinson, 43 Fairfield Avenue, Felixstowe, for his model diagrams.

To Mr A.J. Russell, Managing Director, Lledo (London) Ltd, for giving permission to quote his company's trademarks.

To Ray Bush, editor 'LLEDO CALLING' Collectors Club, 1 Tor Road, Hartley, Plymouth, Devon PL3 5TD, for his kind permission to use his club magazine for reference purposes.

Also for kind permission to refer to information contained in 'UK Matchbox Club' magazines.

To Andrew Perkins, 'The Chimneys', Hall Road, Hemsby, Great Yarmouth, Norfolk, for the special attention to the photography.

NOTES

NOTES

NOTES

NOTES

NOTES

219

A ROUND TUIT

32-34 Dickson Rd. BLACKPOOL. FY1 2AJ.
TELEPHONE (0253) 20367

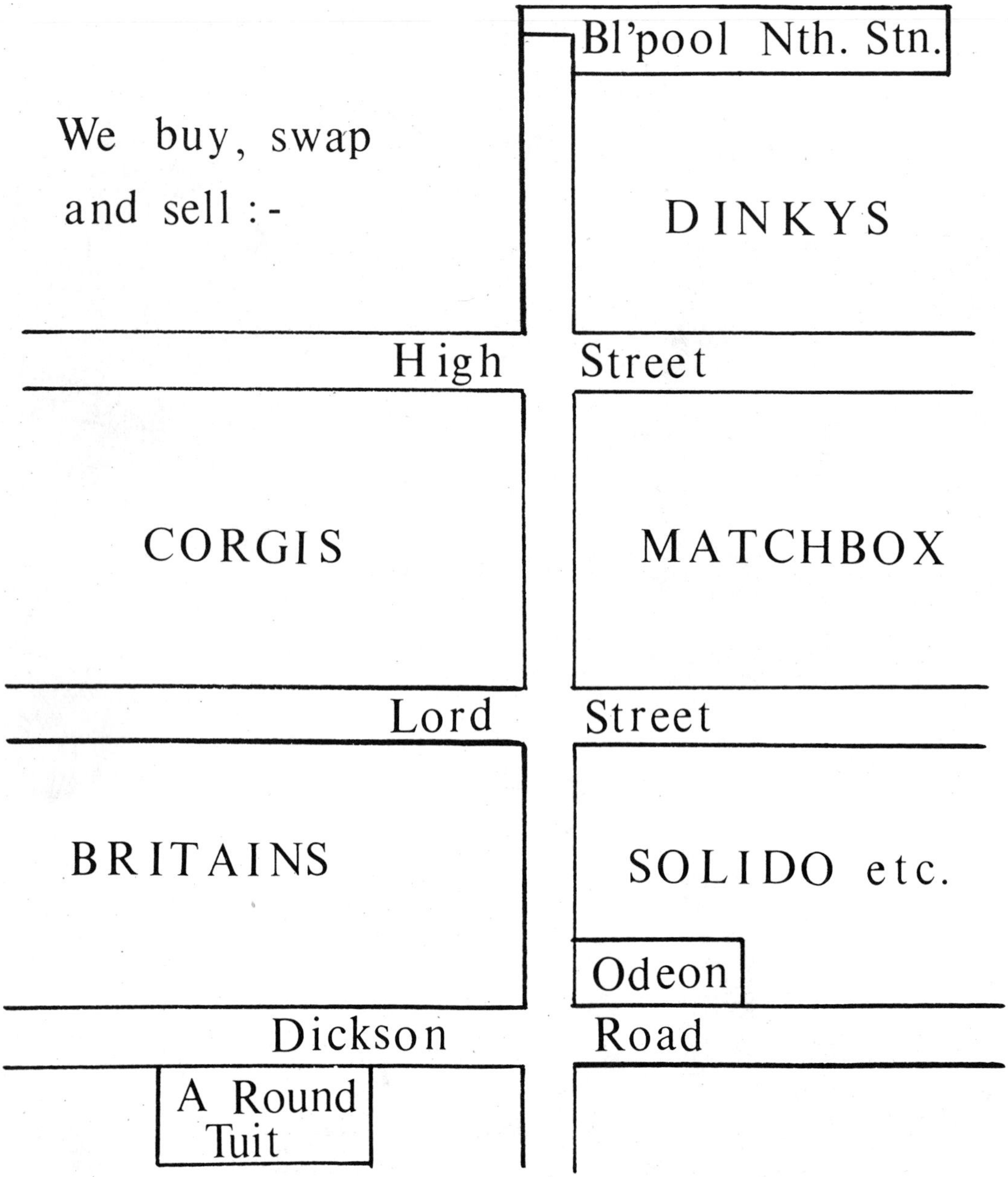

Bl'pool Nth. Stn.

We buy, swap
and sell :-

DINKYS

High   Street

CORGIS   MATCHBOX

Lord   Street

BRITAINS   SOLIDO etc.

Odeon

Dickson   Road

A Round
Tuit